THE PINEAL GLAND

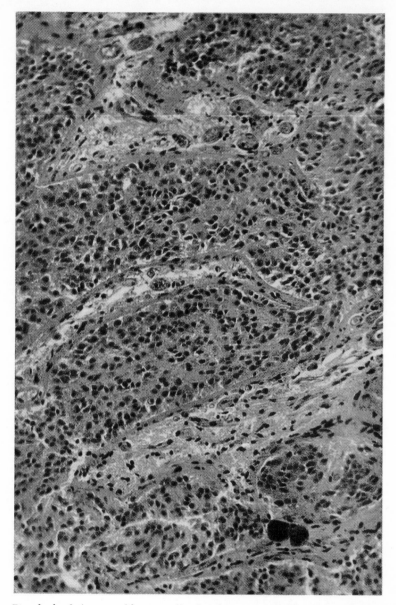

Pineal gland (presumably normal) of a forty-six-year-old woman. X 190. Tissue fixed in Zenker's solution and stained with phloxine and methylene blue. The slide was donated by Dr. Leopold Reiner.

The Pineal Gland

A REVIEW OF THE PHYSIOLOGIC LITERATURE

By JULIAN I. KITAY
and MARK D. ALTSCHULE

PUBLISHED FOR THE COMMONWEALTH FUND

BY HARVARD UNIVERSITY PRESS, CAMBRIDGE, MASS.

1954

Published for
The Commonwealth Fund
By Harvard University Press
Cambridge, Massachusetts

For approximately a quarter of a century THE COMMONWEALTH FUND, through its Division of Publications, sponsored, edited, produced, and distributed books and pamphlets germane to its purposes and operations as a philanthropic foundation. On July 1, 1951, the Fund entered into an arrangement by which HARVARD UNIVERSITY PRESS became the publisher of Commonwealth Fund books, assuming responsibility for their production and distribution. The Fund continues to sponsor and edit its books, and cooperates with the Press in all phases of manufacture and distribution.

Distributed in Great Britain
By Geoffrey Cumberlege
Oxford University Press, London

Preface

The pineal gland was named at least two thousand years ago. The organ is not mentioned in the Hippocratic writings, but it was described before A.D. 200. Galen said that it was called *conarium* by "those who concern themselves with dissections." Since most medical writings between 500 B.C. and Galen's time have been lost, the identity of these anatomists is uncertain; they may well have included Herophilus and Erasistratus, whose contributions to our knowledge of the anatomy of the brain are well known. However, as Bacon put it, "those who write upon the first inventors of things, and the origin of the sciences, rather celebrate chance than art"; the growth of knowledge that follows a discovery is more important than the discovery itself. Up to the last decade the history of the pineal gland revealed no such increase of knowledge.

Herophilus and his followers revived an earlier idea that the ventricles were the seat of the mind and concluded that the pineal body was a sphincter that regulated the flow of thought. This concept persisted until Galen's time; however, Galen showed that the organ could not possibly be a sphincter* and was probably a gland, perhaps similar to lymph glands.

The seventeenth century saw a revival of interest in the pineal body after Descartes designated it as the seat of the soul. This idea, supported by the authority of Descartes's name, aroused much interest—and in the long run probably retarded the advancement of knowledge about the organ. The concept continued to enjoy prominence despite the objections of some leading physicians of the era, including Bartholin and Wharton. Thomas Gibson, whose *Epitome*

*Galen believed that the cerebellar vermis was the thought sphincter. The idea of a thought valve was reintroduced into western Europe when the works of the Arab Galenists were translated in the twelfth century.

of Anatomy was published in 1763, also took issue with Descartes's theory. He revived Galen's ideas, in a slightly modified form, employing the same genital analogies that Galen had applied to the general area of the pineal body, and described the organ itself as an endocrine gland:

The first is *Glandula pinealis,* or Penis; because it representeth the Pine-nut, or a Man's Yard. It is seated in the beginning of that Pipe, by which the third and fourth Ventricles are united. Its basis is downwards, and its apex or end looks upwards. It is of a substance harder than the Brain, of a pale colour, and covered with a thin Membrane. This Gland *des Cartes* thinks to be the primary seat of the Soul, and that all animal operations draw their origine from it. But *Bartholin* has sufficiently confuted that opinion; for it seems to be but of the same use as other Glands, and particularly the *Glandula pituitaria* placed near it, viz. to separate the *Lympha* from the Arterial blood; which *Lympha* is resorbed by the Veins (or it may be by *Vasa lymphatica*) as was shown from *Dr. Lower.* Near to this on both sides of this third Ventricle four round bodies appear. The two upper are lesser, and are called *Testes:* the two greater are lower, and are called *Nates.* The chink betwixt the *Nates* is called *Anus.*

Three ideas about pineal function have persisted since the seventeenth century. They are: (1) that the organ is a sphincter; (2) that it is the seat of the mind; and (3) that it is a gland, having endocrine functions.*

The first of these—the ancient Greek belief that the pineal gland was a sphincter—was upheld in part in the early nineteenth century by Magendie, who concluded that it regulated the flow of spinal fluid. De Cyon adhered to this view as late as 1907.

The second idea is reflected in Günz's report in 1753 of five cases of pineal calcification with psychosis. Morgagni in 1779 expressed doubt that there was a *constant* relation between psychosis and calcification of the pineal gland. Nevertheless, he went on to say: "And although you have heard above that this disorder has been found with madness and without it also, yet I would not have you

*Much of the early history of the pineal and other glands was discussed by Rolleston in *The Endocrine Organs in Health and Disease, with an Historical Review* (London: Oxford University Press, 1936).

forget there is not any one disorder wherewith it is so frequently found to be join'd, as with madness."

The third idea has an interesting history. A case report published in 1898 described precocious bodily and sexual development in a boy in whom autopsy had revealed a pineal tumor. A few years later Pellizzi described two cases of pubertas praecox and declared that the symptoms had been due to pineal tumors, although post-mortem examinations had not been made. Reports of similar cases soon brought about the formulation of theories about the hormonal function of the pineal gland. These may be grouped as follows: (1) that the gland stimulates bodily and sexual development; (2) that it inhibits such development; and (3) that it has neither effect. No decisive evidence on these matters has ever been presented in the published clinical studies. Through the years the list of organs that the pineal body is believed to affect has been extended to include not only the gonads but the pituitary, adrenal, thyroid, and parathyroid glands and the pancreas, the thymus, the brain, etc.

During the past decade many excellent experiments have been reported—chiefly in Japan and continental Europe. These studies, which shed much light on pineal physiology, are largely unknown to biologists—at least in this country, where it is generally believed that the organ is a functionless vestige of a primitive eye. The belief is apparently based on a few American reports that it has no function; these negative studies have been given prominence out of all proportion to their value. The work reviewed in this monograph shows (1) that the pineal gland cannot be considered either functionless or vestigial and (2) that it definitely meets the criteria of physiologic activity.

Misinterpretation of the past is more misleading than ignorance of it; both phenomena have helped to establish negative ideas about the gland. Moreover, these ideas, where held, have discouraged research and have vitiated much of what has been done. Claude Bernard pointed out that "a discovery is generally an unforeseen relation not included in theory, for otherwise it would be foreseen" and also that "men who have excessive faith in their theories or ideas are not only ill prepared for making discoveries; they also make poor observations. They can see only a confirmation of their theory." Bacon described the fate of new ideas: "The human mind is often so awkward and ill-regulated in the career of invention that it is at first diffident, and then despises itself. For it appears at first incredible that any such discovery should be made, and when it has been made, it appears incredible that it should so long have escaped men's research."

The reader must judge for himself the value of the experiments reported in the hundreds of papers reviewed here. At any rate, the need for a compilation such as the present work requires no emphasis. Bacon's words seem most pertinent:

For as water, whether of the dew of heaven or spring of the earth, would speedily lose itself in the ground unless collected into conduits and cisterns, so it seemeth this excellent liquor of knowledge, whether it descend from the Divine inspiration or spring from human sense, would soon hide itself in oblivion unless collected in books, traditions, academies, and schools, it might find a permanent seat, and a fructifying union of strength.

J. I. K.

M. D. A.

Acknowledgments

Drs. Roy O. Greep and Paul L. Munson read the manuscript and made valuable comments. Its preparation was greatly aided by the sound and discerning editorial advice of Miss Evelyn Russ.

Miss Katherine Merrill's part in the project was of major importance; she not only translated most of the Japanese papers reviewed here but scanned the indices for pertinent articles and enlisted friends in Japan in the task of securing material not readily available. Dr. Otto Krayer's advice helped us to secure certain information from Austria. The Charles M. Tuttle Company of Rutland, Vermont, and Tokyo, Japan, and the Fondazione Mario Donati of Milan, Italy, expedited the flow of photostats from several areas that were inaccessible to us.

The bulk of the material available in this country was obtained from the Armed Forces Medical Library; we are particularly indebted to the Misses Marguerite M. Correll and Eleanor Johnson and to Mr. Robert B. Austin of that institution. Also helpful in this respect were the Misses Gretchen Reiss and Catherine Binderup, of the Library of the Harvard Medical School; Miss Marie Parsons, of the Library of the Harvard Dental School; and Miss Wilma Folkerth, of the New York Academy of Medicine.

A nearly complete list of the libraries that sent us material follows. Their cooperation is gratefully acknowledged.

American Medical Association Library, Chicago, Ill.
American Museum of Natural History Library, New York, N.Y.
Armed Forces Medical Library, Washington, D.C.
Armed Forces Medical Library, History of Medicine Division,
    Cleveland, Ohio
Bibliothèque Nationale, Paris, France
Boston Medical Library, Boston, Mass.
Boston University School of Medicine Library, Boston, Mass.
College of Physicians of Philadelphia Library, Philadelphia, Penn.

Columbia University Medical Library, New York, N.Y.
Cornell University Library, Ithaca, N.Y.
Finska Läkaresällskapet Bibliotek, Helsinki, Finland
Harvard University Libraries, Cambridge, Mass.
    Arnold Arboretum
    Biological Laboratories
    Museum of Comparative Zoology
    Widener Library
Harvard University Schools of Medicine and Public Health Libraries, Boston, Mass.
Indiana University Library, Indianapolis, Ind.
John Crerar Library, Chicago, Ill.
Keiō Gijuku University Medical School Library, Tokyo, Japan
Kyōto University Medical School Library, Kyōto-shi, Japan
Library of the Medical Society of the County of Kings and Academy of Medicine of Brooklyn, Brooklyn, N.Y.
Medizinische Lesehalle, Munich, Germany
Nagoya University Medical School Library, Nagoya-shi, Japan
National Diet Library, Tokyo, Japan
New York Academy of Medicine Library, New York, N.Y.
The New York Public Library, New York, N.Y.
Ohio State University Library, Columbus, Ohio
Pan-American Sanitary Bureau Library, Washington, D.C.
Public Library of the City of Boston, Boston, Mass.
Rockefeller Institute for Medical Research Library, New York, N.Y.
Technische Hochschule Bibliotek, Hannover, Germany
Tufts College Medical and Dental School Library, Boston, Mass.
United States Department of Agriculture Library, Washington, D.C.
United States Library of Congress, Washington, D.C.
University of Toronto Library, Medical Reading Room, Toronto, Canada
Vanderbilt University School of Medicine Library, Nashville, Tenn.
Yale Medical Library, New Haven, Conn.

The cost of translations and the other expenses incurred in the preparation of this monograph were met by grants from the Wilson Laboratories, of Chicago, Illinois, the Proctor Fund of Harvard University, and the Commonwealth Fund.

[x]

Contents

LIST OF ILLUSTRATIONS

Introduction

Ideas about the function of the pineal gland have not heretofore been based on critical analysis of available evidence. This review aims to provide material for formulating valid concepts of pineal function. It includes only those reported experimental data and direct observations that relate to pineal physiology. Speculative discussions have largely been omitted; this accounts for the disparity between the length of the bibliography and that of the text. Only original papers have been cited here (with a few exceptions), since many abstracts were found to be incomplete, misleading, or inaccurate; the same criticism also applies to most previous reviews.

The present work makes available a great deal of data that heretofore has largely been ignored. This neglect of previous research has led many investigators to repeat experiments that were inadequately designed and poorly executed; the literature has thus been enlarged without being enriched. The inadequate observations and fragmentary data contained in many reports created problems of presentation. These problems have been met by classifying the findings somewhat arbitrarily. The plan of organization used here is perhaps open to criticism, and indeed is probably imperfect; however, at times "truth emerges more readily from error than from confusion."

The procedure used for tabulating this material was dictated by the need for conciseness. The bibliographic numbers of the papers reviewed are grouped in tables, mainly according to results observed and animals used. This device has been employed solely for the purpose of categorizing the findings, and is not presented as a method of weighing the evidence. Detailed evaluations of data, as well as extended consideration of appropriate papers, are contained in the text.

The chief criterion used in selecting papers for detailed discussion in this book was statistical significance. Disregard of statistics in the past has frequently led to invalid conclusions; accordingly, statistical information has been given here when available, or when the data have permitted statistical calculations. Unless otherwise indicated, mean values are always accompanied by the standard error of the mean. Lord Kelvin wrote:

> I often say that when you can measure what you are speaking about, and express it in numbers, you know something about it; but when you cannot measure it, when you cannot express it in numbers, your knowledge is of a meagre and unsatisfactory kind; it may be the beginning of knowledge, but you have scarcely, in your thoughts, advanced to the state of *Science,* whatever the matter may be.

Any conclusions presented here are supported by sound statistical considerations. However, it should be apparent that these conclusions are set down merely to suggest additional definitive experiments.

Part One

PINEAL PHYSIOLOGY

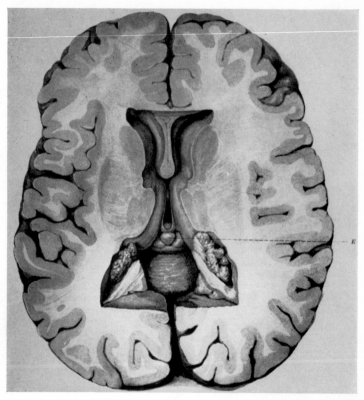

E

FIGURE 1. Horizontal section through the brain of a thirty-year-old man, showing position and anatomic relations of the pineal gland (E). From W. Bargmann, "Die Epiphysis cerebri," in *Handbuch der mikroskopischen Anatomie des Menschen* (W. von Mollendorff, ed.), vol. 6, part 4, pp. 309–502. Berlin: Springer Verlag, 1943. Reproduced by permission of the publisher.

CHAPTER I

Characteristics of the Pineal Gland

The human pineal gland is a small, conical organ, gray in color, that lies deep in the brain along the quadrigeminate groove between the superior colliculi (Figure 1). It is attached anteriorly to the posterior wall of the third ventricle by the pineal stalk, which is continuous with the superior habenular and posterior commissures. Embryologically it is derived from neural ectoderm. Histologic descriptions of the gland are varied and controversial; most authorities agree that it contains at least two types of cells—parenchymal cells and neuroglia (frontispiece)—and some workers have described additional types. The parenchymal cells resemble epithelium and consist of abundant cytoplasm surrounding pale, rounded nuclei; they are markedly irregular in shape, owing to long protoplasmic processes that radiate in all directions from each. A survey of the literature on pineal anatomy, histology, and embryology is beyond the scope of this work; however, a list of relevant papers is included in Appendix I, and a number of reviews are listed in Appendix II. The best review of pineal histologic studies is that of Bargmann (App. II, ref. 13). An excellent review of pineal embryology and comparative anatomy is included in the monograph on the pineal gland by Gladstone and Wakeley (App. I, ref. 174).

A tract connecting the pineal gland and the habenular nucleus was reported to have been demonstrated in the rat by the finding of retrograde degeneration after pinealectomy (178); this observation was not confirmed in the cat (252). Bilateral removal of the superior cervical ganglia in the rat caused no change in nerve terminations in the pineal gland (137); however, complete degeneration of these nerve endings was observed after the habenular and posterior commissural tracts had been severed.

Histochemical studies of the pineal gland of the monkey carried out by Wislocki and Dempsey (462) showed basophilic cytoplasmic granules that stained specifically for ribonucleoprotein. Desoxyribonucleoprotein was found in nucleoli and nuclear chromatin. Glycogen was demonstrated in the cytoplasm, and alkaline phosphatase was noted in both cytoplasm and nucleus. Similar examinations by Mikami (281) in the pig, horse, goat, and sheep confirmed these findings. Leduc and Wislocki studied the pineal gland of the rat (240); they demonstrated acid phosphatase in parenchymal cells, particularly in the nuclei. Moderate succinic dehydrogenase activity was observed in the cytoplasm, whereas nonspecific esterase activity was slight. Alkaline phosphatase was found in the walls of blood vessels but not in the parenchymal cells. Wislocki and others showed that in the rat the pineal gland and a few small adjacent areas—in contrast to the rest of the brain—were readily stained *intra vitam* with trypan blue (58, 211, 463) and silver nitrate (463); however, neither substance penetrated the pineal parenchymal cells themselves.

The pineal uptake (specific activity) of radioactive phosphorus in the cat, guinea pig, rabbit, pig, and rat was reported to be three times that of the pituitary gland and twenty times that of the cerebellum (32, 33). The high specific activity was apparently independent of blood activity, since it was not removed by perfusion with an isotonic saline solution. Forty minutes after injection of P^{32}, 65 per cent of the activity was found in the form of acid-soluble phosphate ester and 25 per cent as phosphate ion; 10 per cent was insoluble in trichloracetic acid. P^{32} specific activity in the pineal gland of rats was found to be lowest in infancy, consistently high in maturity, and even higher in senility (31). Other authors (356) confirmed in the rat the finding that the pineal uptake of P^{32} (per 100 mg. of fresh tissue) was higher than that of any other part of the brain; moreover, the P^{32} uptake of the gland was found to be greater than that of any other bodily organ studied. Similarly, the pineal uptake of radioactive iodine was higher than that of any other organ except the thyroid gland.

Reports based on fragmentary studies of the age at which pineal weight is greatest describe wide variations (8, 238, 361, 411). However, several extensive studies of the weights of normal human pineal glands show fair agreement (23, 25, 177, 318, 434, and Table 1); in adults the gland usually weighs between 140 and 200 mg. All the data show that pineal weight does not decrease with puberty—contrary to common belief.

The chemical composition of the gland has been described in detail (110, 353, 363, and Tables 2, 3, and 4). The amounts of water and protein found in pineal tissue are about the same as those reported for pituitary tissue (381). The presence of vitamin B (405) and vitamin C (58, 141) has also been reported. Study of the antigenic properties of the pineal glands of oxen revealed that the organ-specific component is probably an albuminoid protein that is heat labile and insoluble in alcohol (464). Tissue cultures of rabbit pineal glands have been successfully prepared in a medium consisting of

Table 1

Weights of normal human pineal glands

Ref. no.	Total no. of cases	Decade								
		1st (mg.)	2nd (mg.)	3rd (mg.)	4th (mg.)	5th (mg.)	6th (mg.)	7th (mg.)	8th (mg.)	9th (mg.)
23	139	137	162	162	189	139	188	173	116	—
25	56	106	152	172	173	162	138	129	—	—
177	332	—	115	125	124	121	127	121	109	—
318	227	82	161	153	139	141	152	124	130	—
434	71	136	158	146	145	209	159	215	129	136

[5]

Table 2

Composition of the pineal gland in cattle, sheep, and lambs

(Fenger, 110)

Fresh glands	Cattle	Sheep	Lambs
No. of glands examined	1458	1348	5062
Average weight of gland	0.18 gm.	0.12 gm.	0.08 gm.
Minimum weight of gland	0.09 gm.	0.05 gm.	0.04 gm.
Maximum weight of gland	0.35 gm.	0.25 gm.	0.18 gm.
Moisture in fresh tissue	81.6%	82.7%	83.5%
Petroleum-ether soluble material	2.8%	2.5%	2.5%
Yield of dessicated fat-free material	15.6%	14.8%	14.0%
Fat-free dessicated material			
Moisture	5.10%	5.65%	6.25%
Ash	8.10%	8.20%	7.05%
dry basis	8.53%	8.69%	7.52%
Phosphorus pentoxide	3.75%	3.44%	3.16%
dry basis	3.95%	3.65%	3.37%
Total nitrogen	12.68%	12.68%	12.83%
dry basis	13.31%	13.44%	13.69%
Protein (N x 6.25)	78.94%	79.25%	80.19%
dry basis	83.19%	84.00%	85.56%

Table 3

Composition of the pineal gland in oxen

(Roux, 363)

A. Water and solid material (400 glands analyzed):
   1. Average weight 0.199 gm.
   2. Water 79.2%.
   3. Solids 20.8%.
B. Mineral content by calcination (248 glands analyzed):
   1. Average weight 0.192 gm.
   2. Average mineral content 2.3%.
C. Fat content (51 glands analyzed):
   1. Average weight 0.185 gm.
   2. Average fat content 3.5%.
D. Protein content (120 glands analyzed):
   1. Average weight 0.214 gm.
   2. Average protein content 13.1%.
E. Miscellaneous: 1.9%.

Table 4

Mineral content of pineal tissue in sheep and oxen—spectroscopic analysis

(Press and Fearon, 353)

	Sheep	Oxen		Sheep	Oxen
Aluminum	(+)	+	Strontium	(+)	0
Copper	+	+	Calcium	+++	+++
Potassium	++	+	Magnesium	+++	+++
Sodium	+++	+++	Iron	+++	+++
Manganese	(+)	+	Lead	(+)	+
Zinc	0	0	Silicon	+	+
Tin	(+)	(+)	Rubidium	(+)	0

heparin, plasma, and pituitary and spleen extracts; epithelial (paren-chymal) cells, glia fibrils, endothelial cells, and fibroblasts grew in these cultures (202).

COMMENT

The available anatomic data suggest that the pineal stalk contains neuronal communications between pineal nerve endings and adjacent brain centers. The reported histochemical and isotope-uptake data indicate that in the animals studied there is no impediment to diffusion between the blood and the pineal gland such as exists between the blood and the brain parenchyma (the blood-brain barrier). The findings are consistent with an active rate of metabolism in the parenchymal cells; they suggest that the gland has a specialized function.

CHAPTER II

Chief Methods of
Investigating Pineal Function

PINEALECTOMY

Excision, first described by Exner and Boese in 1910 (106), has so far proved the most fruitful means of studying pineal function. The operation has most frequently been performed in rats, rabbits, and fowl. The usual method is surgical removal, although thermo-cauterization and stereotaxic ablation have also been employed. The procedure is difficult, and the operative mortality ranges up to 98 per cent. Death has mainly been due to uncontrollable hemorrhage from closely adjacent large blood vessels. Another difficulty is presented by the fact that the gland becomes progressively more inaccessible with ascending phylogenetic development; it is located at a depth of 2 to 3 mm. in the immature rat but is 3 to 4 cm. deep in the immature dog. Incomplete excision, postoperative infection, and the strong likelihood of trauma to neighboring structures are further complications. Accordingly, many investigators have found it difficult to accumulate pinealectomized animals in sufficiently large numbers to permit statistical analysis of results.

Our modification of the technique of pinealectomy in the rat employed by Borell (31), which we have found effective (212), is illustrated in Figure 2.

Anesthesia is maintained with ether. The dorsum of the head and neck is shaved and a 2- to 3-cm. midline incision is made over the occipital region. A rectangular flap is cut in the skull with a dental

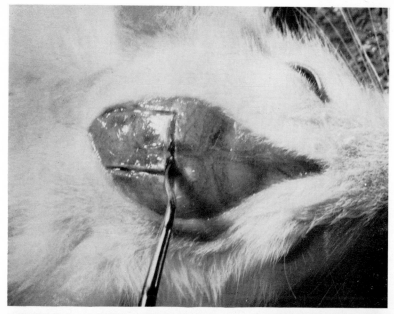

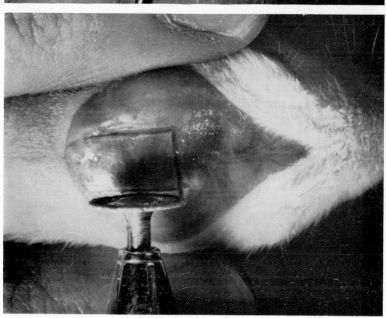

FIGURE 2. Technique of pinealectomy in the rat (see text).

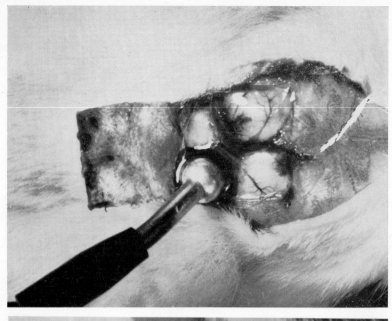

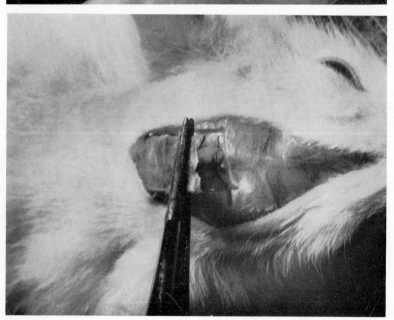

FIGURE 2. Technique of pinealectomy in the rat (see text).

C   D

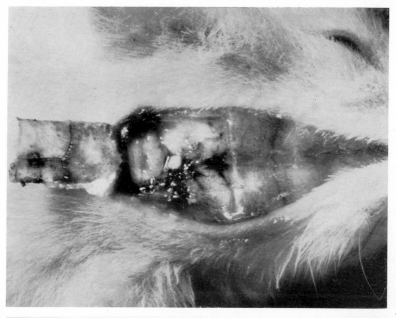

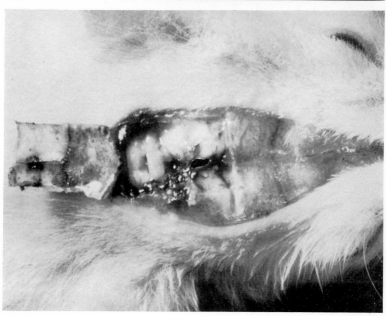

FIGURE 2. Technique of pinealectomy in the rat (see text).

E

F

drill fitted with a diamond cutting disk (Figure 2A). The flap is raised above the level of the skull with a probe (Figure 2B) and is carefully peeled from the underlying dura with a hemostat (Figure 2c). One of the lateral sinuses is coagulated with an electrocautery (Figure 2D). The dura is cut parallel to the longitudinal and confluent sinuses; the presenting portion of the confluent sinus is carefully raised and the pineal gland is thus exposed (Figure 2E). The gland is removed with iris forceps; bleeding from the pineal site (Figure 2F) is controlled with cotton pledgets and gelfoam sponge. The bone flap is replaced and the incision closed with Michel wound clips.

Several authors have published detailed papers on methods of pinealectomy (13, 30, 214, 406). Additional information on operative techniques is contained in the various experimental reports cited in Table 5.

Table 5

References on pinealectomy in various animals

Animal	Reference numbers
Cat	65, 252, 253
Catfish	468
Dog	29, 64, 65, 253, 377, 392, 413
Fowl	19, 50, 56, 57, 120–122, 186–188, 227, 280, 324, 325, 328, 329, 383, 384, 386, 428, 436, 471
Guinea pig	56, 57, 166
Lamprey	474
Lizard	54, 55
Mouse	138, 203, 276
Phoximus	135, 379
Rabbit	2, 3, 17, 56, 57, 106, 180, 182–185, 217, 219, 254–259, 273, 275, 304–306, 373, 377, 417, 470, 473
Rat	7, 11, 31, 48, 62, 65, 85, 91, 94, 121, 153, 158, 178, 179, 189–195, 201, 204–206, 212, 215, 252, 276–278, 307–309, 317, 357, 390–396, 403, 412, 413, 438, 448, 450
Sheep	67–69
Tadpole	5, 16, 168

PINEAL-EXTRACT ADMINISTRATION

Most studies of pineal function have been based on administration of the pineal gland by feeding the gland or by injecting extracts (Table 6). The results of this type of investigation are less clear-cut than those reported for pinealectomy and are more difficult to evaluate. This is chiefly owing to poor control of one or more of the following variables:

1. Source of tissue
   a. Species of animals used as donors
   b. Age of donor animals
   c. Sex of donor animals
   d. Physiologic state of donor animals (pregnancy, disease, etc.)
2. Condition of tissue
   a. Time interval between removal and preparation
   b. Methods of preservation
   c. Degree of decomposition
3. Method of preparation
   a. Solvent(s)
   b. Degree of purification
   c. Concentration
   d. Time interval between preparation and administration
4. Activity of preparation
   a. Standardization by assay
   b. Types of activity in various fractions
5. Mode of administration
   a. Oral
   b. Parenteral
6. Amount administered
7. Duration of administration

In most instances each investigator prepared his own extract—usually aqueous—and used it as such or with slight modifications. Chloroform, glycerine, ether, and alcohol have occasionally been employed as solvents. Fischer (115), Hanson (151), and Steinberg

Table 6

References on pineal-extract administration in various animals

Animal	Reference numbers
Axolotl	175
Cat	28, 63, 75, 198, 246, 322
Dog	20, 43, 44, 63, 76, 82, 133, 154, 157, 166, 169, 198, 220, 248–250, 264, 336, 341, 348, 355, 419, 423, 459, 460
Fish	139, 155, 223, 224, 269, 474
Fowl	53, 97, 229, 326, 327, 335, 339, 340, 342, 383, 384, 408, 430
Frog	24, 84, 207, 208, 440, 472
Goat	320, 321
Guinea pig	20, 28, 63, 91, 94, 131, 260, 261, 264, 265, 279, 303, 359, 378, 402, 423, 425, 455
Hedgehog	6
Horse	108, 164, 170–174, 380, 399, 400, 479
Insects	363
Man	9, 10, 12, 14, 18, 21, 22, 26–28, 39, 41, 44–47, 49, 60, 63, 109, 132, 134, 136, 140, 142, 148, 149, 159–163, 218, 226, 232, 235–237, 242–244, 251, 262, 263, 270, 271, 283, 284, 295–297, 310, 311, 314, 315, 331, 333, 334, 337, 338, 343, 349–352, 362, 374, 389, 418, 420–422, 424, 426, 427, 435, 437, 439, 444, 445, 453, 454, 459–461, 465, 466
Mouse	26, 39, 77, 78, 86, 88–90, 93, 98, 101–103, 114, 115, 150, 165, 181, 232, 276, 277, 292, 303, 375, 410, 446, 447, 449, 451, 452, 456–458, 461
Paramecium	116, 266, 467
Pig	40, 400
Python	225
Rabbit	28, 52, 59, 61, 63, 89, 100, 112, 113, 118, 123, 125–128, 181, 198, 216, 229, 232, 239, 245, 247, 272, 274, 322, 345, 348, 354, 398, 443, 448, 452, 453, 459, 460
Rat	1, 85, 87–89, 92, 95–97, 99, 129, 151, 153, 167, 181, 204, 213, 232, 277, 282, 285–291, 293, 294, 303, 308, 330, 332, 363–368, 397, 419, 423, 425, 432, 446, 447, 449, 451, 452, 455
Sheep	198
Tadpole	4, 14, 16, 34, 147, 175, 209, 266–268, 298, 360, 363, 404
Toad	34

(401) devised more elaborate methods of preparation.

The use of three commercial extracts has been reported. Epiglandol, prepared by Hoffman-LaRoche, Inc., in Switzerland, was utilized in clinical research from about 1910 to 1930 (382). It was an aqueous preparation of bovine glands freed of proteins by treatment with metaphosphoric acid. Its manufacture was discontinued because its biologic action was not dependable. Epiphysan is an aqueous extract first manufactured by the Richter Company in Budapest and now sold by several European pharmaceutical firms (38, 385). Epiphysormone is an aqueous alkaline extract of bovine glands manufactured by a laboratory in Bucharest and apparently used only by Rumanian investigators (323).

Several procedures have been proposed for assaying the potency of pineal extracts; these include observation of quantitative decreases in melanophore size in the toad (34) and in sperm count in the rat (288). Another suggested method is to determine the minimum amount of extract required to inhibit ovarian changes in the rat that have been produced by injecting a measured quantity of pituitary gonadotrophin (96). Still another proposed criterion is the duration of retardation of opening of the mouse vaginal membrane (114).

PINEAL IMPLANTATION

Pineal implantation has been used less frequently than the other methods (Table 7). The preceding comments concerning dosage, source and condition of tissue, and duration of administration apply here as well as to extracts. Few implantation experiments have employed enough animals to yield significant data.

Table 7

References on pineal implantation in various animals

Animal	Reference numbers
Axolotl	442
Chick	221
Guinea pig	42, 88, 199, 200, 302
Man	374
Mouse	117, 312, 376, 388, 410, 447
Pigeon	146
Rabbit	83, 106
Rat	1, 42, 85, 153, 234, 299, 300, 447
Tadpole	156, 404

CHAPTER III

Bodily Growth and Development

PINEALECTOMY

Accelerated bodily growth and development have frequently been reported in pinealectomized animals (Table 8). A variety of immature animals have been used, and body weights have been determined at times ranging from a week to over a year after operation. Weight increase has been the chief criterion of growth, although body length and height also have been employed. More specific developmental characteristics, such as bone age, have been studied occasionally, but never systematically. The single report of growth retardation was apparently based solely on weight findings, since body height and length were normal.

Although the over-all pattern of change reported is apparently consistent, few papers present enough data to analyze statistically.

Table 8
References on the effects of pinealectomy on growth

Animal	Stimulation	Inhibition	No change
Cat	65, 252, 253		
Dog	65, 253, 377		29, 64, 413
Fowl	186–188, 227, 280, 428, 471		19, 50, 384
Rabbit	180, 257, 275, 377, 473		106
Rat	65, 121, 189, 190, 195, 201, 252, 276, 438, 448, 450		11, 48, 153, 158 212, 215, 357, 413
Sheep		67–69	168
Tadpole	5		

Table 9

References on the growth of offspring of pinealectomized animals

Animal	Stimulation	No change
Fowl	57	
Guinea pig	56	
Rabbit	56, 273, 275	
Rat	62	85, 189, 403, 448

Moreover, those data that can be analyzed usually yield no convincing results. Only two papers that report growth acceleration include significant data. Izawa (190) pinealectomized twenty-day-old Wistar rats and found that their body weights at eighty-five days of age differed significantly but not strikingly from those of control animals. Twelve male rats had a mean body weight of 171.8 ± 8.9 gm.* as compared with 11 control animals, whose mean weight was 146.7 ± 9.8 gm., a difference of no significance. On the other hand, 10 pinealectomized female rats had a mean body weight of 155.2 ± 5.5 gm., whereas an equal number of control animals weighed 136.9 ± 5.4 gm. The latter difference is significant at the 5 per cent level of confidence. Data of greater statistical significance have been reported (275); however, these results were based on a very small number of animals. Those workers who report no change in body weight after pinealectomy likewise have employed small numbers of animals. However, two studies using large series of experimental, sham-operated, and intact control animals have demonstrated no change in rate of growth in the chick (384) and the rat (212).

Several investigators have reported growth acceleration in the offspring of pinealectomized animals (Table 9); however, examination of the data shows that the findings were equivocal. For example, Mesaki (275) pinealectomized immature rabbits, followed them through pregnancy, and determined the birth weights of their off-

---

*Mean body weight ± standard error of the mean. Throughout this book mean values are accompanied by the *standard error of the mean*, unless otherwise indicated.

Table 10

Body weights of offspring of pinealectomized rabbits
(Mesaki, 275)

	Pinealectomized rabbits		Control rabbits	
No. of litters	5		5	
Total no. of fetuses	27		34	
Mean litter size	5.4		6.8	
Sex	*Male*	*Female*	*Male*	*Female*
No. of fetuses	12	15	17	17
Body weights ± S.E.	51.7 ± 2.9 gm.	55.1 ± 2.6 gm.	47.5 ± 1.5 gm.	48.2 ± 1.7 gm.
P	> 0.10	< 0.05	—	—

spring. The differences were not striking (Table 10), and they might easily be explained by the fact that the pinealectomized rabbits had smaller litters than the controls.

PINEAL-EXTRACT ADMINISTRATION

In general, the reported results of extract administration have been inconclusive and inconsistent (Tables 11 and 13). Although findings in a few species—the cat, the guinea pig, and the tadpole—are consistent for each animal, the data presented are too scanty to permit any definitive conclusion. Rowntree and his coworkers (151, 364–368) recorded growth retardation in six generations of rats treated with a picric-acid-precipitated extract; however, they also reported accelerated maturity. These results have been listed under "retardation," although the changes were too complex for so simple a designation. Effects on offspring of treated animals have been studied infrequently (Table 12), and with equally unconvincing results.

PINEAL IMPLANTATION

Data on the effects of implants on growth are fragmentary and inconclusive (Table 14).

Table 11

References on the effects of pineal-extract administration on growth

Animal	Stimulation	Inhibition	No change
Cat	28, 63		
Dog	220, 264	154, 220	
Fowl	339, 408	229	340, 384
Guinea pig	28, 63, 264, 265, 279, 425		
Guppy		223	
Insects			363
Mouse		39, 276, 447, 449	456, 457
Paramecium	266		467
Perch		224	
Python		225	
Rabbit	28, 63	229, 274, 354, 460	
Rat	129, 286, 289, 363, 425	85, 88, 151, 364–368, 447, 449, 452	153, 167, 397
Tadpole	4, 147, 209, 266, 298, 360, 363		14

Table 12

References on the effects of pineal-extract administration on growth of offspring of treated animals

Animal	Stimulation	Inhibition
Guinea pig	378	279
Rabbit		272, 274
Rat	363	85, 151, 363–368

Table 13

References on modes of pineal-extract administration and effects on growth

Mode	Stimulation	Inhibition	No change
Epiphysan injection	339, 425	279	340, 384
Epiphysan feeding	220, 408	154, 220	
Epiphysormone injection	286, 289, 425		
Pineal-extract injection	129	39, 88, 229, 274, 276, 354, 447, 449, 452, 460	153, 340, 384, 456, 457
Fischer's extract injection			384
Hanson's extract injection		151, 364–368	384
Steinberg's extract injection		85	
Pineal feeding	4, 28, 63, 147, 209, 264–266, 298, 360, 363	223–225	14, 167, 363, 397, 467

Table 14

References on the effects of pineal implantation on growth

Animal	Stimulation	Inhibition	No change
Axolotl			442
Chick			221
Guinea pig		42	
Mouse		447	312
Rabbit	83		106
Rat		42, 447	85, 153, 234, 299, 300
Tadpole	156		

MISCELLANEOUS METHODS AND FINDINGS

Pinealectomy in the rat produced changes in brain and spinal-cord weights that are not statistically significant (191, 194). Pineal injection in rats was reported to inhibit the effect of pituitary growth hormone on body weight (87). Injecting melted paraffin in the pineal region of one dog resulted in failure to gain weight in comparison with a control animal (313). Feeding epiphysan to dogs was reported to produce hypertrophy of cartilage cells (154). Pineal-extract administration in fowl had varying effects on plumage (335). The ratio of pineal weight to body weight has been reported as correlated with longevity in vertebrates (230).

COMMENT

To date there is little evidence that the pineal gland has any direct effect on bodily growth and development.

CHAPTER IV

The Pituitary Gland in General

PINEALECTOMY

The effects of pinealectomy on the pituitary gland have consistently been reported either as no change or as simple hypertrophy and hyperplasia, particularly of the acidophilic cells in the anterior lobe (Table 15). However, the small numbers of animals and the inadequacy of techniques used prevent reaching any firm conclusions.

One group reported that pinealectomy in the rat increased the rate of anaerobic glycolysis in the pituitary gland (206, 307, 309).

Table 15

References on the effects of pinealectomy on the pituitary gland

Animal	Hypertrophy	No change
Cat	65, 252, 253	
Chicken	188, 436	280, 384
Dog		64
Rabbit	17, 305, 306, 417	
Rat	179, 193, 194, 308, 309, 394, 438	11, 201, 357, 403*
Sheep	68	

*403 No change in offspring of pinealectomized rats

PINEAL-EXTRACT ADMINISTRATION

Few workers have reported changes in the pituitary gland following extract administration (Table 16); the findings of only two authors merit analysis. Shellabarger (384, 385) performed two experiments and found in both that pineal extract decreased pituitary weight when injected daily for twenty days in male chicks that had been castrated when nineteen days old. In one experiment the pituitary glands of 12 control capons showed the usual castration hypertrophy and weighed an average of 6.60 ± 0.2 mg., whereas the glands of 12 pineal-treated capons weighed an average of 5.82 ± 0.2 mg. The difference between means is significant at the 5 per cent level. The mean pituitary weight found in the treated capons was not significantly different from that found in an equal number of intact untreated animals. In effect, pineal injection was found to inhibit the pituitary hypertrophy usually associated with castration. Wakida's experiments (452), though based on small numbers of animals, indicated that two weeks of extract administration in mice decreased the weight of the adenohypophysis, particularly in male animals (Table 17).

Table 16

References on the effects of pineal-extract administration on the pituitary gland

Animal	Hypertrophy	Atrophy	No change
Capon		384	
Chick			384
Dog		220	
Duck	339		
Mouse		452	
Rabbit		247	
Rat			167

Table 17

Effects of pineal-extract injection on pituitary weight in mice
(Wakida, 452)

	Male mice		Female mice	
	Pineal-treated	Control	Pineal-treated	Control
No. of animals	8	5	8	3
Weight range	4.0–5.0 mg.	5.5–6.5 mg.	5.0–7.0 mg.	6.0–8.0 mg.
Mean weight	4.5 mg.	6.0 mg.	6.1 mg.	7.3 mg.

CHAPTER V

Pituitary Gonadotrophin and the Gonads

RELATION TO GONADAL DEVELOPMENT

Pinealectomy

Gonadal hypertrophy. Early reports that sexual development was apparently influenced by pineal tumors stimulated many experimental attempts to demonstrate such a relation. Most such investigations have been limited to determining gonadal weights at various times after pinealectomy. Gonadal hypertrophy has frequently been noted in every species of animal studied (Table 18).

Although many findings are inconclusive, enough data are now available to indicate that there probably is a functional relation between the pineal body and the gonads. Among the best studies are those of Shellabarger (384, 386); this investigator removed the pineal gland from two-day-old male white Leghorn chicks and found marked testicular hypertrophy at autopsy at forty-two, fifty, fifty-four, sixty, and seventy days of age. The operative site was examined macroscopically and histologically to ascertain that excision had been complete. It was found that testis weight did not increase significantly before forty-two days or at ninety-four days of age. Subsequent calculations, based on testis weight per 100 gm. of body weight (385), demonstrated that the statistical significance of the gonadal hypertrophy observed at fifty-four, sixty, and seventy days of age was independent of variations in body weight. In each series the pinealectomized animals were compared with sham-operated and intact con-

Table 18

References on the effects of pinealectomy on the gonads

Animal	Hypertrophy	Atrophy	No change
Cat	65, 252, 253		
Dog	65, 253, 377, 392, 413		29, 64
Fowl	56, 57, 120–122, 186–188, 280, 384, 386, 428, 471; 227*	50, 280, 383, 386, 428	19
Guinea pig	57, 166		
Lizard	55		
Rabbit	17, 57, 306, 377, 473		106
Rat	65, 121, 189, 192, 194, 195, 212, 252, 308, 391–393, 395, 396, 412, 413, 448, 450		11, 153, 158, 201, 212, 215, 357, 438
Sheep	67–69		

*227: Comb hypertrophy in the cock; gonads not examined

trol chicks. No significant difference in mean testis weights of the latter two groups was observed. For example, the average testis weight of 12 pinealectomized chicks at autopsy at sixty days of age was 66.9 ± 4.1 mg. per 100 gm. of body weight. The average testis weight in 10 sham-operated chicks was 49.1 ± 5.1 mg. per 100 gm. of body weight; in 12 intact animals it was 50.0 ± 5.5 mg. per 100 gm. of body weight. The differences between the means of the pinealectomized chicks and those of either of the control groups is significant at the 2 per cent level of confidence. The results obtained at autopsy of fifty-four- and seventy-day-old chicks are summarized in Table 19. Further experiments demonstrated that the injection of pineal extract in pinealectomized animals significantly diminished testicular hypertrophy.

Simonnet and his coworkers (389A, 393) operated on twenty-two-day-old, 30-to-50-gm. female Wistar rats and autopsied them five weeks later. In one series, 11 pinealectomized rats were found to have an average ovary weight of 34 ± 3.1 mg. per 100 gm. of body weight. The average ovary weight of 7 control animals was

Table 19

The effects of pinealectomy on testis weight in the chick
(Shellabarger, 384, 386)

	Pinealectomized	Sham-operated control	Intact control
Age at autopsy	54 days	54 days	54 days
Number	20	17	20
Testis weight* ± S.E.	42 ± 3.2 mg/100 gm.	27 ± 3.9 mg/100 gm.	33 ± 3.1 mg/100 gm.
P		< 0.01	< 0.05
Age at autopsy	70 days	70 days	70 days
Number	10	5	5
Testis weight* ± S.E.	67 ± 6.7 mg/100 gm.	35 ± 3.5 mg/100 gm.	34 ± 4.3 mg/100 gm.
P		< 0.01	< 0.01

*Expressed as mg/100 gm. of body weight

23 ± 2.6 mg. per 100 gm. of body weight; the difference between means is significant at the 2 per cent level of confidence in this series. The results in another series were significant at the 1 per cent level; 8 pinealectomized rats had an average ovary weight of 38 ± 3.3 mg. per 100 gm. of body weight, whereas values for 5 control animals were 18 ± 1.5 mg. per 100 gm. of body weight. In a third series of 7 pinealectomized and 10 control animals the ovarian hypertrophy observed in the pinealectomized animals was not found to be significant when body weights were taken into account; however, the difference in gross ovary weights between the two groups was significant at the 5 per cent level. Increased numbers of corpora lutea were noted in the ovaries of the pinealectomized rats in all three series. A fourth experiment (389A, 396) included sham-operated as well as intact control rats. Ten pinealectomized rats were found to have an average ovary weight of 80 ± 1.9 mg. per 100 gm. of body weight. Values for 5 sham-operated and 5 intact control rats were 63 ± 5.9 mg. per 100 gm. of body weight and 58 ± 3.7 mg. per 100 gm. of body weight respectively. The difference between the pinealectomized group and each of the two control groups was significant

at the 2 per cent level of confidence. Furthermore, a marked "decidual" reaction was observed in the uteri of the pinealectomized rats, whereas no change was found in those of the control animals.

The same investigators (392) have also reported gonadal hypertrophy in pinealectomized male Wistar rats. Although these results are not susceptible of further statistical analysis (Table 20), the difference in testis and seminal-vesicle weights between the experimental and control groups is large and apparently significant. Body weights for these animals were not reported.

Nakashita (306) pinealectomized 8 immature rabbits whose body weights were approximately 1600 gm. Autopsy was performed twenty to forty days later, and 4 control rabbits of the same age and body weight were selected for comparison. The mean testis weight for the pinealectomized rabbits was 1.210 ± 0.026 gm. per kg. of body weight, as compared with a value of 1.025 ± 0.014 gm. per kg. of body weight for the control animals; this difference is significant at the 1 per cent level. Differences in seminal-vesicle and prostate weights were equally significant.

Table 20

The effects of pinealectomy on testis weight in the rat
(Simonnet et al., 392)

	Pinealectomized	Control
Age at autopsy	2 mo.	2 mo.
Number of animals	25	7
Testis weight ± M.D.*	1.336 ± 0.06 gm.	0.702 ± 0.06 gm.
Seminal-vesicle weight ± M.D.*	48 ± 2.0 mg.	21 ± 1.0 mg.
Age at autopsy	3 mo.	3 mo.
Number of animals	22	8
Testis weight ± M.D.*	2.014 ± 0.20 gm.	1.378 ± 0.08 gm.
Seminal-vesicle weight ± M.D.*	113 ± 9.0 mg.	79 ± 2.9 mg.

*Mean deviation

Izawa (192) has also reported gonadal hypertrophy following pinealectomy. He operated on twenty-day-old Wistar rats and examined the genital tracts at eighty-five days of age; the completeness of excision was later determined through serial sections. Twelve pinealectomized male rats were found to have an average body weight of 171.8 ± 8.9 gm. and an average testis weight of 2.200 ± 0.10 gm. Values for 11 control animals were 146.7 ± 9.8 gm. and 1.691 ± 0.14 gm. The difference in mean testis weights is significant at the 1 per cent level. The seminal-vesicle weights were 40.1 ± 6.5 mg. and 16.7 ± 5.0 mg. for the pinealectomized and control animals respectively. This difference is also significant at the 1 per cent level of confidence. The difference in body weights is not statistically significant. Ten pinealectomized female rats were found to have an average body weight of 155.2 ± 5.2 gm. and an average ovary weight of 76.4 ± 6.0 mg. Body and ovary weights for 10 control animals were 136.9 ± 5.1 gm. and 59.9 ± 3.7 mg. respectively. The difference in ovary weights is significant at the 5 per cent level of confidence. Uterus weights in pinealectomized and control animals were 408.6 ± 17.4 mg. and 315.3 ± 15.3 mg. respectively; this difference is significant at the 1 per cent level. Body weights for the two groups of female rats differed significantly at the 5 per cent level.

Kitay (212) reported that pinealectomy resulted in ovarian hypertrophy in the immature rat. Three small series of rats were prepared, each consisting of 8 to 10 pinealectomized animals and an equal number of sham-operated animals. Statistically significant ovarian hypertrophy was obtained in the pinealectomized rats in the first series. The mean ovary weights for the pinealectomized and control groups in Series 2 and 3 did not differ significantly. However, the difference in mean ovary weights in Series 3 approximated that observed in Series 1. In view of these contradictory findings, a fourth series was prepared, which consisted of a total of 96 female Wistar rats operated on when twenty-six days old. Three groups—pinealectomized and sham-operated and intact control rats—were used, each including 32 animals. Mean ovary weights for these groups were respectively 42.6 ± 1.4 mg., 35.7 ± 1.6 mg., and 36.2 ± 1.5 mg. at autopsy at fifty days. In this series the differences in ovary weights between the pinealectomized animals and either the sham-operated or the intact control rats were significant at the 1 per cent level of confidence. Analysis of covariance demonstrated that the same level of significance obtained when adjustment was made for variation in body weights.

Gonadal atrophy. The few instances of gonadal atrophy following pinealectomy (Table 18) are interesting in that the condition was observed only in male chicks and that all but one of the authors reported testicular hypertrophy in other series of pinealectomized chicks. The gonadal changes observed in these experiments varied according to the age at operation and the age at autopsy (Table 21). The only results that can be analyzed statistically were presented by Shellabarger. This investigator performed two experiments on white Leghorn cockerels; in both studies the animals were pinealectomized at two days of age and autopsied when nineteen or twenty days old. In one series (383), 26 pinealectomized chicks were found to have a mean testis weight of 44 mg. as compared with 51 mg. in 36 sham-operated control animals. This difference is significant at the 1 per cent level. Data on body weights were not supplied. Another series

Table 21

Time relations in experiments resulting in testis atrophy and hypertrophy in the chick

Ref. No.	Testis atrophy			Testis hypertrophy		
	Age at operation (days)	Age at autopsy (days)	Interval (days)	Age at operation (days)	Age at autopsy (days)	Interval (days)
50	?	?	210–240	—	—	—
280	1–2	240	238–239	1–2	45–90	44–89
383, 386	2	19–20	17–18	2	42–70	40–68
428	113	298	185	8	176	168

[27]

(386) also included a group of intact control chicks. Since information on body weights for this series has been made available (385), the results are presented in the form of testis weight per 100 gm. of body weight. The mean testis weight for 15 pinealectomized chicks was 32 ± 1.8 mg. per 100 gm. of body weight, whereas values for equal numbers of sham-operated and intact control animals were 40 ± 1.6 mg. and 36 ± 1.4 mg. respectively. The difference in mean gonad weights between the pinealectomized and sham-operated control chicks is significant at the 1 per cent level. However, the difference in values between the pinealectomized and intact control chicks is not statistically significant.

No change. Examination of the papers that report no gonadal change after pinealectomy actually reveals very little substantial evidence to support this finding. The chief criticism of most of these reports is that they were based on inadequate numbers of animals. Indeed, Dandy (64) did not even state how many dogs he studied. The information given in his paper indicates that only a very small number of animals could have been used, and that an unspecified number of these were still living when the report was made and therefore had not been examined. Furthermore, the autopsied animals were sacrificed at various ages between three and fifteen months (a range not likely to yield results susceptible of comparison) and the criteria employed in tissue examination were not clearly described. Nevertheless, this experiment has been cited by many reviewers as an outstanding proof that pinealectomy causes no gonadal change. Another paper frequently quoted in support of this belief is that of Andersen and Wolf (11); these investigators reported that pinealectomy in male rats at one to three days of age had no effect on testis weight at autopsy at sixty or seventy days. Both sham-operated and intact control animals were used for comparison. Since about 50 per cent of the rats developed infections, findings in these animals were presented separately (Table 22). Moreover, although female rats also were studied, no ovarian weights were reported. The authors themselves stated that their data were based on so few animals that their statistical computations were not reliable. The reports of no change published by Badertscher (19), Biedl (29), Exner and Boese (106), Hofmann (158), Kanamori (201), Kolmer and Löwy (215), and Vecchi (438) were fragmentary and were based on fewer than 4 pinealectomized animals in any one series. However, Hofmann did report seminal-vesicle hypertrophy in pinealectomized male rats, and Vecchi found uterine hypertrophy in pinealectomized female rats.

The remaining studies in this group demonstrate that pinealectomy performed in immature animals does not affect gonadal weight in such animals at maturity. Hartog Jager and Heil (153) reported that the gonad weights of 8 male and 17 female pinealectomized rats did not differ significantly from those of 8 male and 12 female sham-operated control rats. Ages at operation and autopsy were not specified, but average body weights at autopsy were said to be 200 and

Table 22

The effects of pinealectomy on testis weight in the rat

(Andersen and Wolf, 11)

Age at autopsy (days)	Group	Infection	No. of animals	Body weight ± S.E. (gm.)	Testis weight ± S.E. (gm.)
60	Pinealectomized	No	2	178	2.48
60	Sham-operated	No	0	—	—
60	Intact	No	4	169 ± 7	2.29 ± 0.07
60	Pinealectomized	Yes	5	144 ± 11	1.90 ± 0.24
60	Sham-operated	Yes	6	162 ± 12	2.20 ± 0.26
60	Intact	Yes	4	137 ± 17	1.98 ± 0.16
70	Pinealectomized	No	6	184 ± 17	2.16 ± 0.38
70	Sham-operated	No	4	190 ± 3	2.55 ± 0.21
70	Intact	No	5	194 ± 3	2.56 ± 0.22
70	Pinealectomized	Yes	3	177 ± 17	2.41 ± 0.17
70	Sham-operated	Yes	1	150	1.28
70	Intact	Yes	2	189	2.56

175 gm. for the male and female rats respectively. In another experiment described in the same paper, sixty-one-day-old female rats were described as weighing 91 gm. Apparently gonad weights were determined at 100 to 130 days of age—at least in fully mature animals. These authors did report that the average seminal-vesicle weight in the pinealectomized male rats was double the average weight in the control animals. In view of this finding, it is unfortunate that the testes were not examined histologically. Renton and Rusbridge (357) reported that pinealectomy in 11 female and 5 male albino rats produced no significant gonadal changes as compared with results in an equal number of control animals at autopsy at 340 days of age. Many of the fragmentary experiments (106, 158, 215, 438) mentioned in the preceding paragraph might also be included in this group of reports on animals autopsied when too old to show changes.

Miscellaneous findings. Several authors administered pineal extracts and implants to pinealectomized animals and reported that normal gonadal development was maintained (306, 383, 384, 392, 412, 413).

Metabolic studies on the gonads of pinealectomized rats have been published. A decreased uptake of P^{32} occurred in the ovaries (31). An increased uptake of P^{32} by the testes was reported by one group (31), but this finding was not confirmed by others (390). However, the total testicular phosphate content was increased; although the adenosine triphosphate fraction decreased, the glucose-bound phosphate increased markedly (390, 391, 392). Pinealectomy was reported to increase the rate of aerobic (316, 317) and anaerobic (206, 307, 309) glycolysis in the vaginal mucous membrane.

Gonadal development in the offspring of pinealectomized animals has been studied by only two investigators. Mesaki (273, 275) found that the gonads of the offspring of female rabbits that had been pinealectomized while immature were markedly larger at birth than those of the offspring of a sham-operated control group. It should be noted that the hypertrophy was significant when computed in

Table 23

The effects of pinealectomy in the rabbit on gonad weight in offspring
(Mesaki, 275)

	Offspring of pinealectomized rabbits	
No. of litters	5	
Total no. of fetuses	27	
Mean litter size	5.4	
Sex	*Male*	*Female*
No. of fetuses	12	15
Gonad weight ± S.E.	13.1 ± 0.8 mg.	6.3 ± 0.3 mg.
P	< 0.02	< 0.001
Gonad weight* ± S.E.	25.3 ± 0.5 mg/100 gm.	11.6 ± 0.5 mg/100 gm.
P	< 0.01	< 0.001
	Offspring of control rabbits	
No. of litters	5	
Total no. of fetuses	34	
Mean litter size	6.8	
Sex	*Male*	*Female*
No. of fetuses	17	17
Gonad weight ± S.E.	10.8 ± 0.4 mg.	4.1 ± 1.2 mg.
P		
Gonad weight* ± S.E.	22.8 ± 0.7 mg/100 gm.	8.6 ± 0.2 mg/100 gm.
P		

*Expressed as mg/100 gm. of body weight

terms of both mg. of gross ovary weight and mg. per 100 gm. of body weight (Table 23). Sullens and Overholser (403) reported no gonadal changes in the offspring of pinealectomized rats. Autopsies were performed at sixty days—an age not likely to demonstrate the effects of pinealectomy on intra-uterine development.

Pineal-Extract Administration

Many papers have been published concerning the effects of pineal-extract administration on the gonads (Tables 24 and 26) and genital tracts (Tables 25 and 26) of treated animals. However, all but a few of these studies are fragmentary, inconclusive, and statistically inevaluable. Only the following studies merit comment.

Gonadal hypertrophy. Shellabarger (383) injected aqueous pineal extract in 32 five-day-old white Leghorn cockerels daily for fourteen days. Twenty-six cockerels received an equivalent amount of brain-tissue extract, and 36 animals served as untreated controls. Testis weights were determined at autopsy at twenty days of age on the day following the last injection. The mean testis weight for the pineal-treated group was 55 mg., compared with 48 mg. for the group treated with brain extract and 51 mg. for the untreated group. Analysis of variance revealed that the mean testis weight of the pineal-treated group was significantly greater (at the 1 per cent level of confidence) than the mean testis weight of the two control groups combined. However, further information (385) concerning the body weights of the animals used in this experiment suggests that the aforementioned difference in testis weights is not significant when variation in body weights is taken into account.

Gonadal atrophy. Shellabarger (384, 385) also has reported gonadal atrophy in white Leghorn cockerels treated with aqueous pineal extract. Sixteen twenty-day-old cockerels were injected with pineal extract daily for sixteen days and 13 control animals were injected with water. Mean testis weights, as determined at autopsy on the day following the last injection, were 177 ± 22 mg. for the

Table 24

References on the effects of pineal-extract administration on the gonads

Animal	Hypertrophy	Atrophy	No change
Dog	220	220	423
Fowl	383	339, 340, 384, 430	384
Guinea pig		279, 303, 455	423
Mouse		89, 303, 449	114, 292, 375, 457
Rabbit	345	89, 345, 460	
Rat	282	89, 213, 303, 432, 449, 452	153, 167, 397, 423, 455

pineal-treated group and 261 ± 25 mg. for the water-treated group. This difference is significant at the 5 per cent level of confidence. A second experiment involving the use of brain-extract-treated as well as pineal- and water-treated groups yielded results that were equally significant. The author stated that the testis atrophy ob-

Table 25

References on effects of pineal-extract administration on the genital organs where no changes or observations on the gonads were recorded

Organ	Animal	Stimulation	Inhibition	No change
Penis (erection)	Rat		285	
Prostate gland	Mouse and rat		303	
Sperm (count)	Rat		288	
Spermatic vesicles	Mouse	375	303	
	Castrated mouse			88
	Rat		303	
Uterus	Guinea pig			359
	Castrated guinea pig			88
	Mouse	375		

Table 26

References on modes of pineal-extract administration and the effects on the genital tract

Mode	Hypertrophy	Atrophy	No change
Epiglandol injection			359
Epiphysan injection	345, 375	279, 339, 340, 345	375, 384
Epiphysan feeding	220	220	
Epiphysormone injection	282	285, 288	292
Pineal-extract injection	383	89, 213, 303, 340, 384, 430, 432, 449, 452, 455, 460	88, 153, 423, 455, 457
Fischer's extract injection			114, 384
Hanson's extract injection			384
Pineal feeding			167, 397

tained in these experiments may not be related to variation in body weight, since no differences in mean body weights were observed between the experimental groups and their respective control groups.

Kitay and Altschule (213) administered an aqueous pineal extract to three series of female Wistar rats. The 19 animals in Series 1, started at thirty-two days of age, were given 0.5 ml. of pineal extract daily for fourteen days. Series 2 (21 rats) and Series 3 (18 rats), started at thirty and forty-five days of age respectively, were given 1.0 ml. per day of the same extract for the same period of time. Each series included a control group of equal size that was treated with an equivalent volume of distilled water. Ovary and body weights in all three series were measured at autopsy on the day following the last injection. The mean ovary weights of the various pineal-treated and control groups are presented in Table 27. Analysis of covariance of ovary weight and body weight was made for each group; the mean ovary weights, adjusted for variation in body weights, also are shown in the table. Diminution of ovary weight in the pineal-treated groups was observed in all three series. The observed decrease in mean ovary weight in Series 1 is not statistically significant of itself. However, when variation in body weight is taken into account through analysis of covariance, the difference proves to be significant at the 5 per cent level of confidence. The ovaries of the rats in this series did not differ in appearance from those of control animals. The mean ovary weight of this pineal-treated group in Series 2 was 36 per cent less than that of the control group. This difference is significant at the 0.1 per cent level, and the significance is unchanged by analysis of covariance. In Series 2, 19 of the 21 control rats had hemorrhagic ovarian follicles, whereas only 3 pineal-treated animals showed such findings. This difference also is significant at the 0.1 per cent level of confidence. The decrease in mean ovary weight in the pineal-treated rats of Series 3 is significant at the 5 per cent level. However, this difference is not significant when variation in body weight is

[34]

Table 27

Effects of pineal-extract administration on ovary weight in the rat
(Kitay and Altschule, 213)

Series	Age at onset (days)	Age at autopsy (days)	No. of rats	Treatment	Mean ovary wts. ± S.E.* (mg.)	P	Mean ovary wts. ± S.E.† (mg.)	P
1	32	47	19	Pineal	29.7 ± 2.4	> 0.05	30.3 ± 1.0	< 0.05
			19	Water	34.0 ± 1.7		33.4 ± 0.9	
2	30	45	21	Pineal	18.7 ± 1.1	< 0.001	18.8 ± 1.0	< 0.001
			21	Water	29.3 ± 1.5		29.1 ± 1.5	
3	45	60	18	Pineal	40.4 ± 2.8	< 0.05	42.7 ± 1.6	> 0.05
			18	Water	49.0 ± 2.4		46.7 ± 2.1	

*Mean ± standard error of the mean
†Adjusted mean ± standard error of the mean after correction by analysis of covariance

taken into account through analysis of covariance. The ovaries of the animals in this series did not differ in appearance from those of the control animals.

No change. Shellabarger (384) found that injection of either epiphysan or pineal extract prepared according to the method of Hanson or Steinberg did not affect testis weight in the white Leghorn cockerel. Weinberg and Fletcher (457) reported that pineal injection did not change testis weight in immature mice treated three times weekly for four weeks. Their results are questionable, since the pineal-treated animals were found to be cachectic and moribund at autopsy.

Miscellaneous findings. Mesaki (272, 274) reported that after pineal extract was administered to rabbits, their offspring showed gonadal atrophy when examined at birth.

Pineal Implantation

Studies of gonadal development following pineal implantation have been based on experimental groups that were too small to permit any conclusions (Table 28).

Miscellaneous Methods

The injection of melted paraffin in the pineal region of one dog apparently retarded its genital development in comparison with that of an intact control animal (313). Hemisection of the brain stem in

Table 28

References on the effects of pineal implantation on the gonads

Animal	Atrophy	No change
Chick		221
Guinea pig	42, 199, 200	
Mouse		312
Rabbit		106
Rat	42, 234, 299, 300	85, 153

immature female dogs, with consequent destruction of the pineal gland, was reported to retard genital development (210). In view of the methods used in both these studies, it is possible that the findings were the effects of nonspecific trauma.

RELATION TO VAGINAL OPENING

Pinealectomy

Acceleration. Pinealectomy in the rat has been reported to accelerate opening of the vaginal membrane (392, 393, 396, 448). In one experiment 28 female rats of the Wistar strain were pinealectomized at twenty-two days of age. At fifty-three days the vaginal orifice was patent in 18 of these but had opened in only 4 of 15 control animals of the same age (393). Data in the remaining papers are fragmentary.

No change. On the other hand, two papers reported no change. Andersen and Wolf (11) concluded that vaginal opening in the rat was not affected by pinealectomy, on the basis of the data summarized in Table 29. Del Castillo (48) found that the date of vaginal opening did not differ significantly among 6 pinealectomized, 2 sham-operated, and 2 intact rats.

The age at vaginal opening was reported as unchanged in the offspring of pinealectomized rats (85, 403).

Table 29

The effects of pinealectomy on age at vaginal opening in rats

(Andersen and Wolf, 11)

Group	No. of animals	Mean age (days)	Age range (days)
Pinealectomized	6	41	41–43
Sham-operated controls	4	44	40–46
Intact controls	7	44	41–47

Table 30

References on retardation of vaginal opening by administration of pineal extract

Animal	Reference numbers
Guinea pig	455
Mouse	101, 102, 114, 115, 303, 447, 449
Rat	303, 447, 449, 455

Pineal-Extract Administration

Retardation. Pineal-extract administration was consistently found to retard the opening of the vaginal membrane in guinea pigs, mice, and rats (Table 30). The duration of retardation was reported to vary with the concentration of the extract (101, 114, and Figure 3).

Miscellaneous findings. One group (85, 151, 364–368) reported earlier vaginal opening in the offspring of rats treated with pineal extract.

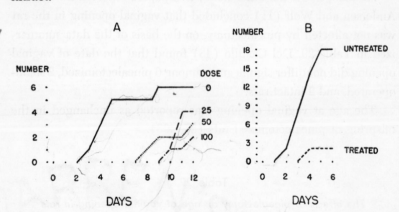

FIGURE 3. Effects of daily pineal-extract administration on vaginal opening in 22-day-old 8-gram mice. The ordinate indicates the number of mice with patent vaginal orifices and the abscissa the number of days of extract injection. Graph A, adapted from Fischer (114), illustrates results following daily injection of 0, 25, 50, or 100 gamma of pineal extract to groups of six mice each. Graph B, adapted from Engel (101), illustrates the effect of daily injection of 3 to 6 gamma of extract. The treated and untreated groups included 18 animals each.

[38]

Retardation. Pineal implants have been observed to retard vaginal opening (300, 302, 447).

RELATION TO THE ESTRUS CYCLE

Pinealectomy

Stimulation. Pinealectomy has usually been reported to prolong estrus and shorten diestrus (Table 31). Katagiri (203) pinealectomized mature white mice during the indifferent stage and examined vaginal smears daily for two weeks. His 20 experimental animals had a mean of 10 ± 0.3 days of estrus, whereas 20 control animals had a mean of 3.7 ± 0.3 days. The difference is significant at the 1 per cent level.

Inhibition. One investigator (252, 253) reported a delayed onset of the first estrus in pinealectomized cats.

No change. Andersen and Wolf (11) stated that the regularity of estrus cycles was unchanged in pinealectomized rats, but they did not specify the lengths of their observation periods or mention the relative durations of estrus and diestrus. Another worker (153) who reported no change based his conclusion solely on age at the onset of the first estrus cycle.

Pineal-Extract Administration

The most frequently reported effects of pineal extracts are retardation of the onset of estrus and prolongation of diestrus (Table 32). However, since most of the data are not statistically significant and since other workers have reported both stimulation and no change, definite conclusions cannot be made.

Pineal Implantation

Studies on the influence of pineal implants on the estrus cycle have yielded inconclusive results (Table 33).

Table 31

References on the effects of pinealectomy on the estrus cycle

Animal	Stimulation	Inhibition	No change
Cat		252, 253	
Mouse	203, 276		
Rat	201, 205, 276, 307, 309		11, 153

Table 32

References on the effects of pineal-extract administration on the estrus cycle

Animal	Stimulation	Inhibition	No change
Dog		43	
Guinea pig		279	
Mouse	88, 93, 388	39, 150, 165, 276, 303, 447, 449, 451, 452	410
Pig	40	40	
Rat	282	303, 432, 447, 449, 451, 452	1, 419, 446

Table 33

References on the effects of pineal implantation on the estrus cycle

Animal	Stimulation	Inhibition	No change
Guinea pig		302	
Mouse		117, 447	376, 410
Castrated mouse	376, 388		410
Rat		447	1, 153

Miscellaneous Findings

Certain investigators (119, 205, 347, 475, 476, 477) claimed to have isolated in the urine of children a factor that inhibited estrus in the rat; they alleged that this undefined substance originated in the pineal gland.

[40]

Pinealectomy

Studies on pinealectomized animals suggest that the operation increases gonadotrophin secretion or enhances sensitivity to gonadotrophin or both. Mesaki (277) reported that injection of 0.8 to 3.0 rat units of pituitary gonadotrophin in pinealectomized immature rats resulted in the appearance of macroscopic follicles and corpora lutea in ovaries examined three days after the first injection. Five of the 8 experimental animals showed 10 or more mature follicles and corpora lutea each; the remaining 3 showed 4 to 9 each. Of the 6 sham-operated control animals similarly handled, not one produced visible mature follicles. Furthermore, in 4 of the 6 controls neither mature follicles nor corpora lutea could be found on microscopical examination.

Sakurane (373) injected early pregnancy urine in pinealectomized, unilaterally orchidectomized male rabbits. In each case the remaining testis showed further accelerated growth (i.e., hypertrophy, hyperplasia, and increased spermatogenesis) as compared with those of unilaterally orchidectomized but unpinealectomized control animals.

Nakashita (306) injected blood serum from pinealectomized male rabbits in cocks; he reported that hypertrophy of the comb and testes occurred. He also found that when pinealectomized rabbits were either hypophysectomized or given pineal implants, blood serum from these animals had no such effect in the cock, whereas blood serum from hypophysectomized (and pinealectomized) rabbits that had received pituitary implants did produce hypertrophy of the cock comb and testes. A similar change was produced by the serum from a few rabbits in each of which three pituitary glands had been implanted but which were otherwise intact. The active fraction of the serum was found to be a water-soluble protein that was insoluble in ether or alcohol. Neither castration, adrenalectomy, nor thyroidectomy affected the activity of serum from the pinealectomized rabbits. Comparable results were obtained by using male rabbits as donors and mice as assay animals (305, 417) and by using female rabbits and mice in the same respective capacities (417). Most of these studies were based on very small numbers of animals.

Testis size and phosphorus content were said to have increased in pinealectomized rats and to have returned to normal after hypophysectomy (391).

A poorly documented study stated that injection of pregnancy urine in pinealectomized female rats caused no change in ovary weight in comparison with similarly treated control animals (153). Administration of a pituitary preparation containing both gonadotrophic and thyrotrophic activity was alleged to decrease the weights of the preputial glands, the uteri, and the Fallopian tubes of pinealectomized rats, as compared with those of similarly treated control animals. Pinealectomy in the rat has been reported to prevent the formation of antihormone in the serum after subcutaneous injection of anterior pituitary gonadotrophin (91, 94).

The gonadotrophin content of the adenohypophysis of male chicks pinealectomized at two days of age was found to be significantly decreased at autopsy at twenty days of age (383). However, a statistically significant increase in gonadotrophin content was found when autopsy was performed at forty to forty-five days of age in other chicks so treated (384).

Pineal-Extract Administration

Relation to pituitary gonadotrophin. Injection of pineal extract has almost invariably inhibited the effect of pituitary gonadotrophin injected at the same time (Table 34). The bulk of the data is in agreement with the following examples: Wakida (452) injected anterior pituitary extract alone in 17 young female rats that served as controls; corpora lutea were produced in all the animals, an average of 7 being found (in both ovaries) in each animal. He then injected both pituitary and pineal extracts in 38 animals; only 8 of these

Table 34

References on the relation of pineal-extract administration to the action of injected pituitary gonadotrophin

Animal	Target organ	Inhibition	No change
Bird	Testicle	53	
Mouse	Vagina (estrus)	277	
	Ovary	86, 89, 181, 461	446
	Seminal vesicles and prostate gland	89	
Rabbit	Ovary	59, 89, 100, 181, 448	118
	Seminal vesicles and prostate gland	89	
Rat	Vagina (estrus)	96, 277	
	Ovary	89, 95, 96, 99, 181, 277, 452	446
	Seminal vesicles and prostate gland	89	

showed corpora lutea, with an average of 3 for both ovaries together.

Mesaki (277) reported that pineal extract prevented pituitary gonadotrophin from inducing estrus in mature mice. The vaginal smear was first observed daily for three weeks to determine regularity of cycles; injections were then made on the first subsequent day of diestrus. Six animals given gonadotrophin alone developed estrus after exactly four days, whereas 10 animals given both pineal extract and gonadotrophin developed it only after 5.2 ± 0.2 days. This difference is significant at the 1 per cent level.

Engel (96) found that extracts prepared from human pineal glands also prevented pituitary gonadotrophin from inducing corpus luteum formation in rats; this inhibiting effect was produced by extracts made from 25 human glands.

Injection of simple aqueous pineal extracts has been reported to decrease the gonadotrophin content of the pituitary glands of forty-seven-day-old male chicks (384) and of guinea pigs (303), mice (303), rats (303), and rabbits (452). Epiphysan and Hanson's and Fischer's extracts had no effect on pituitary gonadotrophin content in male chicks (384).

[43]

Table 35

*References on the relation of pineal-extract administration to the action
of injected placental gonadotrophin*

Animal	Target organ	Synergism	Inhibition	No change
Frog	Spermatozoa		440	
Mouse	Ovary	114, 292	181	232, 446
Rabbit	Ovary	443	52, 100, 181	232
Rat	Ovary		97, 181	232, 446

Relation to placental gonadotrophin. The effects of pineal extracts
on the action of placental gonadotrophin have been investigated; the
results are confusing, in that synergism, inhibition, and no change
have all been reported (Table 35).

Pineal Implantation

One investigator reported that pineal implants in the rat produced testicular atrophy and that normal testicular development was
restored in these animals by pituitary implants (200).

RELATION TO ACTIONS OF ESTROGEN AND ANDROGEN

Pinealectomy

Pinealectomy in immature rats did not affect the estrus-producing
action of injected estrogen (277). Pinealectomy in the mature rat
increased aerobic glycolysis in the vaginal mucous membrane, and
injected estrogen accelerated this glycolysis more in the pinealectomized animals than in the controls (317).

Pineal-Extract Administration

Administration of pineal extracts has consistently been observed
to have no effect on estrus cycles that were produced by estrogen
injected at the same time (Table 36). Extracts have been reported
to have no effect on urinary estrogen excretion in women (12). Pineal
extract given to cocks did not alter comb hypertrophy produced by

[44]

Table 36

References on the relation of pineal-extract administration to the action of injected estrogen

Animal	Inhibition	No change
Mouse		277
Castrated mouse	39	150, 277, 452
Rat		277
Castrated rat		277, 452

testosterone (97). On the other hand, epiphysormone administered to rats was found to inhibit penile erection caused by testosterone (285).

The effects of pineal injection on urinary 17-ketosteroid excretion are presented in Chapter VI.

RELATION TO FECUNDITY AND PREGNANCY

Pinealectomy

Pinealectomy produced no change in litter size in the guinea pig (56) and the rat (189, 448). Studies of litter size in the rabbit were inconclusive (56, 106, 275). A number of dead and dying animals were noted in the litters of cats (65, 252, 253) and rats (278) that had been pinealectomized before impregnation. Pregnancy occurred at an earlier age in the rat after operation (189, 448). Pinealectomy shortened the duration of pregnancy in the rabbit (273, 275) but did not change it in the rat (153).

Pineal-Extract Administration

Pineal extracts have had varying effects on litter size (Table 37). Hanson's extract produced blindness, passivity, and weakness in the offspring of rats that had received it (151, 364–368). Extracts lowered the age at first impregnation in the guinea pig (264, 265) and prolonged the duration of pregnancy in rabbits (272, 274).

[45]

Table 37

References on the effects of pineal-extract administration on litter size

Animal	Increase	Decrease	No change
Dog			419
Guinea pig		279	425
Rabbit	272	274	
Rat		330	419, 425

Pineal Implantation

Pineal implantation did not affect litter size in the rabbit (106).

Miscellaneous Studies

The ratio of pineal weight to body weight was reported to be correlated with fecundity in mammals (230, 231). The ratio of pituitary weight to pineal weight was also found to be correlated with fecundity in 19 mammalian species and 29 avian species (229). A uniformly low ratio (i.e., large pineal gland) is related to low fecundity in birds. In birds the ratios range between 1.3 and 7.5, with an average of 3.0. Mammals such as the rat and mouse have high ratios and are very fecund—e.g., mouse 48 and rat 31, as compared with cow 15 and man 4.

COMMENT

The data discussed in this chapter represent the bulk of those observations on pineal function that can be statistically analyzed. Studies made by five investigators have been cited in support of the concept that pinealectomy causes gonadal hypertrophy. Three of these (212, 384, 396) represent the best evidence available. The remaining data cannot be relied on, since sham-operated control animals were not used. Furthermore, in two experiments on rats (192, 392), gonadal hypertrophy was not conclusively demonstrated, since variations in body weight were not taken into account. More extensive studies, using larger numbers of animals and including observations on the aforementioned factors, are indicated.

The data purporting to show gonadal atrophy following pineal-ectomy are questionable because none of the reports demonstrate that the observed decrease in testis weight was independent of variation in body weight. Furthermore, the alleged statistical significance was based solely on differences between pinealectomized and sham-operated chicks; comparison of pinealectomized and intact control animals did not yield significant results.

Reports that gonadal hypertrophy follows pineal-extract administration (383, 385) are equally open to question. On the other hand, data demonstrating gonadal atrophy after pineal-extract injection (213, 384, 385) are statistically significant; apparently they were not influenced by variation in body weight.

The observed effects of pinealectomy on the vaginal membrane (acceleration of opening) and on the estrus cycle (prolongation of the estral phase) are uniform, and the data cited are statistically significant. Similarly, the inhibitory effects of pineal-extract injection on vaginal opening and on the action of pituitary gonadotrophin are also consistent. Further studies should be undertaken, since not enough evidence is available to permit final conclusions. It is still not clearly understood how injected gonadotrophin acts in pineal-ectomized animals; this might be learned by using animals that had been both pinealectomized and hypophysectomized. Investigators should use larger numbers of animals than previously. These considerations also apply to future studies on the inhibitory effect of pineal extracts on injected pituitary gonadotrophin. Observations on the effects of pinealectomy and pineal-extract administration on the gonadal hormones, though not wholly consistent, suggest that the hormonal action is not affected by either. Further documentation is required here as well.

CHAPTER VI

Corticotrophin and the Adrenal Cortex

PINEALECTOMY

The commonest reported results of pinealectomy are adrenal hypertrophy and hyperplasia (Table 38). However, the validity of the findings is questionable because too few animals were used and statistical significance was not demonstrated. A few studies of changes in adrenal cholesterol and ascorbic acid in the rat are subject to similar criticism (391, 392, 395, and Table 39). No significant change was found in the rate of anaerobic glycolysis in the adrenal glands of pinealectomized rats (206, 309).

PINEAL-EXTRACT ADMINISTRATION

Studies of changes in the adrenal gland following pineal-extract administration are few and inconclusive (Table 40).

A number of workers have studied the effects of pineal injection on the biochemical changes caused by adrenocortical hormones. Administration of extracts in the rabbit was reported to prevent the hyperglycemia (125) and the rises in blood ketone bodies (112), phosphate (113), and magnesium (113) that were produced in control animals by injecting anterior pituitary extracts, which presumably contained ACTH. The marked fall in postoperative ketonemia produced by pineal injection in human subjects (18) may represent an analogous change. In other experiments rabbits were subjected to high external temperatures after half of them were given pineal

Table 38

References on the effects of pinealectomy on the adrenal glands

Animal	Hypertrophy	Atrophy	No change
Cat	65, 252		
Dog			64
Fowl	186, 188		280, 384
Rabbit	17		
Rat	193, 194, 201, 308, 309, 391, 392, 395, 438, 448	392, 395	11, 153, 357
Sheep	68		

Table 39

The effects of pinealectomy on adrenal ascorbic acid and cholesterol in the rat (Simonnet et al., 392)

	Pinealectomized rats		Control rats	
	Male	Female	Male	Female
Number of animals	14	8	11	5
Mean adrenal weight	32 mg.	40 mg.	40 mg.	37 mg.
Adrenal weight*	26 mg/100 gm.	37 mg/100 gm.	33 mg/100 gm.	28 mg/100 gm.
Total cholesterol (per 100 gm. of gland)	1.30 gm.	1.86 gm.	1.90 gm.	1.58 gm.
Ascorbic acid (per 100 gm. of gland)	109 mg.	235 mg.	180 mg.	262 mg.

*Expressed as mg/100 gm. of body weight

Table 40

References on the effects of pineal-extract administration on the adrenal glands

Animal	Hypertrophy	Atrophy	No change
Dog		220	
Fowl	339, 340		384
Rat		332, 450	153, 167, 452

extract. The treated group had slightly more initial hypothermia and less final hyperthermia than the control animals; decreased hyperglycemia and increased water retention were also noted, but the results were not statistically significant (245). Pineal extracts given to human subjects in one study caused no significant change in the twenty-four-hour 17-ketosteroid excretion after treatment for varying lengths of time (47, 362); however, adequate control levels were not determined. In a more carefully controlled study (136), 10 male patients were treated with epiphysan for four days; a significant decrease in 17-ketosteroid excretion was reported. The mean fall was 3.2 ± 0.75 mg., a value significant at the 1 per cent level of confidence. In still another study, pineal extract significantly decreased urinary ketosteroid excretion for two weeks when administered daily to one thoroughly studied patient (10).

Administration of corticotrophin in the rat was found to restore the pineal uptake of P^{32} to normal after hypophysectomy had markedly increased it (356).

COMMENT

Pineal extracts apparently inhibit changes in blood chemistry that are consistent with the action of corticotrophin and the adrenocortical hormones; they also decrease 17-ketosteroid excretion.

CHAPTER VII

Thyrotrophin and the Thyroid Gland

PINEALECTOMY

The effects of pinealectomy on the thyroid gland are variously reported as (1) no change and (2) hypertrophy and hyperplasia (Table 41). These data must be interpreted with caution, since very few animals were used in most of the studies and thorough histologic studies were rarely made. An increased rate of anaerobic glycolysis was observed in the thyroid gland of the rat after pinealectomy (206, 307, 309).

Pinealectomized rabbits were reported to be resistant to antipyretic drugs and abnormally sensitive to pyrogenic substances (217, 304). Additional studies on these abnormal febrile responses are difficult to interpret and accept (217, 304); they purport to relate

Table 41

References on the effects of pinealectomy on the thyroid gland

Animal	Hypertrophy	No change
Cat	65	
Dog		64
Fowl	186, 188	280, 384
Rabbit	17, 304	
Rat	193, 194, 201, 308, 448	7, 11, 153, 357, 438; 403*
Sheep	68	

*403: No change observed in thyroid glands of offspring of pinealectomized rats

the observed changes to altered thyroid function following pinea-lectomy.

PINEAL-EXTRACT ADMINISTRATION

The described effects of pineal extract on the thyroid gland are also inconclusive (Table 42). Epiphysan was reported to synergize the action of injected thyroxin in guinea pigs—merely on the basis of the finding that it caused an even greater fall in body weight and in the weights of the liver, spleen, testes, and adrenal glands than was produced by thyroxin alone (260). These changes do not by any means establish synergism.

Epiphysormone inhibited the action of injected thyrotrophin on the thyroid gland of rats, as indicated by decreased gland weight, flatter follicle cells, and increased follicle diameter in comparison with controls treated with thyrotrophic hormone alone (290). Administration of epiphysormone to partially thyroidectomized rats was reported to diminish the compensatory thyroid hypertrophy normally found in hemithyroidectomized animals (291). Histologic examination of these pineal-treated animals showed increased colloid content, increased follicle diameter, and flattening of the follicle cells. Injecting epiphysan in the guinea pig has been reported both to inhibit (91, 94) and to synergize (261) the effects of injected thyrotrophic hormone on the thyroid gland. These data, as reported, do not permit statistical evaluation.

Table 42

References on the effects of pineal-extract administration on the thyroid gland

Animal	Hypertrophy	Atrophy	No change
Dog		220	
Fowl	339, 340		
Guinea pig			261, 402
Rat		289, 290	153, 167

CHAPTER VIII

Pancreas, Parathyroid Glands, and Thymus

PANCREAS

Pinealectomy

The effects of pinealectomy on the pancreas have been reported as: no change in the dog (64) or rat (403, 438) and hypertrophy in the rat (193, 194).

Pineal-Extract Administration

Epiphysan seemingly produced pancreatic hypertrophy in the female dog and decreased pancreas weight in the male (220). Epiglandol was reported to inhibit the hypoglycemic effect of insulin in human subjects (350), whereas a chloroformic pineal extract apparently synergized insulin action in the rabbit (126).

PARATHYROID GLANDS

Pinealectomy

Pinealectomy produced no change in the parathyroid glands of the dog (64) and the chick (280), but was reported to cause parathyroid hypertrophy in the rabbit (304). A complicated study was made that allegedly demonstrated a relation between parathyroid and pineal functions (304). This report must be regarded with skepticism, since small numbers of animals were used.

Pineal-Extract Administration

Epiphysormone administration in the rat was said to increase the number, the central distribution, and the vacuolization and transparency of the principal cells of the parathyroid glands (293); the oxyphil cells were decreased. Hyperemia, parenchymal hyperplasia, and decrease of connective tissue were also reported. Epiphysor-mone, administered to thyro-parathyroidectomized dogs, was report-ed to lessen spasticity, rigidity, and convulsions and to increase blood calcium and phosphate concentrations (341).

THYMUS

Pinealectomy

The effects of pinealectomy on the thymus are inconclusive (Table 43). An increased rate of anaerobic glycolysis was reported in the thymus of the rat after pinealectomy (206, 307).

Pineal-Extract Administration

The reported effects of extract administration on the thymus gland are inconclusive (167, 220, 287, 339, 340).

Table 43
References on the effects of pinealectomy on the thymus

Animal	Hypertrophy	Atrophy	No change
Dog			64
Fowl			280
Rat	193, 201, 308, 448	438	11

CHAPTER IX

Skin Pigmentation

PINEALECTOMY

Pinealectomy in the tadpole had no effect on pigmentation and did not alter the "silvery reaction" produced by previous hypophysectomy (16). The operation in the eyeless catfish (468) and in the minnow (135, 379) did not affect the pigmentary response to changes in illumination. On the other hand, removal of the pineal eye in larval lampreys was reported to abolish the normal photo-pigmentary response and to produce continuous dark pigmentation of the skin (474). Further studies by the same investigator revealed that pinealectomy did not affect the paleness produced by previous hypophysectomy. Moreover, administration of an extract of the pineal organs of lampreys to pinealectomized lampreys did not alter their dark pigmentation. Covering the pineal eye in the lizard (344) did not change the skin reaction to light, whereas similar treatment produced dark pigmentation of the skin in teleosts (37). A number of studies have been published on the role of the pineal eye as a photoreceptor (e.g., 36, 54, 55), but a review of this phase of pineal function would be beyond the scope of this book.

ADMINISTRATION OF PINEAL SUBSTANCE AND EXTRACT

Feeding pineal glands from various species has consistently produced melanophore contraction with consequent decreased pigmentation in test animals, particularly the tadpole (Table 44); pineal implants have been reported to have a similar effect (404). Injecting an extract of a human pineal gland caused this reaction in toads (34).

Table 44

References on the effects of pineal administration on skin pigmentation

Animal	Decrease	No change
Axolotl		175
Fish	139, 469	155
Tadpole	4, 16, 34, 147, 175, 267, 268, 363, 404	209
Toad	34	

COMMENT

These findings suggest that the pineal gland affects the function of melanophore cells.

CHAPTER X

Carbohydrate, Lipid, Protein, and Electrolyte Metabolism

CARBOHYDRATE METABOLISM

Glucose

Pinealectomy. Pinealectomy produced a slight but significant blood sugar rise in mature rabbits within ten to twenty-five days after operation (2). The average blood sugar at this time was 114 ± 1.8 mg. per 100 ml. in 14 experimental animals and 96.8 ± 2.0 mg. per 100 ml. in the same number of control animals. When immature rabbits were used the values were 112.7 ± 2.0 mg. per 100 ml. in 10 pinealectomized animals and 98.2 ± 1.7 mg. per 100 ml. in 10 control animals. These differences are significant at the 1 per cent level of confidence. The glucose concentration in the pinealectomized rabbits was reported to be unchanged after injections of pituitary extract and gonadal hormones but to respond normally to administration of adrenalin and insulin (3). Pinealectomy in fowl produced only an insignificant tendency toward a blood sugar rise (324). Two other studies on blood sugar changes in pinealectomized animals have been reported (301, 470), but the data are fragmentary.

Pineal-extract administration. Pineal injection has had various effects on blood sugar concentrations (Table 45). The most consistent results have been reported by Frada (125), who found hypoglycemia after administering aqueous extracts and hyperglycemia after giving chloroformic extracts. Aqueous pineal extract was found to inhibit the hyperglycemia produced by adrenalin in the rabbit

[57]

Table 45

References on the effects of pineal-extract administration on blood glucose concentrations

Animal	Increase	Decrease	No change
Dog	459		82, 336
Man	41		18, 350
Rabbit	125, 126, 128, 131, 459	125, 127, 128, 131	

(127). Administration of an aqueous pineal extract to two psychotic patients, whose glucose-tolerance curves were elevated, resulted in a lowering of the curve in each instance (10). Various pineal extracts have been reported to produce glycosuria in the rabbit (198) and the cat (322).

Glycogen

Pinealectomy. Hepatic glycogen was not affected in pinealectomized fowl (328).

Pineal-extract administration. Pineal injection in the duck (339, 342), guinea pig (131), and rat (294) had no conclusive effects on hepatic glycogen. Similarly inconclusive changes in muscle glycogen were observed in the rat (294) and duck (326).

LIPID METABOLISM

Blood and Liver Lipids

Pineal-extract administration. No change was observed in the blood lipid concentration of fowl (339, 340) after treatment with epiphysan. The effects of epiphysan on hepatic lipids in the guinea pig (131) and fowl (340) also have been inconclusive.

Ketone Bodies

Pineal-extract administration. Pineal injection in human subjects has been reported to produce a marked decrease in hyperketonemia caused by the stress of surgical operation (18) and by various diseases, particularly diabetes (45, 46). No change in blood ketone-body concentration was observed in normal rabbits (112) or dogs (355) that received pineal extracts.

Cholesterol

Pinealectomy. Inconclusive variations in blood cholesterol concentration were observed in pinealectomized fowl (325).

Pineal-extract administration. Pineal injection in dogs (336) and fowl (339, 340) produced no significant change in blood cholesterol concentration.

PROTEIN METABOLISM

Plasma Protein

Pineal-extract administration. Epiphysan has been reported to raise the plasma protein concentration in fowl (340).

Blood Amino Acids

Pineal-extract administration. The blood amino-acid concentration in human subjects was found to be increased after injection of epiphysan (41).

Blood and Urine Uric Acid

Pineal-extract administration. Epiphysan has had inconclusive effects on blood and urine uric-acid concentrations in human subjects (134).

Blood Glutathione

Pineal-extract administration. Pineal-extract administration caused a mean increase in the blood glutathione concentration of 7.5 ± 1.0 mg. per 100 ml. of erythrocytes in 9 psychotic patients (10). This rise is significant at the 1 per cent level of confidence.

Urinary Nitrogen Excretion

Pinealectomy. Pinealectomy in mature rabbits has been reported to cause a 10 to 25 per cent fall in total urinary nitrogen excretion within three to five weeks after operation; the greatest fall was observed in the excretion of urea nitrogen, allantoin nitrogen, and ammonia nitrogen (254). Normal nitrogen balance was found to be restored in these rabbits by the administration of pituitary extracts (255) or gonadal hormones (256). On the other hand, in young rabbits the operation produced a negative nitrogen balance (257).

Pineal-extract administration. On the basis of fragmentary studies, pineal extracts were reported to produce a negative nitrogen balance in human subjects (63).

ELECTROLYTE METABOLISM

Calcium

Pinealectomy. No significant change in blood calcium concentrations was observed in pinealectomized fowl (324).

Pineal-extract administration. The effects of pineal injection on blood calcium concentrations in dogs (44, 336), fowl (339, 340), man (44), and rabbits (113, 183) have been inconclusive.

Phosphorus

Pinealectomy. Pinealectomy was observed to produce a slight but statistically significant decrease in blood phosphate concentration in rabbits, coincidentally with an increase in blood sugar (2, 3). No change was observed in pinealectomized fowl (329).

Pineal-extract administration. Blood phosphate concentration in the rabbit (113) and muscle inorganic-phosphate content in fowl (327) were not significantly changed by injection of pineal extracts.

Potassium

Pinealectomy. Pineal excision in fowl produced no significant change in serum potassium concentration (324).

Pineal-extract administration. Epiphysan injection in dogs (336) and ducks (339) was found to have no significant effect on serum potassium concentration.

Magnesium

Pineal-extract administration. The blood magnesium concentration in rabbits was unchanged by pineal injection (113).

Pineal-extract administration. Epiphysan produced no significant changes in muscle hydration in fowl (327).

Acid-Base Balance

Pineal-extract administration. Epiglandol caused a slight metabolic alkalosis in human subjects (445); another extract increased the plasma alkaline reserve in rabbits (239).

COMMENT

Significant rises in blood sugar and decreases in blood inorganic-phosphate concentration and in urinary nitrogen excretion have been reported in pinealectomized rabbits. Pineal-extract administration in psychotic patients caused significant elevation of blood glutathione; hyperketonemia due to surgical operations was lowered by such extracts.

CHAPTER XI

Tumor Growth

PINEALECTOMY

Pinealectomy has been reported to accelerate the growth of sarcoma transplants in the rat (204, 309). A contradictory report that it inhibits the growth of spontaneous and inoculated carcinoma in mice also has been published (138).

PINEAL ADMINISTRATION

All papers on pineal injection and implantation (Table 46) report inhibition of the growth of spontaneous and inoculated neoplasms.

Table 46

References on the effects of pineal administration on tumor growth

Animal	Inhibition	No change
Man	26, 297, 374	
Mouse	26, 77, 78, 88, 90, 98, 103	88
Rat	204, 308	

CHAPTER XII

Relations of Various Factors to the Pineal Gland

PINEAL ADMINISTRATION

Pineal weight did not change significantly in male chicks treated daily with various pineal preparations for twenty to twenty-five days (384); histologic examination of these glands was not reported. However, administration of aqueous pineal extract to capons caused a significant fall in pineal weight (384, 385). Castration alone was found to produce pineal hypertrophy; the average pineal weight in 12 forty-day-old capons was 3.44 ± 0.2 mg., as compared with 3.00 ± 0.1 mg. in intact control chicks. However, 12 capons of the same age given pineal extract for twenty days were found to have a mean pineal weight of 2.84 ± 0.1 mg. after twenty days. These results are significant at the 5 per cent level of confidence.

Hoskins (167) reported no changes in pineal weight in rats fed pineal substance; this work is inconclusive, since very few animals were used.

ACTIVITY OF ENDOCRINE GLANDS

Gonads

In general, the effects of castration on pineal histologic structure have been too variable to permit drawing conclusions (Table 47). However, one report presented results that merit comment. Shellabarger (384, 385) found that male chicks that had been castrated at nineteen days of age showed pineal hypertrophy when autopsied

Table 47

References on the effects of castration on the pineal gland

Animal	Hypertrophy	Atrophy	No change
Cat		15	
Cattle		51, 441	144, 145
Chick	384		
Horse	229	480	
Pig	228, 229, 233		
Rabbit	346, 370	371, 372	
Rat	369		58, 215

at forty days. In one series, 12 of these caponized animals had an average pineal weight of 3.44 ± 0.2 mg., whereas 12 intact control chicks had an average pineal weight of 3.00 ± 0.1 mg.—the difference being significant at the 5 per cent level. Injection of pineal extract in the capons restored their average pineal weight to a normal level (see above). Unilateral gonadectomy in the rabbit was reported to cause a decrease in pineal argyrophil staining reaction that was later followed by a rise (387); this finding is nonspecific (see *Adrenal Glands* and *Thyroid Gland*, below). Castration in the rat was reported to produce an increased pineal uptake of P^{32}, particularly in the female (31).

A confusing variety of histologic changes in the pineal gland have been reported to occur with functional changes in the gonads (70, 72, 73, 152, 269). Pineal hyperchromatophilia, cytoplasmic swelling, increased intercellular colloid formation, increased granularity, and increased vascularization have been reported to follow administration of testosterone in male rats and administration of estrogen or chorionic gonadotrophin in female rats (415, 416). On the other hand, administration of progesterone, estradiol, stilbestrol, or testosterone propionate to male chicks was reported to have no effect on pineal weight or histologic appearance (384). Reports of histologic changes in the pineal gland during pregnancy are varied

Table 48

References on the effects of pregnancy on the pineal gland

Animal	Hypertrophy	Atrophy	No change
Bird		71, 74	
Cat	15		
Cow	407	111, 407	144, 145
Guinea pig	105, 378		
Man			35, 124, 196
Pig			35
Rabbit	378		
Sheep			66

(Table 48). An x-ray study of 120 women of childbearing age revealed that the incidence of pineal calcification in 40 pregnant women was 40 per cent, as compared with 15 per cent in 40 women who had never been pregnant. The incidence in 40 subjects who had been pregnant in the past was also 40 per cent (130).

Pituitary Gland

Hypophysectomy in the rat and guinea pig had no effect on the histologic appearance of the pineal gland (152) but did increase pineal uptake of P^{32} and I^{131} by 70 to 900 per cent in the rat (356).

Adrenal Glands

Adrenalectomy in the rat produced no change in the pineal gland eight days after the operation (58)—an interval too brief to permit the development of definitive effects. Unilateral adrenalectomy in the rabbit was reported to cause a decrease in the pineal argyrophil staining reaction that was later followed by an increase (387); these changes were probably nonspecific. Administration of corticotrophin or cortisone was reported to have no effect on pineal weight or histologic appearance in the male chick (384).

Thyroid Gland

Thyroidectomy in the goat was reported to cause marked changes

[65]

in the pineal gland (429). Increased connective tissue, regression of parenchymal cells, sheathing of blood vessels, glial infiltration, nerve-fiber degeneration, decreased vascularization, and deposition of calcium were observed. No change in pineal weight or histologic appearance was found after thyroidectomy in the male chick (384). Hemithyroidectomy in the rabbit was reported to cause a nonspecific decrease in the pineal argyrophil staining reaction, followed by a later increase (387). Pineal weight was reported as unchanged after injection of thyrotrophic hormone in the rat (58). Administration of thyroxin or thiouracil had no effect on pineal weight or histologic appearance in the male chick (384).

Pancreas and Thymus

Pancreatectomy in the cat (222) and thymectomy in the cat, dog, and pig (241) were reported to be followed by pineal hypoplasia and atrophy.

ELECTRICAL STIMULATION

Direct electrical stimulation of the intact pineal gland in the rabbit was reported to result in contraction of the gland (61)—a finding that suggests vasoconstriction. Faradic stimulation of the superior cervical ganglion in cats was said to cause changes suggestive of increased pineal secretion; thickening of neurofibrils, hyperchromatization and "sclerosis" of parenchymal-cell nuclei, and irregular deposition of clusters of pigmented granules in the parenchymal cells were described (414).

NUTRITIONAL STATES

Avitaminosis E in the rat had no effect on the pineal gland (104). Hypervitaminosis B_1 was reported to produce hypertrophy and hyperplasia of the pineal parenchymal cells in the rabbit (358). A calcium-free diet in fowl was described as being followed by pineal gliosis and parenchymal-cell atrophy (409).

MISCELLANEOUS PROCEDURES

Experimental rib fractures in rats were reported to cause pineal parenchymal-cell hypertrophy involving both nuclei and cytoplasm (319); increased vascularization, with thinning of cytoplasm and decrease of chromatin, was also described. Deep roentgen-ray irradiation of the heads of rabbits was found to result in pineal congestion, hemorrhage, and nuclear transparency and degeneration (176). Large doses of diphtherotoxin administered to rabbits initially produced histologic signs suggestive of increased function—i.e., nuclear and cytoplasmic changes with deposition of granules and increased ascorbic-acid content (79, 80, 81). Prolonged administration of the toxin produced regressive changes and a decrease in ascorbic-acid content.

CHAPTER XIII

Miscellaneous Studies in Pinealectomized Animals

Adrenalin injected in pinealectomized rabbits was reported to raise the intrabronchial pressure and lower the carotid blood pressure and the depth of respiration. These effects were directly opposite to those found in normal control animals (219).

Pinealectomy in the rabbit was said to alter sensitivity to various anesthetic agents. In addition, it increased sensitivity to some convulsants (caffein sodium benzoate, picrotoxin, and cardiazol). Pineal extract restored these responses to normal (184, 185).

An increase in body temperature was found after pinealectomy in the rabbit (182, 217) and the sheep (68, 69), but no such change occurred in the rat (158). The hyperthermia in the rabbit was resistant to antipyretics and abnormally responsive to pyrogens (182, 183); it was abnormally affected by injection of various inorganic cations (sodium, calcium, and magnesium). Pineal extracts and implants restored normal responses.

Injection of a variety of substances, including gonadal hormones (259), adrenalin (258), and atropine (258), in pinealectomized rabbits resulted in inconclusive variations in blood pressure.

CHAPTER XIV

Immediate Effects of Pineal Extracts

CARDIOVASCULAR CHANGES

Pineal extract given parenterally was reported to produce tachycardia in the intact dog (248) and also in the perfused cat heart (198). It caused no change in the intact cat (75) or in the perfused frog heart (24, 207). Small doses were found to increase the heart rate in the rabbit, whereas larger doses caused bradycardia and pulsus trigeminus (61). The force of contraction was observed to be increased in the rabbit (61) and in the excised cat heart (198). Dilute extracts were reported to produce a mild increase in contractile force in the excised frog heart; a concentrated preparation produced a rise after a transient fall (207). This effect was found to be independent of innervation (208). No change in force of contraction was observed in the intact cat (75). Cardiac output was increased in the perfused frog heart (24).

Extracts have most frequently been reported to have a hypotensive effect (Table 49). They were found to inhibit the pressor action of epinephrine in the frog (24) and to cause vasodilatation in the dog (133, 348), the rabbit (348), and man (243).

RESPIRATORY CHANGES

The effects of pineal extracts on respiratory rate and depth in the hedgehog (6), cat (75), dog (198), and sheep (198) are inconclusive.

[69]

Table 49

References on the effects of pineal-extract administration on blood pressure

Animal	Rise	Fall	No change
Cat	322*	75, 198	
Dog		133, 166, 169, 198, 248–250, 460*	63
Man		132, 283, 460*	
Rabbit	354*	61, 198, 398	453
Sheep		198	

*Reaction preceded by brief change in opposite direction

HEMATOLOGIC CHANGES

Pineal-extract injection was said to shorten blood coagulation time and bleeding time in human subjects. Platelets and blood viscosity were reported as increased, and no change was noted in osmotic or mechanical red-blood-cell fragility (459). Corroborative studies (284) revealed that the coagulation time in the human subjects tested was reduced 12 to 57 per cent in one hour and 50 to 80 per cent after three hours. The extract (epiphysormone) was effective in dilutions up to 1/10,000. Similar results have been obtained in the rabbit (453). Epiglandol injected in 10 human subjects produced lymphocytosis in 8 (437). Pineal injection markedly raised the number of circulating eosinophils in 9 psychotic patients (10).

MUSCULAR CHANGES

Treatment with extracts was reported to increase contractility of the uterus of the guinea pig (267), the pregnant rabbit (322), and the rat (452). No significant change was found in the uterus of the virgin guinea pig (110). Increased tonus was observed in the uterus of the pregnant guinea pig; the reverse effect was noted in virgin animals (460). No change was observed in the intestinal volume of the cat (75), but accelerated motility (216) and increased contractile force (322) were observed in the intestine of the rabbit.

[70]

Perfusion of a frog gastrocnemius-muscle preparation with pineal extract was reported to produce a mild increase in work done and to delay the development of fatigue after electrical stimulation (84). No significant change in contraction was observed in a frog sartorius-muscle preparation perfused with pineal extract (472).

MISCELLANEOUS CHANGES

Extracts increased diuresis in the rabbit (198); the response in the cat was variable (75, 322). A galactogenous action was observed in the cat (246) and the goat (320, 321). Cerebrospinal-fluid pressure fell in the dog (157), but no alteration was observed in the rate of secretion (76). Increased intraocular pressure (123) and pupillary dilatation (123, 322) were noted in the rabbit. The rate of callus formation in experimental fractures in the rat was unchanged (92). Increased pulse frequency was observed in the contractile vacuoles of paramecia (116). Extracts produced a moderately increased resistance to anthrax bacillus inoculation in mice (458). Nerve excitability was unaltered in a frog sciatic-nerve–muscle preparation (472). Pineal extract administration was reported to raise body temperature in the guinea pig and dog (20), but it had no effect in the hedgehog (6). Pineal implantation in pigeons was reported to diminish the total depth of pupillary contraction in response to a standard light stimulus (146). Injection of pineal-gland "antibodies" in the rabbit caused insignificant fluctuations in the heterologous agglutinin response to injected human blood cells (433).

COMMENT

Many of the findings reported, such as the cardiovascular and respiratory effects, are nonspecific and are consistent with the results of injection of many different types of crude biologic preparations. The remaining studies are inconclusive.

CHAPTER XV

Clinical Use of Pineal Extracts

Observation of the effects of hormones administered in disease has sometimes yielded clues to their role in normal physiology.

GENITAL DISEASES

Extracts have been reported to be efficacious in a variety of sexual and genital disturbances, including dysmenorrhea, hyperlibidinism, the menopausal syndrome, and uterine and vaginal bleeding. The commercial preparations epiglandol, epiphysan, and epiphysormone have been used most frequently, although other extracts also have been employed (Table 50).

MENTAL DISEASES

Epiphysormone, epiglandol, and epiphysan have all been employed in the therapy of psychosis. Reports on a total of 119 cases

Table 50

References on the use of pineal extracts in genital disorders

Disorder	Epiglandol	Epiphysan	Epiphysormone	Other extracts
Dysmenorrhea	159, 161, 163, 315	163, 461		453
Hyperlibidinism	159–162, 244, 315, 454	21, 162, 232, 439	421	
Menopause		49, 461, 466	466	140
Uterine bleeding		310, 427	262, 331, 427, 444	39, 263, 453
Miscellaneous	22, 161, 226, 242, 243	389, 461		14, 465

[72]

describe presumed remission in 63, improvement in 26, and no change in 30. Schizophrenia has been the disorder most frequently treated (Table 51).

MISCELLANEOUS DISEASES

Pineal extracts have been used with varying results in many other diseases (Table 52).

VETERINARY DISEASES

Epiphysan is alleged to have been effective in the treatment of tetanus (108, 173, 399) and muscle inflammations (171, 174, 479) in horses and in hypersexuality in sows (400) and horses (164, 170, 172, 174, 380, 400).

Table 51

References on the use of pineal extracts in psychosis

Type of psychosis	Epiglandol	Epiphysormone	Other extracts
Juvenile psychosis		420	
Manic psychosis		295, 296, 424	
Puerperal psychosis			352
Schizophrenia	22, 236, 237, 270, 454	337, 338, 343, 418, 427	349
Miscellaneous			426

Table 52

References on the use of pineal extracts in various diseases

Type of disorder	Reference numbers
Neurologic	28, 63, 109, 142, 161, 235, 251, 314
Psychiatric	60, 148, 351, 422
Endocrine	161, 334, 422, 435
Miscellaneous	9, 26–28, 149, 161, 218, 271, 297, 311, 333, 374, 422

[73]

COMMENT

Reports on the use of pineal extract in various diseases thus far afford no information on the physiologic role of the gland. This is owing to the incompleteness or poor quality of most of the reported clinical studies. In addition, the lack of any standard methods of assay makes it impossible to evaluate the dosages used. When extensive, well-controlled, and thorough observations are made, they will undoubtedly contribute to the understanding of pineal function.

Part Two

CLINICAL CORRELATIONS

CHAPTER XVI

Pineal Calcification

The occurrence of pineal calcification in man is well known; it was described in detail in medical publications of the seventeenth and eighteenth centuries. Of these early works, the writings of Collins (581), Günz (660), von Haller (666), Haslam (670), King (732), Morgagni (833), Soemmering (945), and Stalpart van der Wiel (949) are particularly noteworthy. These authors and others described the incidence and appearance of pineal calcification as observed at autopsy. More recent reports (Table 53) have primarily been concerned with the incidence of calcification as determined through large series of skull roentgenograms. Such studies reveal that it has varied between 33 and 76 per cent among subjects of

Table 53

Incidences of pineal calcification in man

Ref. no.	Total no. of cases	Decade									Average
		1st (%)	2nd (%)	3rd (%)	4th (%)	5th (%)	6th (%)	7th (%)	8th (%)	9th (%)	(%)
523	666	2	25	38	59	59	58	69	—	—	45
539	1271	3	26	47	58	58	67	65	73	—	49
553	114	0	60	78	71	75	86	95	70	100	76
554	70	0	25	55	61	69	83	—	—	—	56
607	2724	5	28	49	61	62	66	70	69	100	51
903	375	0	11	42	36	72	45	83	—	—	33

all ages. The incidence is negligible in the first decade of life; it approximates 25 per cent in the second decade, and increases gradually from the third to the eighth decades. No relation has ever been established between the occurrence of calcification and any functional status of the human pineal gland. The incidences of calcification and of its association with various diseases have been described (Table 54); however, the physiologic significance of pineal calcification is not yet certain.

Many workers have used roentgenographically observed calcification in the pineal area as an anatomic landmark (Table 55).

Table 54

References on the association of pineal calcification with various disorders

Disorder	Reference numbers
Epilepsy	572, 859
Hypertension, etc.	539, 881
Muscular dystrophy	972
Paget's disease	558
Psychosis	539, 584, 660, 670, 732, 833
Sexual disorders	520, 539, 575, 576, 612, 886, 908, 909, 940, 965
Tuberous sclerosis	859
Miscellaneous	544, 722, 734, 785, 789, 870, 977, 986, 1014

Table 55

References on the use of the calcified pineal gland as a roentgenographic landmark

Reference numbers
491, 493, 496, 557, 565, 570, 585, 602, 606, 610, 611, 627–631, 648, 658, 671, 680, 683, 775, 781–783, 785, 787, 815, 842, 908, 930, 946, 947, 958, 988, 993, 994, 1013

CHAPTER XVII

Pineal Tumors

The literature on pineal tumors reveals much that is not directly pertinent to pineal function. Accordingly, the material has been presented in tabular form without discussion, except where findings have physiologic implications. More detailed information on the clinical and pathological features of pineal disease may be found in appropriate textbooks or in the original papers listed in Tables 59–66.

Neoplasms are the most common pineal lesions; however, their incidence is low in most series of intracranial tumors. Only 473 cases have been reported in any detail; 97 additional cases are mentioned in reports on series of brain tumors (521, 730, 802, 838). Over 50 per cent of the total have been reported in patients twenty years of age or younger (Table 56). The incidence is three times as frequent in men as in women. Histopathological descriptions are varied and confusing, and more than 25 types of tumor have been described. Table 57 represents an attempt to systematize the nomenclature. This classification is used for convenience only and does not purport to be definitive. The incidences of the various types of pineal tumors are shown in Table 58. It is interesting that mixed tumors have occurred almost entirely in male patients, whereas cysts are chiefly found in women. About 50 per cent of the tumors described are of parenchymal origin. The remaining tables (Tables 59–67) summarize the age and sex incidences of each type of tumor. Individual cases are indicated by the bibliographic numbers of the papers in which they were reported.

Table 56

Age and sex incidences of all pineal tumors

Age	Male	Female	Totals
1–5	14	8	22
6–10	44	10	54
11–15	72	12	84
16–20	80	13	93
21–25	56	11	67
26–30	26	18	44
31–35	29	10	39
36–40	12	8	20
41–45	7	13	20
46–50	10	6	16
51–55	1	1	2
56–60	4	3	7
61–65	2	0	2
66–70	0	0	0
71–75	1	2	3
76–80	1	0	1
81–85	1	0	1
Totals	360	115	475
Age and sex unreported			34
Cases from series	58	39	97
Grand totals	418	154	606

The basis used here for categorizing the histologic composition of each tumor was the diagnosis reported by the observer. The accuracy of some of these diagnoses has been questioned by various workers, and the tables of incidence would probably be altered somewhat if each paper were re-examined and the histopathologic descriptions classified according to more rigorous standards of nomenclature. If this were done, many tumors originally reported as sarcomas or carcinomas would probably be classified as pinealomas or teratomas.

Table 57

Suggested classification of pineal tumors

A. Parenchymal-cell tumors
1. Pinealoma (pinealoblastoma)
2. Adenoma
3. Simple hypertrophy

B. Mixed tumors
1. Teratoma
2. Chorionepithelioma
3. Dermoid

C. Supporting-tissue tumors
1. Gliomas
   a. Astroblastoma
   b. Astrocytoma
   c. Ependymoma (and -blastoma)
   d. Glioblastoma
   e. Glioma (neurospongioma, neuroglioma)
   f. Medulloblastoma
   g. Spongioblastoma
2. Sarcomas

D. Cysts

E. Miscellaneous tumors
1. Carcinoma
2. Cholesteatoma
3. Fibrolipoma
4. Germinoma
5. Meningioma (psammoma)
6. Nerve-cell tumors
   a. Ganglioneuroma
   b. Neural
   c. Neuroepithelioma
7. Tuberculoma
8. Tumors of vascular and perivascular structures
   a. Angioma
   b. Hemangioblastoma
   c. Perithelioma

F. Tumors with unspecified histopathology

G. Tumors metastatic to the pineal gland

H. Ectopic pinealoma

I. Suspected tumor; no autopsy

Table 58

Age and sex incidences of various types of pineal tumors

Age	Parenchymal-cell		Mixed		Supporting-tissue		Cystic		Miscellaneous		Unspecified	
	M	F	M	F	M	F	M	F	M	F	M	F
1–5	4	4	5	2	4	—	—	2	1	—	—	—
6–10	17	7	19	—	6	1	1	—	1	1	—	1
11–15	44	6	22	2	4	2	1	2	1	—	—	—
16–20	44	8	18	1	7	1	4	2	6	—	1	1
21–25	29	4	7	—	8	—	2	2	7	3	3	2
26–30	11	9	3	1	2	6	2	2	7	—	1	—
31–35	14	1	1	—	7	4	5	4	—	—	2	1
36–40	3	3	—	—	5	—	2	4	2	—	—	1
41–45	2	3	—	—	3	3	—	7	1	—	1	—
46–50	6	1	—	—	2	1	—	4	2	—	—	—
51–55	—	1	—	—	—	—	1	—	—	—	—	—
56–60	—	2	—	—	1	—	2	—	1	1	—	—
61–65	1	—	—	—	—	—	1	—	—	—	—	—
66–70	—	—	—	—	—	—	—	—	—	—	—	—
71–75	—	—	—	—	—	—	1	2	—	—	—	—
76–80	1	—	—	—	—	—	—	—	—	—	—	—
81–85	—	—	—	—	—	—	1	—	—	—	—	—
Totals	176	49	75	6	49	18	23	31	29	5	8	6
Age and sex unreported	17		3		2		9		2		1	
Cases from series	70		9		—		—		5		13	
Grand totals	312		93		69		63		41		28	

Another cause of inaccuracy has been the use of the term "pinealoma" to describe any tumor found in the pineal gland. The term was introduced by Krabbe in 1915 to designate tumors composed solely of pineal parenchymal cells. This limitation was initially respected, but "pinealoma" is now often used as an anatomic classification—e.g., "pinealoma, astrocytomatous form," which is intended to describe an astrocytoma of the pineal gland. This confusion can be obviated only by the universal acceptance of a terminology based on histologic appearance.

[82]

Table 59

References on cases of parenchymal-cell tumors

Age (years)	Male	Female
1–5	514 (2 cases), 603, 652	490, 644, 727, 912
6–10	495, 505, 639, 645, 693, 695, 696, 717, 780, 814, 816, 826, 843, 906, 912, 942, 998	498, 605, 650, 695, 816 (2 cases), 912
11–15	494, 516, 528 (2 cases), 589, 639, 653 (2 cases), 690, 695, 698, 706, 709, 719, 720, 745 (2 cases), 755, 812, 823, 827, 843 (2 cases), 845, 849, 878 (4 cases), 882, 896, 899, 912, 918, 922, 944, 978, 1002 (2 cases), 1016, 1028 (4 cases)	481, 498, 586, 653, 695, 742
16–20	498 (2 cases), 512, 517, 518, 525, 636, 638, 645, 652, 653, 659, 668, 695 (2 cases), 698, 699, 716, 720, 733, 746, 755, 758, 794, 804, 812 (2 cases), 823, 847, 849, 858, 867, 873, 878, 896 (2 cases), 912 (2 cases), 919, 920, 956, 959, 987, 1022	486, 562, 652, 742, 796, 812, 934, 1003
21–25	499, 512, 524, 577, 661, 686, 695 (2 cases), 699, 742, 759, 776, 784, 797, 799, 808, 820, 823, 857, 878, 912, 952, 962, 1002 (2 cases), 1017, 1023, 1028 (2 cases)	694, 926, 1018, 1028
26–30	501, 510, 638, 652, 696, 742, 804, 834, 866, 957, 1002	498, 508, 560, 589, 590, 695, 1002, 1028 (2 cases)
31–35	498, 512, 521, 533, 633, 646, 652, 662, 735, 742, 792, 1002, 1010, 1019	694
36–40	653, 691, 997	854, 888, 890
41–45	535, 699	681, 692, 954
46–50	512, 812, 944, 989, 1028 (2 cases)	521
51–55		618
56–60		614, 674
61–65	652	
80	901	

Additional cases in which age and sex were not reported:

Pinealoma   498, 639 (6 cases), 970 (2 cases), 1017 (3 cases), 1028 (2 cases)

Adenoma   986

Hypertrophy   527, 600

Cases of hypertrophy in table   501, 524, 605, 755 (2 cases), 814, 901, 926, 934, 978, 987, 998, 1003

Cases of adenoma in table   758, 808, 820, 827, 942, 1016

[83]

Table 60

References on cases of mixed tumors

Age (years)	Male	Female
1–5	561, 626, 695, 748, 935	779, 788
6–10	513, 545, 546, 589, 591, 632, 664, 684, 707, 719, 728, 767, 793, 861, 876, 885, 911, 985, 1012	
11–15	497, 514, 515, 518, 580, 586, 601, 624, 642, 647, 649, 736, 744, 765, 774, 821, 911, 937, 938, 955, 1008, 1026	804, 875
16–20	494, 507, 508, 529, 608, 613, 625, 637, 651, 654, 702, 721, 731, 846, 875, 927, 961, 992	742
21–25	731 (2 cases), 875, 896, 927, 960, 1005	
26–30	632, 853, 1005	871
31–35	632	

Parapineal teratoma (not included above)   685, 798, 813
Additional cases of teratoma (age and sex not specified)   632 (2 cases), 844
Cases of dermoid in table   497, 742, 871
Cases of chorionepithelioma in table   507, 508, 591, 654, 955, 992, 1012
Adenoid carcinoma with cartilage in table   580, 613

Table 61

References on cases of supporting-tissue tumors

Age (years)	Male	Female
1–5	556, 689, 714, 864	
6–10	688, 846, 868, 883, 893, 900	801
11–15	494, 836, 852, 1027	568, 586
16–20	573, 616, 772, 843, 896, 902, 974	795
21–25	540, 604, 649, 656, 669, 860, 923, 983	
26–30	905, 932	559, 596, 788, 803, 852, 986
31–35	487, 673, 701, 739, 830, 843, 894	645, 742, 868, 1000
36–40	532, 588, 620, 896, 923	
41–45	740, 907, 1026	665, 970, 995
46–50	489, 896	665
51–55		
55–60	986	

Additional cases in which age and sex were not specified   982, 1001

Table 62

References on cases of cystoma

Age (years)	Male	Female
1–5		718, 950
6–10	898	
11–15	519	655, 760
16–20	500, 641, 943, 1020	492, 921
21–25	749, 910	921, 933
26–30	870, 951	492, 870
31–35	522 (2 cases), 527, 567, 583	566, 567 (2 cases), 856
36–40	567, 582	522 (2 cases), 549, 843
41–45		564, 582 (2 cases), 667 (2 cases), 778, 870
46–50		492, 522, 850, 870
51–55	522	
56–60	567 (2 cases)	
61–65	522	
66–70		
71–75	522	500, 582
76–80		
81–85	715	

Additional cases in which age and sex were not specified   566, 571, 870 (6 cases), 891, 910

Table 63

References on cases of tumors of unspecified histologic appearance

Age (years)	Male	Female
1–5		
6–10		915
11–15		
16–20	622	915
21–25	483, 599, 925	895, 915
26–30	969	
31–35	542, 592	712
36–40		503
41–45	777	

Additional case (age and sex not specified)   865

[85]

Table 64

References on cases of miscellaneous tumors

Age (years)	Male	Female
1–5	508	
6–10	632	632
11–15	632	
16–20	632 (4 cases), 806, 863	
21–25	587, 632 (4 cases), 679, 1026	632, 731, 897
26–30	632 (5 cases), 819, 824	
31–35		
36–40	543, 696	
41–45	504	
46–50	634, 928	
51–55		
56–60	635	504

Classification of cases:

A.	Carcinoma	587, 679, 806, 824, 897
B.	Cholesteatoma	
C.	Fibrolipoma	508
D.	Germinoma	632 (10 cases)
E.	Meningioma	504 (2 cases), 543, 635, 1026
F.	Nerve-cell tumors:	
	1. Ganglioneuroma	696, 928
	2. Neural	632 (7 cases)
	3. Neuroepithelioma	634
G.	Tuberculoma	
H.	Tumors of vascular and perivascular structures:	
	1. Angioma	731
	2. Hemangioblastoma	863
	3. Perithelioma	819

Additional case of neural tumor (age and sex not specified)   632
Additional case of fibrolipoma (age and sex not specified)   508

Table 65

References on cases of tumors metastatic to the pineal gland

Ref. no.	Sex	Age (years)	Tumor
550	Male	38	reticulosarcoma
574	Male	47	carcinomatosis
619	Male	37	"medullary tumor"
711	Female	21	sarcoma
877	Male	44	carcinoma
877	Female	62	carcinoma
877	Female	46	carcinoma
877	Male	52	adenocarcinoma
877	Male	61	epithelioma
973	Female	40	carcinoma
1007	Female	60	carcinoma

Table 66

References on cases of ectopic pinealoma

Ref. no.	Sex	Age (years)	Status of the pineal gland	Associated gonadal changes
484	Male	22	normal	hypogonadism
514	Female	9	?	none
530	Male	26	normal	none
583	Male	35	cyst	hypogonadism
643	Female	5	destroyed	none
653	Male	30	normal	none
653	Male	2	normal	none
698	Male	12	normal	none
911	Male	14	normal	none
911	Female	10	normal	none
979	Male	14	?	precocious puberty

Table 67

References on cases of suspected pineal tumors—no autopsy

Cases with neurologic symptoms only:

  Male   481, 488, 550, 595, 697 (3 cases), 720 (2 cases), 741, 810, 822, 829 (2 cases), 970 (4 cases), 975, 990, 991, 1006, 1021

  Female   609, 687, 697, 829 (2 cases), 970

Cases with symptoms of sexual precocity:

  Male   482, 541, 548, 551, 594, 597, 617, 663, 675–677, 738, 766, 818, 819, 828, 837, 851, 862, 879, 880, 889 (2 cases), 892, 913, 914, 916, 963 (2 cases), 964, 980, 981, 984, 1011

  Female   511, 547, 551, 615, 678, 710, 723, 771, 805, 809, 817, 832, 855, 939, 948

Gonadal Changes Associated with Pineal Tumors

Observed changes in sexual development are apparently the only findings associated with pineal tumors that have so far contributed to current knowledge of pineal function. Precocious puberty is the most important of these changes; it is here considered in detail. First described by Heubner in 1898, this syndrome has been observed in 46 patients with verified pineal tumors (Tables 68, 69, 70); all these patients were boys under seventeen years of age. The total number of pineal tumors reported in children from one to sixteen years old is 178; 145 of these were found in boys (Table 71). Accordingly, the over-all incidence of precocity associated with pineal tumors is 26 per cent, and the incidence in boys alone is 32 per cent. The neoplasms found in association with the syndrome include many cell types; they chiefly comprise parenchymal, mixed, and supporting-tissue tumors.

Examination of the literature reveals that two different hypotheses have been propounded to explain the relation between pineal tumors and sexual precocity. The first of these, formulated half a century ago by Marburg, is that sexual precocity is due to decreased secretion of a pineal hormone that is presumed to retard gonadal development, under normal conditions, until puberty. This decreased production is believed to be caused by the destruction of pineal parenchymal cells by neoplasms. This hypothesis has been viewed with skepticism for some time; apparently the chief reason for this attitude is that the experimental evidence on pineal function is almost entirely unknown. A second hypothesis, currently accepted by most authorities, is that a pineal tumor can cause precocious puberty through indirect stimulation of the pituitary gland (App. II, refs. 64, 181, 188, 197). It is argued that the expanding tumor compresses or destroys hypothalamic areas that control anterior pituitary function and that this trauma increases the secretion of gonadotrophins, with consequent precocity. Support of this hypothesis has been based on interpretations of case reports of sexual precocity associated with intracranial lesions not of pineal origin. Its proponents label the pineal body as a non-functioning organ; furthermore, they consider the histologic composition of its tumors of no importance.

A preliminary evaluation of these theories may be made after careful examination of the available literature. The normal pineal gland is composed of two main types of cells: intrinsic parenchymal cells and non-parenchymal cells (chiefly neuroglia). Tumors of this gland may similarly be classified as parenchymal and non-parenchymal neoplasms (Table 72). This classification is based on histopathological diagnoses made at autopsy or operation. Because the reported clinical studies varied greatly both in thoroughness and in length of observation periods, it is impossible to determine precisely the rate of growth of either type of tumor. However, the evidence at hand suggests that it is similar in both types and that both types attain about the same size before operation or autopsy.

Parenchymal and non-parenchymal tumors are equally distributed in children between one and sixteen years of age (Table 71). The data reported here concern this group alone because all the reported cases of sexual precocity occurred in this age range. Ages at autopsy or operation are used, since there is no way of ascertaining ages at onset. According to the pressure hypothesis, the occurrence of precocious puberty is unrelated to the histologic structure of the pineal tumor; therefore, since both types of tumor are found in equal distribution, the condition should be found with equal frequency in

[90]

association with both types. Actually, however, sexual precocity is associated with more than three times as many non-parenchymal as parenchymal tumors (Table 70). The probability that this is a chance disproportion is less than 1/10,000, as computed by the chi-square technique. Statistics for the male cases alone are equally significant. The hypothesis that the sexual precocity associated with pineal lesions is produced merely by pressure on the hypothalamus cannot explain the fact that the incidence of non-parenchymal tumors in precocious puberty is 78 per cent, although their general incidence is only 49 per cent. Chi-square analysis of the incidences of the various types of non-parenchymal tumors and of their association with sexual precocity (Table 73) further reveals that no single non-parenchymal type is significantly associated with the syndrome.

The earlier hypothesis—that the pineal gland is an endocrine organ and its secretion inhibits gonadal development—is consistent with the evidence that precocious puberty is usually associated with non-parenchymal tumors. Since these neoplasms destroy parenchymal tissue, the relatively frequent occurrence of precocity in association with them may very well be due to decrease or loss of pineal secretion. The fact that precocity has occasionally occurred with parenchymal tumors may be explained by the possibility that such tumors do not necessarily secrete. Indeed, some reports have described the pinealomas associated with precocity as composed of cells so undifferentiated and necrotic that secretion is highly unlikely.

An interesting and often overlooked corollary to the aforementioned findings is that pineal tumors have sometimes been associated with hypogonadism (Table 74) — this relationship also being explained as due to pressure. Thirty such cases, all in male patients, have been described; 20 of these (67 per cent) occurred with parenchymal tumors, whereas the remaining patients (33 per cent) had non-parenchymal lesions (Table 75). Although this association of pinealomas and hypogonadism is striking, it is not statistically significant, since it occurred in only 20 cases and hypogenitalism was infrequently observed in cases of pineal tumor in the age range involved (six to thirty-five years). The association of parenchymal tumors with sexual retardation should be examined further.

The hypotheses discussed above do not explain the fact that neither precocious puberty nor hypogonadism has ever been reported in female patients with pineal tumors. A subsidiary factor may be the very low incidence of pineal tumors in girls.

A tentative conclusion suggested by the data reviewed here is that the gonadal abnormalities found in patients with pineal tumors are not caused by pressure on the hypothalamus. Pressure cannot be entirely excluded as an etiologic factor, however, since it is possible that gonadal abnormalities associated with extrapineal intracranial tumors are caused by the compression of appropriate hypothalamic centers. On the other hand, the pressure hypothesis does not explain the gonadal syndromes associated with pineal disorders, in view of the evidence discussed above.

The observations on pineal–gonadal relations discussed here are in accord with the experimental studies discussed in Chapter V.

Table 68

References on cases of parenchymal tumors in patients with precocious puberty

Age (years)	Reference numbers
6–10	693, 696, 717, 826, 942
11–15	528, 690, 709, 823, 922

Table 69

References on cases of non-parenchymal tumors in patients with precocious puberty

Age (years)	Reference numbers
1–5	561, 626, 689, 695, 714, 748, 864, 935
6–10	513, 546, 591, 632 (2 cases), 664, 684, 846, 861, 868, 876, 885, 893, 911, 985, 1012
11–15	514, 624, 647, 744, 765, 774, 821, 937, 938
16	654, 961, 1020

Table 70

Distribution of cases of precocious puberty (all male) associated with pineal tumors

Age (years)	Parenchymal tumors	Non-parenchymal tumors
1–5	0	8
6–10	5	16
11–15	5	9
16	0	3
Totals	10	36

Table 71

Distribution of pineal tumors in male and female patients between one and sixteen years of age

Age (years)	Parenchymal tumors			Non-parenchymal tumors		
	Male	Female	Total	Male	Female	Total
1–5	4	4	8	10	4	14
6–10	17	7	24	27	2	29
11–15	44	6	50	28	6	34
16	7	2	9	8	2	10
Totals	72	19	91	73	14	87

[93]

Table 72

Classification of pineal tumors

Parenchymal tumors	Non-parenchymal tumors
Pinealoma	Mixed tumors
Adenoma	Supporting-tissue tumors
Hypertrophy	Cystoma
	Nerve-cell tumors
	Fibrolipoma
	Germinoma

Table 73

Types of non-parenchymal tumors found in association with precocious puberty

Type of tumor	Cases of precocity	Total no. of male cases	Total no. of all cases
Mixed	28	50	54
Supporting-tissue	6	16	20
Cystic	1	4	9
Neural	1	1	2
Fibrolipoma	0	1	1
Germinoma	0	1	1
Totals	36	73	87

Table 74

References on cases of pineal tumors in patients with hypogenitalism

Parenchymal tumors:	
Pinealoma	495, 505, 512, 533, 577, 633, 698, 706, 720, 745, 784, 849, 858, 878, 919, 952
Adenoma	808
Hypertrophy	755 (2 cases), 987
Non-parenchymal tumors:	
Mixed	518, 529, 721, 1005 (2 cases)
Supporting-tissue	843, 852, 905
Cystic	500
Germinoma	632

[94]

Table 75

Distribution of cases of hypogenitalism in patients with pineal tumors (all male)

Age (years)	Parenchymal tumors	Non-parenchymal tumors
1–5	0	0
6–10	2	0
11–15	5	2
16–20	7	4
21–25	4	2
26–30	0	2
31–35	2	0
Totals	20	10

CHAPTER XIX

Pineal Hypoplasia
Absence of the Pineal Gland

Primary hypoplasia of the pineal gland is rare; only 9 cases have been described. Their salient features have been summarized in Table 76. Atrophy of pineal parenchyma and marked diminution of gland weight were observed in each case. Eight patients showed genital precocity, and 5 of these had associated pituitary lesions as well. It is difficult to evaluate these reports, since pituitary lesions were present in 50 per cent of the cases. The question of the primary etiology of the precocity cannot be resolved. At any rate, pressure on the hypothalamus can be ruled out as an etiologic factor.

Table 76
Cases of pineal hypoplasia

Ref. no.	Sex	Age (years)	Hypergonadism	Other findings
509	Female	23	yes	Microcephaly
598	Female	25	no	Accessory pineal tissue; hirsutism
713	Male	14	yes	Pituitary eosinophilic hyperplasia
751	Male	28	yes	Small pituitary eosinophil adenoma and colloid cyst
752	Male	3 1/2	yes	Pituitary hypertrophy; adreno-cortical adenocarcinoma
755	Male	19	yes	Pituitary colloid cyst
755	Male	35	yes	
755	Male	21	yes	
756	Male	13 1/2	yes	Connective-tissue and eosinophilic hyperplasia in the pituitary gland

Absence of the pineal gland has been reported in 6 instances (Table 77). Hypogonadism was found in 3 of these cases; this contrasts with the hypergonadism observed in the patients with pineal hypoplasia. Further information is required before the inconsistency can be explained.

Specific conclusions concerning the significance of pineal hypoplasia or absence must await more evidence. Unfortunately, the pineal gland is rarely examined at autopsy unless the presence of a tumor is suspected.

Table 77
Cases in which the pineal gland was reported absent

Ref. no.	Sex	Age (years)	Hypogonadism	Other findings
502	Male	4 days	no	Monster
672	Female	26	yes	Adrenal hyperplasia
729	Male	14	no	
825	Male	55	yes	
929	Female	29	no	
1025	Male	16 1/2	yes	Severe anemia

CHAPTER XX

Miscellaneous Findings

A number of miscellaneous lesions have been described in the literature on pineal disease (Table 78). The variety and inconsistency of most of the reports do not permit conclusions concerning the role of the pineal gland in these disorders.

Table 78

References on miscellaneous diseases of the pineal gland

General pathologic studies	552, 578, 579, 703, 704, 705, 757, 761, 762, 789, 790, 791, 800, 833, 848, 869, 870, 874, 887, 967, 968, 986, 1004, 1009, 1015
Pineal diseases:	
1. Animal pathology	768–770
2. Animal tumors	569, 593, 924, 996
3. Hemorrhage	941, 971, 1024
4. Medullary fungus	831
5. Softening	931
6. Trauma	531, 789
Systemic diseases in which changes in the pineal gland were noted:	
1. Carcinomatosis	747
2. Chondrodystrophy	764
3. Leprosy	715, 840, 841
4. Lipodystrophy	737
5. Psychosis	506, 536–538, 563, 584, 623, 657, 811, 839, 870, 884, 1004
6. Sexual disorders	563, 640, 743, 753, 754, 917, 936
7. Syphilis	786
8. Thyroid disease	526, 726, 753, 966, 999
9. Tuberculosis	534, 750, 904

CONCLUDING COMMENT

Concluding Comment

Available evidence lends no support to the notion that the pineal gland is a functionless, vestigial organ in any mammalian species studied. The organ does not undergo atrophy at puberty in man. Several types of findings indicate that it has an active metabolism. For example, histochemical studies of the gland in monkeys, rats, and other animals have demonstrated the presence of ribo- and desoxyribonucleoprotein, glycogen, acid and alkaline phosphatase, and succinic dehydrogenase in its parenchymal cells. In addition, radioisotope experiments in rats have demonstrated that the pineal uptake of P^{32} is greater than that of any other organ studied. Hypophysectomy was reported to cause an even greater P^{32} uptake; corticotrophin administration decreased the uptake to pre-hypophysectomy levels. This high uptake cannot be explained solely on the basis of passive diffusion, since a significant amount of the radioactive phosphate in the gland was found in chemical combination with glucose and protein. The results of the histochemical and isotopic-uptake studies indicate that the parenchymal cells of the pineal gland have metabolic processes similar in rate and complexity to those of specialized organs. In contrast to the brain, the pineal gland is readily stained *intra vitam*. These histochemical observations and the aforementioned isotopic-uptake data indicate that in the animals studied there is no impediment to diffusion between blood and pineal gland such as exists between blood and brain parenchyma (the blood-brain barrier).

Much of the published endocrinologic data either is unsubstantiated or is too fragmentary to warrant positive conclusions at this time. However, a number of reports contain statistically significant findings that are highly suggestive. Accelerated bodily growth and development have frequently been described in pinealectomized animals. Although the reported over-all pattern of change is apparently consistent, few papers present enough data to analyze statistically; when such analyses can be made they seldom yield convincing results. One postulated pineal function—direct control of bodily growth and development—is apparently ruled out by the available information.

The effects of pinealectomy on pituitary morphology have consistently been described either as no change or as simple hypertrophy and hyperplasia. One group reported that pinealectomy in the rat increased the rate of anaerobic glycolysis in the pituitary gland. However, only small numbers of animals were used, and some techniques were inadequate—both of which factors vitiate conclusions based on these reports. Pineal injection was found by one author to suppress the pituitary hypertrophy usually associated with castration in fowl; experiments by another worker indicated that two weeks of extract administration in intact mice decreased the weight of the adenohypophysis, particularly in male animals.

Most of the evidence reviewed suggests that the function of the pineal gland is related to that of the gonads. Pinealectomy in the chick, mouse, rabbit, or rat consistently stimulates the genital system; it causes gonadal hypertrophy, acceleration of vaginal opening in immature animals, and prolongation of estrus with shortening of diestrus in mature animals. Pinealectomy performed in immature animals does not affect the gonadal weight of the mature animal. Pineal-extract administration consistently retards vaginal opening and inhibits the action of injected pituitary gonadotrophin on the genital organs; in addition, in two studies statistically significant gonadal atrophy was produced by injection of pineal extract. These findings are supported by clinical observations on precocious puberty in children who also have pineal tumors; the pineal disorder usually associated with precocious puberty is destruction of the pineal parenchyma. However, the pineal-gonadal relation cannot be precisely defined at present. The data are consistent with any or all of three hypotheses: (1) that the pineal gland directly inhibits the function of the genital organs; (2) that it inhibits the secretion of pituitary gonadotrophin; and (3) that it decreases gonadal responsiveness to this hormone.

The fact that pineal extracts produce melanophore contraction in fish, tadpoles, and toads suggests that the pineal gland inhibits the production or action of another pituitary hormone—intermedin.

Pinealectomy in rabbits increases the blood sugar concentration and decreases blood phosphate concentration and urinary nitrogen excretion. Human patients given pineal extracts show a rise in blood glutathione concentration and decreases in blood ketone bodies and urinary ketosteroid excretion. These findings suggest that the pineal gland influences body metabolism and in particular the metabolic actions of the adrenocortical hormones. Here the possibility suggests itself that the pineal gland inhibits a third pituitary hormone—corticotrophin.

Much additional study is needed to clarify the relations of the pineal body to the pituitary gland, the gonads, the adrenal cortex, and the cutaneous melanophore cells. The relation of the gland to various bodily functions cannot be defined at present. These include: intermediary metabolism, thyroid and thyrotrophin activity, tumor growth, and the functions of the pancreas and of the parathyroid and thymus glands.

Several factors have impeded progress in the field. In the first place, there are no standard methods of preparing and using pineal extracts. Furthermore, nearly all physiologic studies have been limited to chicks, rats, and rabbits—a fact that prevents the drawing of any general conclusions from the available data. No final statement can be made about the nature of pineal function until additional experimental physiologic information has been accumulated.

Clinical observation so far has thrown very little light on pineal function. Several reports have described the incidence of pineal calcification, as determined roentgenographically. The incidence is negligible in the first decade of life; it approximates 25 per cent in the second decade, and increases gradually from the third to the eighth decade. No relation has ever been established between the occurrence of calcification and the status of the human pineal gland as a functioning organ. Neoplasms are the most common pineal lesions in man, but their incidence is low as compared with that of tumors of other organs. More than 50 per cent of them have been reported in patients less than twenty years old; they occur three times as frequently in men as in women. Observed changes in sexual development are apparently the only findings associated with pineal tumors that have so far contributed to our knowledge of pineal function. Precocious puberty, the most important of these changes, may, of course, be caused by a variety of non-pineal lesions, but when it is associated with a pineal tumor the neoplasm is usually non-parenchymal. The high incidence of sexual precocity associated with these tumors may be due to decrease or loss of pineal secretion, since these neoplasms destroy pineal parenchyma. Reports of the occurrence of hypogenitalism in association with pineal parenchymal tumors support the concept of an antagonism between the pineal body and the anterior pituitary gland. It is evident that the observed gonadal changes associated with pineal tumors accord with the experimental physiologic findings that indicate a relation between pineal activity and pituitary gonadotrophin.

Although the available physiologic and clinical data justify the presumption that the gland is functional, its functions cannot yet be defined.

Bibliography
PINEAL PHYSIOLOGY
CLINICAL CORRELATIONS

ABBREVIATIONS

The abbreviations of most of the journal titles used in this bibliography follow the system employed in the Current List of Medical Literature, Armed Forces Medical Library, Washington, D.C. Abbreviations of the older journal titles conform to those used in the various editions of the Index Catalogue of the Surgeon General's Library. The names of journals not included in either of these sources are not abbreviated.

Pineal Physiology

1
Abd-el-Malek, S.   On the relationship between the epiphysis cerebri and the reproductive system, J. Anat. 73: 419–423 (1938–39)

2
Adachi, K.   Shōka-sen no gansui-tanso taisha ni oyobosu eikyō (The effect of the pineal gland on carbohydrate metabolism), Sei-i-kai zasshi 58: 1382–1389 (1939)

3
Adachi, K.   Gansui-tanso taisha yori mitaru shōka-sen to shota naibunpi-sen seizai to no kankei ni tsuite (The relationship between the pineal gland and extracts of various other glands of internal secretion from the stand-point of carbohydrate metabolism), Sei-i-kai zasshi 58: 1767–1784 (1939)

4
Addair, J., and Chidester, F. E.   Pineal and metamorphosis: the influence of pineal feeding upon the rate of metamorphosis in frogs, Endocrinology 12: 791–796 (1928)

5
Adler, L.   Metamorphosestudien an Batrachierlarven; C — Exstirpation der Epiphyse, Arch. Entwmech. 40: 18–32 (1914)

6
Adler, L.   Schilddrüse und Warmeregulation, Arch. exp. Path., Leipzig, 86: 159–224 (1920)

7
Akiyama, S.   Shōka-sen tekishutsu no kōjōsen hatsuiku ni oyobosu eikyō (Influence of pinealectomy on the development of the thyroid), Nippon naibunpigakkai zasshi 3: 1292–1294 (1927)

8
Algranati Mondolfo, A.   Di alcuni ricerche sulla pineale, Arch. ital. anat. pat. 4: 149–189 (1933)

9
Alker, A.   Ueber ovarielle Dysfunktion und Serumkalkspiegel in ihren Beziehungen zur Osteomalacie, Deut. med. Wschr. 51: 151–152 (1925)

10

Altschule, M. D., Siegel, E. P., Goncz, R. M., and Murnane, J. P.   Effect of pineal extracts on blood glutathione level in psychotic patients, Arch. Neur. Psychiat. 71: 615–618 (1954)

11

Andersen, D. H., and Wolf, A.   Pinealectomy in rats, with a critical survey of the literature, J. Physiol. 81: 49–62 (1934)

12

Antognetti, L., and Geriola, F.   Studi sui "Tests" ormonici; nota 11—Comportamento della folliculinuria mensile in seguito allo somministrazione di estratto pineale, Endocr. pat. cost. 11: 99–104 (1936)

13

Arland, J. P.   Excision of the pineal body of a monkey under intra-arterial anesthesia, Indian M. Gaz. 60: 361–362 (1925)

14

Aronstam, N. E.   The pineal gland in relation to the sexual system, M. Rec. 144: 494–496 (1936)

15

Aschner, B.   Schwangerschaftsveränderungen der Zirbeldrüse, Verh. Deut. Ges. Gyn. 15: 231–233 (1913). Also in: Zbl. Gyn. 37: 840–841 (1913)

16

Atwell, W. J.   Further observations on the pigment changes following removal of the epithelial hypophysis and the pineal gland in the frog tadpole, Endocrinology 5: 221–232 (1921)

17

Baba, N.   Shōka-sen tekishutsu kato ni okeru ni-san naibunpi-sen zōki no soshikigaku-teki henka ni tsuite (Histological changes in a few endocrine organs of the pinealectomized rabbit), Sei-i-kai zasshi 57: 2593–2602 (1938)

18

Bachi, S.   Azione di estratti epifisari sull'iperchetonemia postoperatoria, Arch. ital. chir. 47: 317–323 (1937)

19

Badertscher, J. A.   Results following the extirpation of the pineal gland in newly hatched chicks, Anat. Rec. 28: 177–197 (1924)

20

Batelli, F., and Stern, L.   Effets produits par les extraits de la glande pinéale, des capsules surrénales, du foie, du testicule et de l'ovaire injectés dans les ventricules latéraux du cerveau, C. rend. Soc. biol. 86: 755–756 (1922)

21

Bauer, C.   Die Bedeutung der Zirbeldrüsentherapie in der Hypersexualitätsbekämpfung, Wien. med. Wschr. 85: 1009 (1935)

22

Becker, W. H.   Epiglandol bei Dementia praecox, Ther. Halbmonatschr. 34: 667–668 (1920)

23

Berblinger, W.   Zur Frage der genitalen Hypertrophie bei Tumoren der Zirbeldrüse und zum Einfluss embryonaler Geschwülstgewebes auf die Drüsen mit innere Sekretion, Virchows Arch. (suppl.) 227: 38–88 (1920)

24

Bergmann, W.   Wirkung von Pinealisextracten auf das Gefässsystem des Frosches, Arch. néerl. physiol. 24: 391–397 (1940)

25

Bergmann, W.   The Calcified Pineal Gland. Assen: van Gorcum, 1940

26

Bergmann, W., and Engel, P.   Ueber den Einfluss von Zirbelextrakten auf Tumoren bei weissen Mäusen und bei Menschen, Wien. klin. Wschr. 62: 79–82 (1950)

27

Bergmann, W., and Hofstätter, R.   Ist eine Behandlung des Bronchialasthmus durch Zirbelextrakte möglich? Wien. med. Wschr. 101: 964–965 (1951)

28

Berkeley, W. N.   The use of pineal gland in the treatment of certain classes of defective children, M. Rec. 85: 513–515 (1914)

29

Biedl, A.   Innere Sekretion; ihre physiologischen Grundlagen und ihre Bedeutung für die Pathologie; Teil 2—Die Zirbeldrüse, pp. 188–198. Berlin: Urban & Schwarzenberg, 1913

30

Bobkov, I. P.   Ob operativnych podstvpakh k shishkovidnoi zhelezy u sobak (Operative approaches to the pineal gland in dogs), Arkh. biol. nauk 45 (part 2): 197–201 (1937)

31

Borell, U.   Undersökningar över corpus pineales funktion med hjälp av radioaktiv fosfor, Nord. med. 36: 2137–2141 (1947)

32

Borell, U., and Örström, A.   Metabolism in different parts of the brain, especially in the epiphysis, measured with radioactive phosphorus, Acta physiol. scand. 10: 231–242 (1945)

33

Borell, U., and Örström, A. The turnover of phosphate in the pineal body compared with that in other parts of the brain, Biochem. J. 41: 398–403 (1947)

34

Bors, O., and Ralston, W. C. A simple assay of mammalian pineal extracts, Proc. Soc. Exp. Biol. 77: 807–808 (1951)

35

Brandenburg, E. Morphologische Beiträge zur Frage der endokrinen Funktion der Epiphyse, Endokrinologie 4: 81–96 (1929)

36

Breder, C. M., and Rasquin, P. Comparative studies in the light sensitivity of blind characins from a series of Mexican caves, Bull. Am. Mus. Nat. Hist. 89: 319–352 (1947)

37

Breder, C. M., and Rasquin, P. A preliminary report on the role of the pineal organ in the control of pigment cells and light reactions in recent teleost fishes, Science 111: 10–12 (1950)

38

Brücke, F. Personal communication.

39

Burger, K. Tobozmirigy kivonatokkal vegzett kiserletes vizsgalatok (Experiments with pineal extracts), Orv. hetil. 76: 1100–1101 (1932). Also published as: Ueber mit Zirbeldrüsenextrakten ausgeführte experimentelle Untersuchungen und deren therapeutische Möglichkeiten, Vorläufige Mitteilung, Zbl. Gyn. 57: 634–638 (1933)

40

Burkert, J. Pokusy s Extractum epiphysis Spofa u prasnic (Experiments on female pigs, using the epiphysis extract Spofa), Casopis ceskoslovenskych veterinaru 5: 121–125 (1950)

41

Buttaro, C. A., and Rottini, E. Ormoni e tasso amino-acidemico; azione dell'estratto epifisario sul tasso amino-acidemico, Minerva med. 38²: 54–56 (1947)

42

Calvet, J. Expériences sur l'action de l'épiphyse sur les glandes génitales, Bull. Soc. de sexol. 1: 171–180 (1933). Also published as: De l'action de l'épiphyse sur les rats et les cobayes impubères, C. rend. Assoc. anat., 25e Réun., Lisbonne, 28: 118–120 (1933)

43

Calvet, J.   Injections d'extrait épiphysaire chez la femelle en période de rut, Toulouse méd., p. 93, 1934

44

de Candia, S.   Action de l'extrait pinéal sur la calcémie, Rev. fr. endocr. 9: 23–32 (1931)

45

Cannavo, L., and Frada, G.   Studi sull'epifisi; nota 1—Influenza di alcuni estratti epifisari sul tasso chetonemico, Arch. ital. med. sper. 2: 407–436 (1938)

46

Cannavo, L., and Frada, G.   Studi sull'epifisi; nota 2—Azione del calore sugli estratti pineali attivi sulla chetonemia, Arch. ital. med. sper. 2: 1053–1056 (1938)

47

Capretti, G., and Tusini, G.   L'azione degli estratti epifisari sulla eliminazione urinaria dei 17-chetosteroidi, Gior. clin. med. 32: 935–939 (1951)

48

del Castillo, E. B.   Action de la splénectomie et de l'épiphysectomie sur le cycle oestral du rat blanc, C. rend. Soc. biol. 99: 1404–1405 (1928)

49

Cervellati, L.   Epifisi e menopausa, Ann. ostet. gin. 72: 239–251 (1950)

50

Christea, G.   Die Genitalorgane und die Zirbeldrüse, Abstracted in: Münch. med. Wschr. 60: 1051 (1913). Also abstracted in: Zbl. inn. Med. 34: 819 (1913)

51

Cisotti, F.   Sulla citoarchitettonica del corpo pineale, Rendic. Ist. lombardo sci. lett., Classe sci. mat. nat. 76: 79–102 (1942–43)

52

Ciulla, U.   Estratti epifisari e reazione di Friedmann, Atti Soc. ital. ostet. 35: 537–540 (1939)

53

Ciulla, U.   Influenza dell'estratto epifisario sull'azione maturante dei gonadotropi preipofisari sul testicolo degli uccelli, Atti Soc. ital. ostet. 36: 45–48 (1940)

54
Clausen, H. J., and Mofshin, B.   The pineal eye of the lizard (Anolis carolinensis), a photoreceptor as revealed by oxygen consumption studies, J. Cellul. Physiol. 14: 29–41 (1939)

55
Clausen, H. J., and Poris, E. G.   The effect of light upon activity in the lizard, Anolis carolinensis, with especial reference to the pineal body, Anat. Rec. 69: 39–53 (1937)

56
Clemente, G.   Contributo allo studio della glandola pineale nell'uomo e in alcuni animali, Endocr. pat. cost. 2: 44–47 (1923). Also published in: Rendic. R. Accad. naz. Lincei, Roma, 32: 47–51 (1923)

57
Clemente, G.   Contributo allo studio della glandola pineale nell'uomo e in alcuni mammiferi, Gior. biol. med. sper. 1: 76–80 (1923)

58
Collier, R.   Ueber den Feinbau der Epiphysis cerebri von Nagetieren und die Frage seiner funktionellen Veränderungen, Zschr. Zellforsch. 33: 51–67 (1943)

59
Colombo, E.   Valor endocrino de la pineal, Bol. Inst. matern., B. Aires, 12: 32–39 (1943). Also in: Bol. Soc. obst. gin. B. Aires 22: 527–534 (1943); and in: Rev. As. med. argent. 58: 76–78 (1944)

60
Curupi, C.   Szivzavarok es az epiphysis (Cardiac disturbances and the epiphysis), Gyogyaszat 71: 494 (1931)

61
von Cyon, E.   Zur Physiologie der Zirbeldrüse, Vorversuche, Arch. ges. Physiol. 98: 327–346 (1903). Also published as: Tsion, I. (same author). K voprosu o fiziologischeskoi roli gl. pinealis predvakitel'nyie opyty (Physiological role of the pineal gland), Arkh. biol. nauk (suppl.) 11: 297–309 (1904)

62
D'Amour, M. D., and D'Amour, F. E.   Effects of pinealectomy over several generations, Proc. Soc. Exp. Biol. 37: 244–246 (1937)

63
Dana, C. L., and Berkeley, W. N.   The functions of the pineal gland; with report of feeding experiments by H. H. Goddard and W. S. Cornell, Med. Rec. 83: 835–847 (1913). Summarized in: Month. Cyclop. 7: 78–80 (1914)

64
Dandy, W. E.   Extirpation of the pineal body, J. Exp. M. 22: 237–247 (1915)

65
Davis, L., and Martin, J.   Results of experimental removal of the pineal gland in young mammals, Arch. Neur. Psychiat. 43: 23–45 (1940). Abstracted in: Tr. Am. Neur. Ass. 65: 36–40 (1939)

66
Decio, C.   Sulla struttura della ghiandola pineale durante la gravidanza, Riv. ital. gin. 3: 761–775 (1924–25)

67
Demel, R.   Experimentelle Studie zur Funktion der Zirbeldrüse, Teil I, Mitt. Grenzgeb. Med. Chir. 40: 302–312 (1927)

68
Demel, R.   Experimentelle Studie zur Funktion der Zirbeldrüse, Teil II, Arb. neur. Inst. Wien. 30: 13–26 (1927)

69
Demel, R.   Klinisches und Experimentelles zur Funktion der Zirbeldrüse, Beitr. klin. Chir. 147: 66–70 (1929)

70
Desogus, V.   La pineale negli uccelli normali e cerebrolesionati, Riv. biol. 6: 495–504 (1924)

71
Desogus, V.   Contributo allo studio della pineale e dell'ipofisi degli uccelli in stato di maternità, Monit. zool. ital. 37: 273–282 (1926)

72
Desogus, V.   La pinéale chez les mammifères normaux et cérébrolésés, Rev. neur. 2: 362–369 (1927)

73
Desogus, V.   I lipoide della pineale e dell'ipofisi negli uccelli in rapporto al ciclo di ovulazione, Monit. zool. ital. 39: 58–71 (1928). Also in: Atti Soc. sc. med. natur. Cagliari 30: 97–102 (1928)

74
Desogus, V.   Aspetti istologici della pineale in rapporto allo stato gravidico, Riv. pat. nerv. 45: 555–590 (1935). Abstracted in: Atti Soc. ital. anat. 1933; Monit. zool. ital. (suppl.) 44: 147–148 (1933)

75
Dixon, W. E., and Halliburton, W. D.   The pineal body, Q. J. Exp. Physiol. 2: 283–285 (1909)

76
Dixon, W. E., and Halliburton, W. D.   The action of the choroid plexuses on the secretion of the cerebrospinal fluid, Proc. Physiol. Soc., London, March 19, 1910. Published in: J. Physiol. 40: xxx–xxxii (1910)

77
Dobrovolskaia-Zavadskaia, N., and Zephiroff, P.   Effet des produits d'origine épiphysaire et d'origine hépatique sur la croissance des tumeurs chez la souris, C. rend. Soc. biol. 134: 60–63 (1940)

78
Dobrovolskaia-Zavadskaia, N., and Zephiroff, P.   Peut-on influencer l'évolution des tumeurs de souris par des extraits épiphysaires et hépatiques? C. rend. Soc. biol. 134: 79–81 (1940)

79
Dōmoto, S.   Diphtherie-dokuso chūdoku-ji ni okeru sho-naibunpi-zōki no byōri-soshiki-gaku-teki henka narabi-ni Vitamin C gan-yū-ryō no shōchō ni kan-suru jikken-teki kenkyū; shōka-sen no byōri-soshiki-gaku-teki henka (Experimental studies on histopathological changes in all the endocrine organs and variation in their vitamin C content during poisoning with diphtherotoxin; histopathological changes in the pineal gland), Taishitsugaku zasshi 11: 555–568 (1943)

80
Dōmoto, S.   Diphtherie-dokuso chūdoku-ji ni okeru sho-naibunpi-zōki no byōri-soshiki-gaku-teki henka narabi-ni Vitamin C gan-yū-ryō no shōchō ni kan-suru jikken-teki kenkyū; shōka-sen Vitamin C gan-yū-ryō no shōchō (Experimental studies on histopathological changes in all the endocrine organs and variation in their vitamin C content during poisoning with diphtherotoxin; variation in the vitamin C content of the pineal gland), Taishitsugaku zasshi 11: 589–594 (1943)

81
Dōmoto, S.   Diphtherie-dokuso chūdoku-ji ni okeru sho-naibunpi-zōki no byōri-soshikigaku-teki henka narabi-ni Vitamin C gan-yū-ryō no shōchō ni kan-suru jikken-teki kenkyū; zenpen no sōkatsu kōan oyobi ketsuron (Experimental studies on histopathological changes in all the endocrine organs and variation in their vitamin C content during poisoning with diphtherotoxin; summarizing observations on all chapters and conclusions), Nippon biseibutsugaku byōrigaku zasshi 37: 577–593 (1943)

82
Dresel, K.   Ueber den Einfluss von Extrakten aus Drüsen mit innerer Sekretion auf den Blutsucker, Zschr. exp. Path. 16: 365–368 (1914)

83
Dubowik, J. A. Versuch einer hormonalen Beschleunigung des Wachstums junger Tiere, Endokrinologie 11: 15–22 (1932)

84
Eddy, N. B. The action of preparations of the endocrine glands upon the work done by skeletal muscle, Am. J. Physiol. 69: 432–440 (1924)

85
Einhorn, N. H., and Rowntree, L. G. Experimental phases of the pineal problem, Endocrinology 24: 221–229 (1939)

86
Engel, P. Ueber den Einfluss von Epiphysenextrakten auf die Wirkung der Hypophysenvorderlappenhormone, Klin. Wschr. 13: 266–267 (1934)

87
Engel, P. Zirbeldrüse und hypophysäres Wachstum, Klin. Wschr. 13: 1248–1249 (1934)

88
Engel, P. Untersuchungen über die Wirkung der Zirbeldrüse, Zschr. ges. exp. Med. 93: 69–78 (1934)

89
Engel, P. Zirbeldrüse und gonadotropes Hormon, Zschr. ges. exp. Med. 94: 333–345 (1934)

90
Engel, P. Ueber den Einfluss von Hypophysenvorderlappen-hormonen und Epiphysen-hormon auf das Wachstum von Impftumoren, Zschr. Krebsforsch. 41: 281–291 (1934)

91
Engel, P. Investigaciones sobre la genesis de las antihormonas, Arch. Soc. biol. Montevideo 6: 161–179 (1935)

92
Engel, P. Ueber die Beeinflussung der Callus-bildung durch Hormone; ii—Wachstumshormon und Zirbeldrüsenextrakte, Deut. Zschr. Chir. 244: 591–592 (1935)

93
Engel, P. Ueber die Veränderung der Nagerscheide durch Zirbelextrakte, Klin. Wschr. 14: 830–831 (1935)

94
Engel, P. Gegenhormone und Zirbeldrüse, Klin. Wschr. 14: 970–971 (1935)

95
Engel, P.   Ueber die Antigonadotrope Wirkung des Epiphysans, Wien. klin. Wschr. 48: 1160–1161 (1935)

96
Engel, P.   Antigonadotropes hormon in Zirbeldrüse, Blut und Organen, Zschr. ges. exp. Med. 95: 441–457 (1935)

97
Engel, P.   Weitere Untersuchungen über die biologischen und chemischen Eigenschaften des Antigonadotropen Hormons der Zirbeldrüse, Zschr. ges. exp. Med. 96: 328–336 (1935)

98
Engel, P.   Wachstumsbeeinflussende Hormone und Tumor Wachstum, Zschr. Krebsforsch. 41: 488–496 (1935)

99
Engel, P.   Zur Frage der hormonalen Wirkung der Zirbeldrüse, Klin. Wschr. 15: 1281 (1936)

100
Engel, P.   Zur Wirkung des Antigonadotropen Hormon der Zirbeldrüse am Kaninchen, Wien. klin. Wschr. 49: 1018–1019 (1936)

101
Engel, P.   Assay of pineal extracts, Endocrinology 25: 144–145 (1939)

102
Engel, P.   Ensayos sobre la glándula pineal, An. Soc. biol. Bogotá 1: 60–62 (1943)

103
Engel, P.   Influencia de hormonas sobre tumores de benzopirena, An. Soc. biol. Bogotá 4: 27–34 (1950)

104
Escudero, A., Herraiz, M. L., and Polak, M.   Influencia de la vitamina E sobre la estructura de la hipofisis y de la pineal, Tr. Inst. nac. nutr., B. Aires (1940–41), pp. 35–41, 1942

105
Eufinger, H., and Uhing, H.   Untersuchungen über den Einfluss der Gravidität auf den morphologischen Bau des Corpus pineale beim Meerschweinchen, Arch. Gyn. 151: 168–181 (1932)

106
Exner, A., and Boese, J.   Ueber experimentelle Exstirpation der Glandula pinealis, Deut. Zschr. Chir. 107: 182–186 (1910). Abstracted in: Neur. Zbl. 29: 754–755 (1910) and in: Münch. med. Wschr. 58: 154 (1911)

107
Eyster, J. A. E., and Jordan, H. E.   *See* Jordan, H. E., and Eyster, J. A. E., ref. 198.

108
Faustka, K.   Das Epiphysan G. Richter bei einem Pferde mit Starrkrampf, Wien. tieraerztl. Mschr. 37: 778–779 (1950)

109
Fay, H. M.   L'épiphyse en thérapeutique, Bull. Soc. méd. Paris 137: 289–292 (1933). Also published in: J. méd. Paris 53: 614–616 (1933)

110
Fenger, F.   The composition and physiologic activity of the pineal gland, J. Am. M. Ass. 67: 1836–1838 (1916)

111
Ferroni, G. M.   La pineale in gravidanza, Riv. ital. gin. (suppl.) 18: 179–192 (1935–36)

112
Fiandaca, S.   Contributo allo studio delle connessioni funzionali tra epifisi e lobo ipofisario anteriore; Nota i–Azione sulla chetonemia, Biochim. ter. sper. 22: 9–17 (1935)

113
Fiandaca, S.   Contributo allo studio delle connessioni funzionali tra epifisi e lobo ipofisario anteriore; Nota ii–Azione sulla magnesiemia, fosfatemia e calcemia, Biochim. ter. sper. 22: 363–368 (1935)

114
Fischer, O.   Isolation and biological assay of an efficacious fraction of the pineal gland, Arch. internat. pharm. dyn. 59: 340–344 (1938)

115
Fischer, O.   Preparation of an active extract of the pineal gland, Endocrinology 33: 116–117 (1943). Abstracted as: Sobre una fracción activa de la glándula pineal, Bol. Soc. biol. Santiago 1: 7 (1943) and in: Rev. de med. aliment. 5: 303 (1943)

116
Flather, M. D.   The influence of glandular extracts upon the contractile vacuoles of paramecium caudatum, Biol. Bull. 37: 22–39 (1919)

117
Fleischmann, W., and Goldhammer, H.   Nachweis einer oestrushemmenden Substanz in der Zirbeldrüse junger Rattenweibchen, Klin. Wschr. 13: 415 (1934)

118

Fleischmann, W., and Goldhammer, H.   Zur Frage der hormonalen Wirkung der Zirbeldrüse, Klin. Wschr. 15: 1047–1048 (1936)

119

Fleischmann, W., and Goldhammer, H.   Nachweis einer oestrushemmenden Substanz in Kinderharn, Klin. Wschr. 15: 1730–1731 (1936)

120

Foa, C.   Hypertrophie des testicules et de la crète après l'extirpation de la glande pinéale chez le coq, Arch. ital. biol. 57: 233–252 (1912). Also published as: Ipertrofia dei testicoli e della cresta dopo l'asportazione della ghiandola pineale nel gallo, Pathologica 4: 445–454 (1912). Abstracted as: Zoia, C. (Printing of name presumably erroneous), Demonstration von Tieren, denen die Zirbeldrüse entfernt würde, Zbl. allg. Path. 25: 789 (1914)

121

Foa, C.   Nouvelles recherches sur la fonction de la glande pinéale, Arch. ital. biol. 61: 79–92 (1914). Abstracted as: Nuove ricerche sulla funzione della ghiandola pineale, Atti R. Accad. scienze, Torino, 49: 859–872 (1914)

122

Foa, C.   Nuovi esperimenti sulla fisiologia della ghiandola pineale, Arch. sc. biol., Bologna, 12: 306–321 (1928). Abstracted in: Boll. Soc. ital. biol. sper. 3: 385–387 (1928). Also published as: Nouvelles expériences sur la physiologie de la glande pinéale, Arch. ital. biol. 81: 147–158 (1929); and in: Wien. med. Wschr. 84: 1149–1153 (1934)

123

Fontana, G.   Azione dell'estratto epifisario sull'occhio, Lettura oftal., Pistoia, 14: 43–46 (1937)

124

Forlini, E.   Sulle modificazioni della epiphysis cerebri della donna gravida, Riv. ital. gin. 20: 289–342 (1937)

125

Frada, G.   Influenza di alcuni estratti di ghiandola pineale sul tasso glicemico e sull'iperglicemia da prolan, Arch. ital. med. sper. 2: 1105–1114 (1938)

126

Frada, G.   Influenza dell'estratto cloroformico di epifisi sulla curva glicemica da insulina, Biochim. ter. sper. 25: 266–270 (1938)

127

Frada, G.   Azione dell'estratto acquoso di epifisi sulla iperglicemia adrenalinica, Biochim. ter. sper. 25: 315–317 (1938)

128

Frada, G. Correlazioni funzionali in gravidanza tra ipofisi ed epifisi e loro repercussione sul ricambio idrocarbonato, Biochim. ter. sper. 25: 417–422 (1938)

129

Frada, G. Influenza di alcuni estratti di pineale sull'accrescimento e sullo sviluppo sessuale del ratto, Ormoni 1: 673–690 (1939)

130

Frada, G., and Micale, G. Studio clinico-radiologico sulle calcificazioni pineali in gravidanza, Radiologia medica 28: 209–218 (1941). Abstracted in: Ormoni 3: 111–112 (1941)

131

Frada, G., and Tanas, F. Influenza di estratti epifisari sul ricambio glucidico e lipidico, Boll. Soc. ital. biol. sper. 24: 1050–1052 (1948)

132

Fraenkel, L. Besprechung des Vortrages von Basset: Klinische Erfahrungen mit Pituglandol, Mschr. Geburtsh. Gyn. 37: 696 (1913)

133

Fraenkel, L. Wirkung von Extrakten endokriner Drüsen auf die Kopfgefässe, Zschr. exp. Path. 16: 177–185 (1914). Abstracted as: Vasomotorische Phänomene am Kopf durch Extrakte innerer Drüsen, Zbl. ges. Gyn. Geburtsh. 1: 709–710 (1913)

134

Frascarelli, R., and Mescolini, G. Esistono correlazioni tra epifisi e ricambio dell'acido urico? Boll. Soc. ital. biol. sper. 24: 624–625 (1948)

135

von Frisch, K. Beitrage zur Physiologie der Pigmentzellen in der Fischhaut, Arch. ges. Physiol. 138: 319–387 (1911)

136

Gandolfo, G., and Vegna, I. Contributo alla conoscenza della fisiologia pineale; epifisi e androgenuria nell'uomo, Rass. med., Milano, 29: 124–125 (1952)

137

Gardner, J. H. Innervation of pineal gland in hooded rat, J. Comp. Neur. 99: 319–329 (1953). Abstracted in: Anat. Rec. 106: 271 (1950)

138

Georgiou, E. Ueber die Natur und die Pathogenese der Krebstumoren; radikale Heilung des Krebses bei weissen Mäusen, Zschr. Krebsforsch. 28: 562–572 (1929)

139
Gianferrari, L.   Influenza dell'alimentazione con capsule surrenali, ipofisi ed epifisi su la pigmentazione cutanea ed il ritmo respiratorio di Salmo
fario, Arch. sc. biol. 3: 39–52 (1922)

140
Giardinelli, M.   Ricerche cliniche sull'uso dell'increto della ghiandola
pineale nella terapia dei disturbi del climaterio, Minerva med. 40: 663–
665 (1949)

141
Glick, D., and Biskind, G. R.   Studies in histochemistry; viii–Relationship between concentration of vitamin C and development of the pineal
gland, Proc. Soc. Exp. Biol. 34: 866–870 (1936)

142
Goddard, H. H.   The Vineland experiment with pineal gland extract,
J. Am. M. Ass. 68: 1340–1341 (1917)

143
Goddard, H. H., and Cornell, W. S.   See Dana, C. L., and Berkeley, W.
N., ref. 63.

144
Godina, G.   La struttura dell'epiphysis cerebri in rapporto alla castrazione ed alla gravidanza, Riv. pat. nerv. 54: 74–102 (1939)

145
Godina, G.   Il quadro istologico dell'epiphysis cerebri in seguito alla
castrazione e durante la gravidanza, Ormoni 2: 177–182 (1940)

146
Grunewald Lowenstein, M.   Studies on the function of the pineal body,
Exper. Med. Surg. 10: 135–154 (1952)

147
Groebbels, F., and Kuhn, E.   Unzureichende Ernährung und Hormon-
wirkung; Mitteilung iv–Der Einfluss der Zirbeldrüsen- und Hodensub-
stanz auf Wachstum und Entwickelung von Froschlarven, Zschr. Biol. 78:
1–6 (1923)

148
Haagen, R.   Innersekretorische Behandlung der Migräne durch Epiglan-
dol, Münch. med. Wschr. 69: 258–259 (1922). Also published in: Med.
Klin. 18: 481 (1922)

149
Hafermann, —.   Zur antispastichen Wirkung des Epiglandols, Ther. Ge-
genwart 63 (n.s. 24): 475 (1922)

[120]

150

Hano, H. Shōka-sen no yakuri sayo (Pharmacologic action of pineal extracts), Ōsaka igakkai zasshi 42: 2091 (1943)

151

Hanson, A. M. Biologic effects of active thymus and pineal extracts, Minnesota M. 19: 1–4 (1936)

152

den Hartog Jager, W. A. Quelques arguments au sujet de la fonction endocrinienne de la glande pinéale; examen personnel et détails recueillés dans la bibliographie, Acta brevia neerl. 9: 1–4 (1939)

153

den Hartog Jager, W. A., and Heil, J. F. Ueber die Epiphysefrage, Acta brevia neerl. 5: 32–34 (1935)

154

Hellhammer, H. Der Einfluss von Epiphysan, der Kastration und von männlichem Sexualhormon bei weiblichen Tieren und von weiblichen Sexualhormonen bei männlichen Tieren auf die Körperentwicklung und den Knorpel bei jungen Hunden, Inaug. Diss., Vet. Med., Hannover, 1939

155

Hewer, H. R. Studies in colour changes of fish; I—The action of certain endocrine secretions in the minnow, J. Exp. Biol. 3: 123–140 (1926)

156

Hölldobler, K. Weitere Untersuchungen über die Wirkung inkretorischer Drüsensubstanzen auf die Morphogenie; IV—Die Zirbeldrüse, ein inkretorisches Organ mit morphogenetischer Bedeutung, Arch. Entwmech. 107: 605–624 (1926)

157

Hoff, H. Versüche über die Beeinflussbarkeit des Hirndruckes, Arb. neur. Inst. Wien. 24: 397–407 (1922–23)

158

Hofmann, E. Zur Frage der inneren Sekretion der Zirbeldrüse bei der Ratte, Arch. ges. Physiol. 209: 685–692 (1925)

159

Hofstätter, R. Ueber organotherapeutische Versüche mit Epiglandol und Pineal-tabletten, Med. Klin. 10: 1460 (1914)

160

Hofstätter, R. Diskussion zu von Frankl Hochwart, Verein für Psychiatrie und Neurologie in Wien, 1914. Published in: Jahrb. Psychiat. Neur. 35: 161–163 (1915)

161
Hofstätter, R.   Ueber Versüche der therapeutischen Verwendung von Pineal-extrakten, Mschr. Geburtsh. Gyn. 45: 220–239, 316–334 (1917)

162
Hofstätter, R.   Organotherapeutische Versüche mit Hilfe von Zirbelextrakten, besonders bei sexueller Uebererregbarkeit, Wien. klin. Wschr. 49: 136–137 (1936)

163
Hofstätter, R.   Pinealtherapie bei prämenstrueller Anfälligkeit, Zbl. Gyn. 62: 1192–1196 (1938)

164
Hofstra, S. T.   Genezing van hypersexualiteit bij een ruin door middel van Epiphysan "Gedeon Richter," Tijdschrift voor Diergeneeskunde, Utrecht, 66: 1324–1326 (1939)

165
Honda, G.   Shikyū-nenmaku jōhi-saihō oyobi chitsu jōhi-saihō no shiryūtai narabi-ni henryūtai ni kan-suru kenkyū; shoshu naibunpi-sen zōki seibun ga shikyū-nenmaku jōhi-saihō oyobi chitsu jōhi-saihō no shiryūtai narabi-ni henryūtai ni oyobosu eikyō (Studies on the mitochondria and the metachondria of the epithelial cells of the mucous membrane of the uterus and of the epithelial cells of the vagina; the effect of the constituents of various endocrine organs on these epithelial cell mitochondria and metachondria), Jikken igaku zasshi 18: 1439–1445 (1934)

166
Horrax, G.   Studies on the pineal gland; i—Experimental observations, Arch. Int. M. 17: 607–626 (1916)

167
Hoskins, E. R.   The growth of the body and organs of the albino rat as affected by feeding various ductless glands (thyroid, thymus, hypophysis, and pineal), J. Exp. Zool. 21: 295–346 (1916)

168
Hoskins, E. R., and Hoskins, M. M.   Experiments with the thyroid, hypophysis, and pineal glands of Rana sylvatica, Anat. Rec. 16: 151 (1919)

169
Howell, W. H.   The physiological effects of extracts of the hypophysis cerebri and infundibular body, J. Exp. M. 3: 245–258 (1898)

170
Hutschenreiter, C.   Das Epiphysan G. Richter in der Hypersexualitätsbekampfung beim Pferde, Wien. tieraerztl. Mschr. 23: 231–237 (1936)

171
Hutschenreiter, C. Epiphysan G. Richter bei traumatischen und rheumatischen Muskelentzündungen der Pferde, Tieraerztl. Rundschau 43: 75–79 (1937)

172
Hutschenreiter, C. Epiphysan G. Richter als Mittel gegen Hypersexualitätserscheinungen bei Pferden, Tieraerztl. Rundschau 43: 764–767, 775–777 (1937)

173
Hutschenreiter, C. Ein Fall von chronischem Tetanus bei einem Pferde und das Epiphysan G. Richter, Wien. tieraerztl. Mschr. 34: 286–287 (1947)

174
Hutschenreiter, C. Epiphysan G. Richter in seiner hormonalen Reizkörper- und antispasmodischen Wirkung bei Pferden, Wien. tieraerztl. Mschr. 35: 417–435 (1948)

175
Huxley, J. S., and Hogben, L. T. Experiments on amphibian metamorphosis and pigment responses in relation to internal secretion, Proc. R. Soc., London, 93 (series B): 36–53 (1922)

176
Ikoma, M. Shin-bu chiryō-yō roentgen-sen no jikitatsu sayō ni yoru chūsū-shinkei-keitō oyobi shōka-sen nōkasuitai no henka, narabi-ni sono iwayuru entatsu sayō ni yoru jiyo sho-zōki no dai-niji-teki henka ni tsuite (Changes in the central nervous system, the pineal gland, and the hypophysis cerebri caused by the direct action of roentgen rays used for deep therapy, and secondary changes in various viscera caused by the so-called distant effect), Shinkeigaku zasshi 26: 513–552, 589–647 (1926)

177
Ikuta, H. Hito no shōka-sen no soshiki-byōri (Histopathology of the human pineal gland), Keiō igaku 16: 1883–1997 (1936)

178
Ikuta, H. Ueber experimentelle Studien der Zirbeldrüse; I—Veränderungen des Zentralnervensystems bei Exstirpation derselben, Tr. Soc. path. jap. 27: 498–500 (1937)

179
Ikuta, H. Ueber experimentelle Studien der Zirbeldrüse; II—Morphologische Studien über die Hypophyse bei Pinealektomie, Tr. Soc. path. jap. 28: 420–421 (1938)

180
Imura, A. Kato shōka-sen tekishutsu-jutsu narabi-ni shōka-sen ga kato taijū ni oyobosu eikyō ni kan-suru jikken-teki kenkyū chiken hoi (Experimental studies on pinealectomy and the relation of the pineal gland to the body weight of a rabbit), Sei-i-kai zasshi 56: 2045–2048 (1937)

181
Itō, K. Shōka-sen no jikken-teki kenkyū; kō-seishoku-sen sayō ni tsuite (Experimental studies on the pineal gland; anti-sexual gland activity), Chōsen igakkai zasshi 26: 1109 (1936)

182
Itō, K. Shōka-sen no kinō ni kan-suru jikken-teki kenkyū; shōka-sen no taion chōsetsu sayō ni tsuite (Experimental studies on the functioning of the pineal gland; Part I—The body-temperature-regulating action of the pineal gland), Chōsen igakkai zasshi 29: 2501–2532 (1939). Abstracted as: Shōka-sen no jikken-teki kenkyū; shōka-sen no taion chōsetsu sayō (Experimental studies on the pineal gland; the body-temperature-regulating action of the pineal gland), Nippon byōrigakkai kaishi 27: 500–503 (1937)

183
Itō, K. Shōka-sen no kinō ni kan-suru jikken-teki kenkyū; iwayuru enrui-netsu to no kankei (Experimental studies on the functioning of the pineal gland; Part II—Relation to the so-called salt fever), Chōsen igakkai zasshi 30: 22–38, 1940. Abstracted as: Shōka-sen no jikken-teki kenkyū; enrui ni yoru hatsunetsu sono-ta ni-san no jikō to no kankei (Experimental studies on the pineal gland; relation to pyrexia caused by salts, and a few other facts), Chōsen igakkai zasshi 27: 1624–1625 (1937)

184
Itō, K. Shōka-sen no kinō ni kan-suru jikken-teki kenkyū; shōka-sen no masui oyobi keiren ni tai-suru igi ni tsuite (Experimental studies on the functioning of the pineal gland; Part III—The significance of the pineal gland in anesthesia and spasm), Chōsen igakkai zasshi 30: 56–74 (1940). Abstracted as: Shōka-sen no jikken-teki kenkyū; shōka-sen no masui oyobi keiren ni tai-suru igi narabi-ni sore to jōhi-shōtai to no kankei (Experimental studies on the pineal gland; the significance of the pineal gland in anesthesia and in spasm, and the relation of this to the parathyroids), Nippon byōrigakkai kaishi 28: 421–426 (1938)

185
Itō, K. Kenkō kato kessei-nai no kō-masui-sei busshitsu ni kan-suru kenkyū (Studies on the anti-narcotic substance in the blood serum of the normal rabbit), Chōsen igakkai zasshi 29: 2639–2663 (1939)

186
Izawa, Y.   On the experimental removal of the pineal body in chickens, Tr. Soc. path. jap. 12: 139–143 (1922)

187
Izawa, Y.   A contribution to the physiology of the pineal body, Am. J. M. Sc. 166: 185–196 (1923)

188
Izawa, Y.   Further experiments of removal of the pineal body in chickens, Tr. Soc. path. jap. 13: 144–153 (1923)

189
Izawa, Y.   Shiro-nezumi no shōka-sen tekishutsu shiken seiseki oyobi gai-sen-tekishutsu no shussan ni oyobosu eikyō ni tsuite (Results of experiments on excision of the pineal gland of the white rat, and the effect of the excision of this gland upon birth), Nippon byōrigakkai kaishi 16: 166–169 (1926)

190
Izawa, Y.   The effects of pinealectomy at 20 days of age on the growth in body length, body weight, and tail length of male and female albino rats, Tr. Soc. path. jap. 16: 60–69 (1926)

191
Izawa, Y.   The effect of pinealectomy at 20 days of age on the growth of the brain and spinal cord of the male and female albino rat, Tr. Soc. path. jap. 16: 69–72 (1926)

192
Izawa, Y.   The effect of pinealectomy at 20 days of age on the growth of the reproductive system of the male and female albino rat, Tr. Soc. path. jap. 16: 72–78 (1926)

193
Izawa, Y.   The effects of pinealectomy at 20 days of age on the growth of the glands of internal secretion of male and female albino rats, Tr. Soc. path. jap. 16: 78–86 (1926)

194
Izawa, Y.   On some anatomical changes which follow removal of the pineal body from both sexes of the immature albino rat, Am. J. Physiol. 77: 126–139 (1927)

195
Izawa, Y., and Akiyama, S.   Studies on the pineal body; on some anatomical changes following pinealectomy at 20 days of age in both sexes of the albino rat, Tr. Soc. path. jap. 17: 320–324 (1927)

196
Jaffe, —.   Ueber Grosse und Form der Epiphysis, Klin. Wschr. 7: 1663
(1928)

197
Johnson, G. E., and Lahr, E. L.   See Lahr, E. L., ref. 234.

198
Jordan, H. E., and Eyster, J. A. E.   The physiological action of extracts
of the pineal body, Am. J. Physiol. 29: 115–123 (1911–12). Abstracted
in: Eyster, J. A. E., and Jordan, H. E., Effect of intravenous injections
of extracts of the pineal body, Proc. Am. Physiol. Soc., Am. J. Physiol. 27:
xxiii (1911)

199
Jullien, G.   Activité physiologique de l'épiphyse chez l'adulte, C. rend.
Soc. biol. 140: 648–649 (1946)

200
Jullien, G.   Antagonisme épiphyse-hypophyse, C. rend. Soc. biol. 140:
649-651 (1946)

201
Kanamori, T.   Shōka-sen tekishutsu no shi-sei shiro-nezumi ni oyobosu
henka (Changes in the female white rat due to pinealectomy), Ōsaka kōtō
igaku senmongakkō zasshi 9: 624–630 (1942). Abstracted in: Ōsaka igakkai zasshi 41: 600 (1942)

202
Kasahara, S., and Nagai, M.   On the cultivation of the pineal gland, Tr.
Soc. path. jap. 23: 455–456 (1933)

203
Katagiri, E.   Shōka-sen ni kan-suru kenkyū; shōka-sen datsuraku to sei-
shūki (Studies on the pineal gland; pinealectomy and the sexual cycle),
Ōsaka igakkai zasshi 42: 935–938 (1943)

204
Katagiri, E.   Shōka-sen ni kan-suru kenkyū; shuyō zōshoku to shōka-sen
(Studies on the pineal gland; tumor proliferation and the pineal gland),
Ōsaka igakkai zasshi 43: 315–320 (1944)

205
Katagiri, E.   Shōka-sen ni kan-suru kenkyū; shōka-sen tekishutsu ni yoru
hatsujō-kōshin wo yokusei-suru busshitsu (Studies on the pineal gland;
a substance for controlling acceleration of sexual excitement caused by
pinealectomy), Ōsaka igakkai zasshi 43: 573–577 (1944)

206
Katagiri, E.   Shōka-sen ni kan-suru kenkyū; shōka-sen oyobi hoka nai-

bunpi-zōki no gasu-taisha (Studies on the pineal gland; gas metabolism of the pineal gland and of other endocrine organs), Ōsaka igakkai zasshi 43: 578–585 (1944)

207
Katō, S. Shinzō-kinō ni arawaruru sho-hormone seizai no kōka (The effects of various hormone preparations on the functioning of the heart, Part I), Gun-idan zasshi no. 230: 1145–1166 (1932)

208
Katō, S. Shinzō-kinō ni arawaruru sho-hormone seizai no kōka (The effects of various hormone preparations on the functioning of the heart, Part II), Gun-idan zasshi no. 231: 1217–1260 (1932)

209
Katō, S. Fütterungsversuch mit dem Zirbelpräparat an Anurenlarven, Fol. anat. jap. 14: 413–420 (1936)

210
Keller, A. D. Failure of sexual development following lesions in environs of the pineal in "senior" female pups, Fed. Proc., Baltimore, 6: 141 (1947)

211
King, L. S. The hematoencephalic barrier, Arch. Neur. Psychiat. 41: 51–72 (1939)

212
Kitay, J. I. Effects of pinealectomy on ovary weight in immature rats, Endocrinology 54: 114–116 (1954)

213
Kitay, J. I., and Altschule, M. D. Effects of pineal extract administration on ovary weight in rats, Endocrinology (in press)

214
Kolmer, W. Technik der experimentellen Untersuchungen über die Zirbeldrüse, in: Abderhalden, E., Handb. biol. Arbeitsmeth., Abt. V, Teil 3B, 1st Hälfte, pp. 177–194. Berlin: Urban & Schwarzenberg, 1938

215
Kolmer, W., and Löwy, R. Beiträge zur Physiologie der Zirbeldrüse, Arch. ges. Physiol. 196: 1–14 (1922)

216
Komori, S. Shoshu Hormon mata-wa zōki-seizai no shōka-kikan ni oyobosu eikyō ni kan-suru jikken-teki kenkyū; nōkasuitai kōyō-seizai, kanzō-seizai, ichō-Hormon-zai, shōka-sen-zai hōren-sō-seizai, kyōsen-seizai, saitai-Hormon-zai, setsugo-sen-seizai, hifu-seizai, jōhi-shōtai-seizai, taiban-seizai, kokkaku-kin-seizai, oyobi shinzō-Hormon-zai no chōkan-undō ni oyobosu eikyō (Experimental studies on the effects of various kinds of hormones

as well as visceral preparations on the alimentary canal; the effects on the movements of the intestine of preparations of the posterior lobe of the pituitary, the liver, gastrointestinal hormone, the pineal gland, the thymus, umbilical cord hormone, the prostate gland, the skin, the parathyroids, the placenta, skeletal muscle, and cardiac hormone), Kyōto furitsu ika daigaku zasshi 27: 885–898 (1939)

217
Kōmura, G.   Shōka-sen no kinō ni kan-suru kenkyū; shōka-sen no shittsui-shōjō koto-ni kō-antipyrine-sayō ni tsuite (Studies on the function of the pineal gland; results of pinealectomy, particularly resistance to the action of antipyrine), Fol. endocr. jap. 19: 22–26 (1943–44). Abstracted in: Manshū igaku zasshi 37: 808 (1942)

218
Koopman, J.   Mestkuren in de algemeene praktijk; drie gevallen behandeld met pijnappelklier, Geneesk. gids. 6: 485–491 (1928)

219
Kosuga, K., and Imura, H.   Shōka-sen tekishutsu kato kikanshi naiatsu, ketsuatsu narabi-ni kokyū ni oyobosu Adrenalin, Cholin oyobi Histamin no eikyō (The effects of adrenalin, acetylcholine, and histamine on the intrabronchial pressure, the blood pressure, and the respiration of the pinealectomized rabbit), Sei-i-kai zasshi 56: 2243–2248 (1937)

220
Kothmann, K.   Beitrag zur Frage der Beeinflussung der endokrinen Drüsen durch Kastration und Verabfolgung von Hormonpräparaten aus Zirbel und Keimdrüsen, Inaug. Diss., Vet. Med., Hannover, 1939

221
Kozelka, A. W.   Implantation of pineal glands in the Leghorn fowl, Proc. Soc. Exp. Biol. 30: 842–844 (1933)

222
Kraus, E. J.   Pankreas und Hypophyse, Beitr. path. Anat. 68: 258–277 (1921)

223
Krockert, G.   Die Wirkung der Verfütterung von Schilddrüsen- und Zirbeldrüsen-substanz an Lebistes reticulatus (Zahnkarpfen), Zschr. ges. exp. Med. 98: 214–220 (1936)

224
Krockert, G.   Entwicklungsänderungen bei der Fischart Cichliden durch Verabreichung von Schilddrüse, Zirbel- und Thymusdrüse, Zschr. ges. exp. Med. 99: 451–455 (1936)

225
Krockert, G.   Kontinuierliche Hyper-thyreoidisierung und -epiphysierung an Python bivattatus, Vitamine und Hormone 1: 24–31 (1941)

226
Kronfeld, A.   Ueber medikamentose Behandlung der Ejaculatio praecox, Allg. med. Zentr. Ztg. 91: 99 (1922)

227
Kunishige, S.   Kyōsen, shōka-sen narabi-ni hizō to seishoku-sen to no kankei (The relation of the thymus, the pineal gland, and the spleen to the gonads), Okayama igakkai zasshi 50: 570 (1938)

228
von Kup, J.   Wirkung der Kastrierung auf die Zirbeldrüse, Wien. klin. Wschr. 49: 915–917 (1936)

229
von Kup, J.   Der Zusammenhang zwischen der Zirbel und den anderen endokrinen Drüsen, Frankf. Zschr. Path. 50: 152–189 (1937)

230
Kup, G. (von Kup, J.)   Adatok a tobozmirigy es eletkor összefuggesehez, gerinceseken vegzett vizsgalatok kapcsan (Relation between the pineal and longevity, in connection with investigations carried out on verte-brates), Budapesti orv. ujs. 36: 1002–1008 (1938)

231
von Kup, J.   Der Zusammenhang zwischen Zirbelfunktion, Vererbungs-vorgängen, und Rassenanlagen, Frankf. Zschr. Path. 52: 427–432 (1938)

232
von Kup, J.   Ueber den Angriffspunkt der antigonadotropen Epiphysen-wirkung, Frankf. Zschr. Path. 54: 396–412 (1940)

233
Kup, G. (von Kup, J.), and Veghelyi, F.   Castratio hatasa az epiphysisre sertesekben (The effect of castration on the pig epiphysis), Magyar orv. arch. 36: 303–307 (1935)

234
Lahr, E. L.   Pineal implants in rats, Tr. Kansas Acad. Science 35: 102–103 (1932). Abstracted by: Johnson, G. E., and Lahr, E. L., Anat. Rec. 54: 28 (1932)

235
Laignel-Lavastine, M. M., and Fay, H. M.   L'opothérapie épiphysaire dans les troubles de l'évolution du langage, Congrès des Aliénistes, Limoges, pp. 391–395 (1932)

236
Lampl, O.   Ueber Versüche, gewisse Formen der Schizophrenie mit Epiglandol ausserhalb der geschlossenen Anstalt zu behandeln, Münch. med. Wschr. 76: 236–237 (1929)

237
Lampl, O.   Beitrag zur Therapie der Schizophrenie, Med. Klin. 29: 115–116 (1933)

238
Lanz, A.   Ueber das Gewicht der Zirbeldrüse des Pferdes, Berl. Münch. tieraerztl. Wschr., pp. 6–7 (1941)

239
Le Coq, R.   Retentissement de l'extrait épiphysaire, du facteur lipocaïque et de la vagotonine, injectés par voie intraveineuse, sur la réserve alcaline plasmatique du lapin, C. rend. Soc. biol. 145: 217–220 (1951)

240
Leduc, E. H., and Wislocki, G. B.   The histochemical localization of acid and alkaline phosphatases, non-specific esterase and succinic dehydrogenase in the structures comprising the hematoencephalic barrier of the rat, J. Comp. Neur. 97: 241–280 (1952)

241
Lindeberg, W.   Ueber den Einfluss der Thymectomie auf den Gesamtorganismus und auf die Drüsen mit innerer Sekretion insbesondere auf die Epiphyse und Hypophyse, Fol. neuropath. eston. 2: 42–108 (1924)

242
Lindemann, W.   Natur und Verbreitung wehenerregender Substanzen in Körper, Deut. med. Wschr. 39: 2017 (1913)

243
Lindemann, W., and Aschner, B.   Ueber Natur und Verbreitung vasokonstriktorischer und wehenerregender Substanzen in Körper, Münch. med. Wschr. 50: 2779–2782 (1913)

244
Lissman, P.   Die Behandlung nervöser Sexualstörungen, Zschr. ärztl. Fortbild. 17: 225–229 (1920)

245
Lorenzone, C., and Leone, V.   Ormone epifisario e ipertermia passiva, Ormoni 3: 561–576 (1941)

246
Mackenzie, K.   An experimental investigation of the mechanism of milk secretion, with special reference to the action of animal extracts, Q. J. Exp. Physiol. 4: 305–330 (1911)

247

Maeda, M. Pineal (shōka-sen seizai), Oophormin (ōtai igai no ransō jisshitsu seizai) narabi-ni Thyroid (kōjōsen seizai) no kato nōkasuitai zen-yō saihō ni oyobosu sayō ni tsuite (The action of pineal, ovarian, and thyroid preparations on the cells of the anterior lobe of the pituitary gland of the rabbit), Okayama igakkai zasshi 44: 2837–2849 (1932)

248

Malmejac, J., and Desanti, E. Sur les propriétés cardio-vasculaires des extraits épiphysaires, C. rend. Soc. biol. 125: 475–476 (1937)

249

Malmejac, J., and Desanti, E. Extraits épiphysaires et adrénalino-sécrétion, C. rend. Soc. biol. 125: 1077–1078 (1937)

250

Malmejac, J., and Donnet, V. Sur l'action vaso-motrice centrale des extraits épiphysaires, C. rend. Soc. biol. 126: 370–372 (1937)

251

Marburg, O. Versüche einer nicht operativen Behandlung hirndrucksteigernder Prozesse, Wien. klin. Wschr. 37: 1017–1018 (1924)

252

Martin, J. Experimental and clinical observations concerning the results of destruction of the pineal gland, Summaries Doct. Diss. Northwest. Univ. 9: 314–318 (1941). Abstracted in: Arch. Neur. Psychiat. 44: 1146–1148 (1940) and Ann. Surg. 113: 1078 (1941)

253

Martin, J., and Davis, L. Syndrome of destruction of the pineal gland; experimental and clinical observations, Arch. Int. M. 67: 1119–1128 (1941)

254

Masaki, S. Shōka-sen ni kan-suru jikken-teki kenkyū; ɪ—Shōka-sen tekishutsu no kato chisso taisha ni oyobosu eikyō (Experimental studies on the pineal gland; ɪ—The effect of pinealectomy on nitrogen metabolism in the rabbit), Sei-i-kai zasshi 59: 1123–1136 (1940). Summarized in: Nippon yakubutsugaku zasshi 29: 130–131 (1940). Abstracted as: Experimentelle Untersuchung über den Stickstoffwechsel der Zirbeldrüse, Jap. J. M. Sc., Pharm., Proc. 13: 162–163 (1940)

255

Masaki, S. Shōka-sen ni kan-suru jikken-teki kenkyū; ɪɪ—Dainō-suitai seizai no shōka-sen tekishutsu kato chisso taisha ni oyobosu eikyō (Experimental studies on the pineal gland; ɪɪ—The effect of pituitary extracts on nitrogen metabolism in the pinealectomized rabbit), Sei-i-kai zasshi 59: 1137–1159 (1940)

256
Masaki, S.   Shōka-sen ni kan-suru jikken-teki kenkyū; iii—Sei-sen seizai no shōka-sen tekishutsu kato chisso taisha ni oyobosu eikyō (Experimental studies on the pineal gland; iii—The effect of sex gland extracts on nitrogen metabolism in the pinealectomized rabbit), Sei-i-kai zasshi 59: 1262–1287 (1940)

257
Masaki, S.   Shōka-sen ni kan-suru jikken-teki kenkyū; iv—Shōka-sen tekishutsu no yōjaku kato chisso taisha ni oyobosu eikyō (Experimental studies on the pineal gland; iv—The effect of pinealectomy on nitrogen metabolism in young rabbits), Sei-i-kai zasshi 59: 1288–1296 (1940)

258
Masaki, M.   Shōka-sen tekishutsu kato ketsuatsu ni oyobosu shokubutsu-sinkei-doku no eikyō ni tsuite (The effect of vegetative nerve toxins on the blood pressure of the pinealectomized rabbit), Sei-i-kai zasshi 59: 1391–1400 (1940)

259
Masaki, M.   Shōka-sen tekishutsu kato ketsuatsu ni oyobosu sei-sen seizai no eikyō ni tsuite (The effect of sex gland preparations on the blood pressure of the pinealectomized rabbit), Sei-i-kai zasshi 59: 1401–1407 (1940)

260
Massa, M.   Contributo sperimentale alla conoscenza di possibili rapporti fra la pineale e la tiroide, Gior. clin. med. 30: 916–925 (1949)

261
Massa, M.   Ulteriore contributo sperimentale alla conoscenza di possibili rapporti tra epifisi e tiroide, Riv. pat. clin. 5: 264–269 (1950)

262
Mavromati, L.   L'action de l'extrait épiphysaire sur les métrorragies, Bull. Soc. roumain. endocr. 5: 367–368 (1939)

263
Mavromati, L.   Ueber die Behandlung von Meno- und Metrorrhagie mittels Zirbeldrüsenextrakt, Fortsch. Ther. 16: 413–416 (1940)

264
McCord, C. P.   The pineal gland in relation to somatic, sexual, and mental development, J. Am. M. Ass. 63: 232–235 (1914)

265
McCord, C. P.   The pineal gland in relation to somatic, sexual, and mental development, J. Am. M. Ass. 65: 517–520 (1915)

266
McCord, C. P. The pineal gland; the influence of the pineal gland upon growth and differentiation with particular reference to its influence upon pre-natal development, Surg. Gyn. Obst. 25: 250–260 (1917). Abstracted in: Tr. Am. Gyn. Soc. 42: 41–63 (1917)

267
McCord, C. P., and Allen, F. P. Evidences associating pineal gland function with alterations in pigmentation, J. Exp. Zool. 23: 207–224 (1917)

268
Medical Research Council. Function of the pineal, in: Rep. M. Res. Counc., 1936–37, p. 50. London, 1938

269
de Mennato, M. Grassi e lipoidi nell'epifisi cerebrale; modificazioni strutturali in rapporto a stati funzionali, Nuova riv. clin. psichiat. 11: 85–110 (1934)

270
Menninger-Lerchenthal, E. Epiglandol bei Schizophrenie? Psychiat. neur. Wschr. 32: 19–21 (1930)

271
Menninger-Lerchenthal, E. Prophylaxe gegen den aggravierenden Einfluss der Menstruation auf latente und bestehende Krankheiten besonders Psychosen und Lungentuberkulose, Zschr. ges. Neur. Psychiat. 141: 235–245 (1932)

272
Mesaki, T. Shōka-sen kinō ga nin-yō narabi-ni taiji ni oyobosu eikyō ni kan-suru jikken-teki kenkyū; ninshin-chū shōka-sen ext. chūsha ga nin-yō narabi-ni taiji ni oyobosu eikyō (Experimental studies on the effect of pineal function on the pregnant mother and the embryo; Part 1—The effect of injection of pineal extracts during pregnancy on mother and embryo), Sanka-fujinka kiyō 21: 562–593 (1938). Abstracted in: Sanka-fujinka kiyō 21: 797 (1938). Summarized in: Sanka-fujinka kiyō 22: 187–189 (1939)

273
Mesaki, T. Shōka-sen kinō ga nin-yō narabi-ni taiji ni oyobosu eikyō ni kan-suru jikken-teki kenkyū; shōka-sen tekishutsu ga nin-yō narabi-ni taiji ni oyobosu eikyō (Experimental studies on the effect of pineal function on the pregnant mother and the embryo; Part 2—The effect of pinealectomy on the pregnant mother and the embryo), Sanka-fujinka kiyō 21: 594–612 (1938). Abstracted in: Sanka-fujinka kiyō 21: 797 (1938). Summarized in: Sanka-fujinka kiyō 22: 187–189 (1939)

274

Mesaki, T.　Shōka-sen kinō ga nin-yō narabi-ni taiji ni oyobosu eikyō ni kan-suru jikken-teki kenkyū; yōjaku kato shōka-sen ext. chūsha ga nin-yō narabi-ni taiji ni oyobosu eikyō (Experimental studies on the effect of pineal function on the pregnant mother and the embryo; Part 3—The effect of injections of pineal extract from immaturity to maturity on the pregnant mother and the young), Sanka-fujinka kiyō 21: 1344–1373 (1938). Abstracted in: Sanka-fujinka kiyō 22: 563 (1939). Abstracted in English in: Jap. J. Obst. 22: 11–20 (1939). Summarized in: Sanka-fujinka kiyō 22: 187–189 (1939)

275

Mesaki, T.　Shōka-sen kinō ga nin-yō narabi-ni taiji ni oyobosu eikyō ni kan-suru jikken-teki kenkyū; yōjaku-jiki shōka-sen tekishutsu ga nin-yō narabi-ni taiji ni oyobosu eikyō (Experimental studies on the effect of pineal function on the pregnant mother and on the embryo; Part 4—The effect of pinealectomy during the youth of the mother on the pregnant mother and on the embryo), Sanka-fujinka kiyō 21: 1374–1385 (1938). Abstracted in: Sanka-fujinka kiyō 22: 563(1939). Abstracted in English in: Jap. J. Obst. 22: 20–25 (1939). Summarized in: Sanka-fujinka kiyō 22: 187–189 (1939)

276

Mesaki, T.　Shōka-sen kinō ga sei-shūki narabi-ni hoka no sei-Hormon ni oyobosu eikyō ni kan-suru jikken-teki kenkyū; shōka-sen kinō ga sei-shūki ni oyobosu eikyō (Experimental studies on the effect of the functioning of the pineal gland on the sexual cycle and on other sex hormones; Part 1—The effect of the functioning of the pineal gland on the sexual cycle), Sanka-fujinka kiyō 22: 190–205 (1939). Abstracted in: Sanka-fujinka kiyō 21: 1821 (1938). Abstracted in English in: Jap. J. Obst. 22: 26–30 (1939)

277

Mesaki, T.　Shōka-sen kinō ga sei-shūki narabi-ni hoka no sei-Hormon ni oyobosu eikyō ni kan-suru jikken-teki kenkyū; ranpō Hormon no sei-shūki kōshin sayō narabi-ni nōkasuitai zen-yō-Hormon no ranpō seijuku sokushin sayō ni oyobosu shōka-sen no eikyō; hu, zenpen no sōkatu (Experimental studies on the effect of the functioning of the pineal gland on the sexual cycle and other sex hormones; Part 2—The effects of the pineal gland on the action of follicle hormone in accelerating the sexual cycle, and on the action of anterior-lobe pituitary hormone in hastening maturation of the follicles; Supplement, summary of all articles), Sanka-fujinka kiyō 22: 206–220 (1939). Abstracted in: Sanka-fujinka kiyō 21: 1821 (1938). Abstracted in English in: Jap. J. Obst. 22: 30–37 (1939)

278
Meyer, R., and Gaupp, R.   Experimentelle Untersuchungen zur Frage der Zirbelfunktion, Klin. Wschr. 23: 112–113 (1944)

279
Micale, G.   Sui rapporti intercorrente tra ghiandola pineale, funzioni genitali e sviluppo corporeo femminile, Riv. ital. gin. 19: 471–504 (1936)

280
Mikami, S.   Niwatori no shōka-tai jokyo ga karada seichō oyobi hoka no naibunpi-zōki ni oyobosu eikyō ni tsuite (The effect of pinealectomy on body growth and on the other endocrine organs in the domestic fowl), Nippon jūigaku zasshi 12: 267–268 (1950)

281
Mikami, S.   Kachiku no shōka-tai no saihōgaku-teki narabi-ni soshiki-kagaku-teki kenkyū (Cytological and histochemical studies on the pineal gland of domestic animals), Igaku to seibutsugaku 21: 203–206 (1951). Also published in English in: Tohoku J. Agric. Res. 2: 41–48 (1951)

282
Milco, S. M.   L'action de l'extrait épiphysaire sur le cycle oestral de la rate, Bull. Soc. roumain. endocr. 7: 86–92 (1941)

283
Milco, S. M., and Ionesco-Sanger, G.   L'action hypotensive de l'épiphy-sormone, Bull. Soc. roumain. endocr. 6: 138–141 (1940)

284
Milco, S. M., and Pitis, M.   L'action hémostatique de l'épiphysormone, Bull. Soc. roumain. endocr. 6: 162–169 (1940)

285
Milco, S. M., and Pitis, M.   Inhibizione con l'ormone antisessuale pineale dell'irezione spontanea o provocata, Ormoni 3: 609–616 (1941)

286
Milco, S. M., and Pitis, M.   Sur l'existence d'une hormone de croissance dans l'épiphyse, Bull. Acad. méd. Roumanie 7: 230–243 (1942)

287
Milco, S. M., and Pitis, M.   Contributions à l'étude de la corrélation thymo-épiphysaire, Acta endocr. Bucarest 9: 73–75 (1943)

288
Milco, S. M., and Pitis, M.   Technique pour le titrage de l'hormone in-hibitrice sexuelle de l'épiphyse, Acta endocr. Bucarest 10: 44–49 (1944)

289
Milco, S. M., and Pitis, M.   Action de l'épiphyse sur la glande thyroïde, Acta endocr. Bucarest 12: 52–58 (1946)

290

Milco, S. M., and Pitis, M.   L'action de l'épiphysormone sur la thyrotrophine, Acta endocr. Bucarest 13: 7–9 (1947)

291

Milco, S. M., and Pitis, M.   L'épiphysormone et l'hypertrophie de compensation de la thyroïde, Acta endocr. Bucarest 13: 57–59 (1947)

292

Milco, S. M., and Pitis, M.   De l'action soi-disant antagoniste entre l'épiphyse et la gonadotrophine placentaire, Acta endocr. Bucarest 14: 12–15 (1948)

293

Milco, S. M., and Pitis, M.   L'action de l'épiphysormone sur la parathyroïde du rat, Acta endocr. Bucarest 14: 90–94 (1948)

294

Milco, S. M., and Sternberg, I.   L'épiphyse et le métabolisme des glucides; action de l'épiphysormone sur le glycogène hépatique, Acta endocr. Bucarest 12: 117–119 (1946)

295

Milco, S. M., and Tomorug, E.   Deux cas d'agitation maniacale traités par de l'extrait d'épiphyse, Bull. Soc. roumain. endocr. 6: 149–153 (1940)

296

Milco, S. M., and Tomorug, E.   Le traitement de la manie par l'extrait d'épiphyse, Bull. Acad. méd. Roumanie 11: 43–52 (1941)

297

Milco, S. M., and Turai, I.   Tratamentul adenomului de prostata prin extract epifisar, Medicina romana, no. 1, pp. 8–9, July 1, 1946

298

Miyagawa, Y., and Wada, K.   Naibunpi sho-zōki saihō wo motte hikigaeru Bufo japonicus (Schleg.) Rana nigromaculata no shiyō jikken (Experiments in the feeding of the toad, Bufo japonicus Schleg., and of Rana nigromaculata, using cells of various endocrine organs), Jikken igaku zasshi 10: 93–127 (1926). Published in English in: Sc. Rep. Inst. Infects. Dis., Tokyo, 4: 299–329 (1925); and in: Japan. M. World 6: 163–182 (1926)

299

Monnier, M., and Devrient, T.   Les fonctions de la glande pinéale; étude critique et expérimentale, Rev. méd. Suisse rom. 60: 1178–1194 (1940)

300

Monnier, M., and Devrient, T.   Les effets d'implantation répétées de glande pinéale bovine chez le jeune rat, C. rend. Soc. phys. et hist. nat., Genève, 58: 159–163 (1941)

301
Mori, S., Nakamura, M., Hayashi, T., and Miyao, S. Kakushu naibunpi kinō to kettō (Endocrine function of the various glands and the blood sugar), Nippon naibunpigakkai zasshi 6: 149–151 (1930)

302
Moszkowska, A. Différences d'activité entre l'épiphyse de quelques mammifères et l'épiphyse de poule, Ann. endocr. 8: 138–140 (1947)

303
Moszkowska, A. Contribution à l'étude de l'antagonisme épiphyso-hypophysaire, J. physiol., Paris, 43: 827–833 (1951). Also published as: Action des extraits épiphysaires sur les femelles cobayes adultes jeunes, C. rend. Soc. biol. 145: 845–847 (1951), and Action d'extraits aqueux de glandes pinéales de moutons sur les souris mâles et femelles; antagonisme épiphyso-hypophysaire, C. rend. Soc. biol. 145: 847–850 (1951)

304
Nakai, K. Shōka-sen ketsuraku-shōjō no hontai ni kan-suru kenkyū, tokuni ijō enrui-netsu wo shihyō to-shita shōka-sen to kōjō-sen oyobi jōhishōtai to no kankei (Studies on the pathogenesis of deficiency syndromes after pinealectomy, especially the relation between the pineal gland and the thyroid and parathyroid glands as indicated by the abnormal salt fever), Nippon naibunpigakkai zasshi 26: 42–66 (1950)

305
Nakai, K. Shōka-sen ketsuraku-go no seichō sokushin oyobi seiki sōjuku no byōri-hassei ni tsuite (Pathogenesis of the acceleration of growth and precocity of the genitals after pinealectomy), Nippon naibunpigakkai zasshi 27: 89–94 (1951)

306
Nakashita, S. Shōka-sen ketsuraku-go no yū-sei seiki no sōjuku kijo ni kan-suru kenkyū (Studies of the precocious development of the male genital organs after pinealectomy), Nippon naibunpigakkai zasshi 27: 72–81 (1951)

307
Nakatani, M., Nakano, K., and Katagiri, E. Studies on the pineal hormone, Tr. Soc. path. jap. 31: 682–686 (1941)

308
Nakatani, M., Nakano, K., Katagiri, E., Kanamori, T., and Takahashi, S. Shōka-sen narabi-ni kyōsen no kenkyū (Studies on the pineal gland and the thymus), Nippon byōrigakkai kaishi 32: 389–394 (1942)

309
Nakatani, M., Ohara, Y., Katagiri, E., and Nakano, K. Shōka-sen teki-shutsu shi-sei shiro-nezumi no kenkyū (Studies on pinealectomized white rats), Nippon byōrigakkai kaishi 30: 232–236 (1940)

310
Nissim, L. Contributions au traitement des ménorragies par l'extrait épiphysaire, Bull. soc. roumain. endocr. 5: 158–165 (1939)

311
von Noorden, C. Hat es einen Zweck, Epiphysenpräparate bei Mastkuren und Hypophysenpräparate bei Enfettungskuren zu verwenden, Klin. Wschr. 1: 1391 (1922)

312
Norlin, G., and Welin, G. Ueber die Einwirkung der Zirbel auf körper-liche und geschlechtliche Entwicklung, Skand. Arch. Physiol. 69: 293–299 (1934)

313
Novak, J. Ueber künstliche Tumoren der Zirbeldrüsengegend, Wien. klin. Wschr. 27: 974–975 (1914)

314
Oesterreicher, W. Ueber die Behandlung der Epilepsie mit Zirbel-drüsenextrakt, Med. Klin., issue no. 22 (1937). (Article seen in reprint but could not be found in cited journal volume.)

315
Offergeld, —. Hormonale Beeinflussung der weiblichen Libido, Zschr. Sexwiss. 14: 264–270, 301–305, 323–332 (1927)

316
Ohara, Y. Chitsu nenmaku no gasu-taisha; chitsu nenmaku no shūki-sei taisha henka (Gas metabolism of the vaginal mucous membrane; changes in the metabolism of the vaginal mucous membrane during the sexual cycle), Ōsaka igakkai zasshi 39: 1879–1887 (1940)

317
Ohara, Y. Chitsu nenmaku no gasu-taisha; chitsu nenmaku no shūki-sei gasu-taisha ni oyobosu sho-naibunpi-sen tekishutsu no eikyō (Gas metabolism of the vaginal mucous membrane; the effect of the extirpa-tion of the various endocrine glands on the gas metabolism of the vaginal mucous membrane during the sexual cycle), Ōsaka igakkai zasshi 39: 1889–1908 (1940)

318
Ohmura, S. Nippon-jin shōka-sen no kaibōgaku-teki, soshikigaku-teki, narabi-ni byōrigaku-teki kenkyū (Anatomical, histological, and pathologi-

cal study on the pineal gland of the Japanese), Nippon ika daigaku zasshi
2: 30–68, 139–202 (1931)

319
Oka, H.   Naibunpi-sen no kossetsu-sei henka ni kan-suru kenkyū hoi;
kossetsu chiyu sho-ki ni okeru shōka-sen, suizō, daeki-sen oyobi kōgan no
soshikigaku-teki shoken (Supplementary studies on changes in the endocrine glands in fracture; histological observations on the pineal gland, the
pancreas, the salivary glands, and the testes in all stages of healing of
fracture of bone), Okayama igakkai zasshi 51: 288–313 (1939)

320
Ott, I., and Scott, J. C.   Note on the galactogogue action of the thymus,
the corpus luteum, and the pineal body, Month. Cyclop. 4: 99–100 (1911)

321
Ott, I., and Scott, J. C.   The action of animal extracts upon the secretion
of the mammary gland, Ther. Gaz. 27 (series 3): 689–691 (1911)

322
Ott, I., and Scott, J. C.   Action of the corpus luteum and the pineal body,
Month. Cyclop. 5: 207–209 (1912). Abstracted as: A preliminary note
on the pineal body and the corpus luteum, Month. Cyclop. 4: 540 (1911),
and in: Proc. Soc. Exp. Biol. 9: 64 (1911)

323
Parhon, C. I.   L'épiphyse au point de vue endocrinologique, Bull. et mém.
de la Sect. d'endocr. 4: 349–404 (1938)

324
Parhon, C. I., and Cahane, G. M.   Modifications biochimiques après la
cautérisation de l'épiphyse chez les oiseaux, Bull. Soc. roumain. endocr.
5: 165–169 (1939)

325
Parhon, C. I., and Cahana, M. G.   Sur la cholestérolémie des oiseaux
ayant subit la cautérisation de l'épiphyse, Bull. Soc. roumain. endocr.
5: 374–377 (1939)

326
Parhon, C. I., and Cahana, M. G.   Recherches sur le glycogène muscu-
laire après l'injection d'extrait épiphysaire, Bull. Soc. roumain. endocr. 5:
377–378 (1939)

327
Parhon, C. I., and Cahana, M. G.   Recherches sur la hydratation et le
phosphore des muscles après l'administration d'extrait épiphysaire, Bull.
Soc. roumain. endocr. 6: 29–31 (1940)

328

Parhon, C. I., and Cahane, M. G.   Recherches sur le glycogène hépatique chez les oiseaux, après la cautérisation de l'épiphyse, Bull. Soc. roumain. endocr. 6: 96–98 (1940)

329

Parhon, C. I., and Cahana, M. G.   Recherches sur le phosphore sanguin chez les oiseaux après la cautérisation de l'épiphyse, Bull. Soc. roumain. endocr. 6: 147–149 (1940)

330

Parhon, C. I., Crainiceano, A., and Copelmann, L.   L'action inhibitrice de l'extrait épiphysaire sur la fécondité des rats, Bull. et mém. de la Sect. d'endocr. 4: 551–554 (1938)

331

Parhon, C. I., and Milco, S. M.   Action de l'extrait épiphysaire sur la fonction menstruelle, C. rend. Soc. biol. 132: 589–591 (1939)

332

Parhon, C. I., Milco, S. M., and Pitis, M.   Sur les corrélations épiphyso-surrénales, Acta endocr. Bucarest 10: 3–9 (1944)

333

Parhon, C. I., Milco, S. M., and Tomorug, E.   Augmentation pondérale sous l'influence d'un extrait épiphysaire (l'épiphysormone), Bull. Soc. roumain. endocr. 6: 122–126 (1940)

334

Parhon, C. I., and Pitis, M.   Sur le syndrome hypothyro-hyperépiphysaire, Acta endocr. Bucarest 13: 47–51 (1947)

335

Parhon, C. I., and Postelnicu, D.   L'extrait épiphysaire exerce-t-il une influence inhibitrice sur le développement du plumage définitif chez les oiseaux? Acta endocr. Bucarest 11: 136–141 (1945)

336

Parhon, C. I., Stefanescu-Dragomireanu, M., and Marculescu, A.   Action d'un extrait épiphysaire sur quelques constituants biochimiques du sang; augmentation de la potassémie, Bull. Acad. méd. Paris 116: 104–106 (1936)

337

Parhon, C. I., and Tomorug, E.   Sur un cas de skyzophrénie traité par l'épiphysormone avec résultat très favorable, Bull. Soc. roumain. endocr. 6: 141–147 (1940)

338

Parhon, C. I., and Tomorug, E.   Essais sur le traitement épiphysaire de la schizophrénie, Bull. Acad. méd. Roumanie 6: 170–173 (1941)

339
Parhon, C. I., and Werner, G.   Recherches expérimentales sur le syndrome hyperépiphysaire, Bull. et mém. de la Sect. d'endocr. 3: 33–41 (1937)

340
Parhon, C. I., and Werner, G.   Nouvelles recherches sur les syndromes hyperépiphysaires expérimentaux, Bull. Soc. roumain. endocr. 6: 165–171 (1940)

341
Parhon, C. I., and Werner, G.   Action de l'extrait épiphysaire chez les animaux thyro-parathyroïdectomisés, Acta endocr. Bucarest 11: 53–59 (1945)

342
Parhon, C. I., Werner, G., and Cahane, M.   Recherches sur l'action de l'extrait épiphysaire sur le glycogène hépatique, Bull. et mém. de la Sect. d'endocr. 4: 555–557 (1938)

343
Parhon-Stefanesco, C., and Merlesco, G.   Sur le traitement de la skyzophrenie par l'épiphysormone, Bull. Soc. roumain. endocr. 6: 202–204 (1940)

344
Parker, G. H.   The colour changes in lizards, particularly in Phrynosoma, J. Exp. Biol. 15: 48–73 (1938)

345
Passalacqua, N.   Rapporti fra pineale ed organi genitali femminili, Monit. ostet. ginec. 18: 149–168 (1947)

346
Pellegrini, R.   Gli effetti della castrazione sulla ghiandola pineale, Arch. sc. med. 38: 121–145 (1914)

347
Pellegrini, U.   Contributo allo studio di un principio antigonadotropo contenuto velle urine di piccola bambina, Pediatria 49: 502–506 (1941)

348
Pellizzi, G. B.   Sull'azione del succo epifisario, Atti Cong. Soc. ital. neur., Roma, 4: 132–138 (1914)

349
Pilcz, A.   Dementia paranoidea; zur Organotherapie der Dementia praecox, Psychiat. neur. Wschr. 19: 303–305 (1918)

350
Popescu-Inotesti, C.   L'insuline par voie rachidienne; insuline et épiglandole, Rev. fr. endocr. 2: 346–348 (1924)

351
Popovici-Lupa, M., and Popescu-Tanaseanu, A. Ueber die Beeinflussung der kindlichen Enuresis nocturna durch Epiphysenpräparate, Mschr. Kinderh. 86: 400–403 (1941)

352
Prengowski, P. Die Behandlung der Puerperalpsychose mit Zirbeldrüsenhormon, Psychiat. neur. Wschr. 32: 537–538 (1930)

353
Press, R., and Fearon, W. R. Studies on the ultimate composition of biological material; Part III—Glandular tissue, Proc. R. Dublin Soc. 22: 157–159 (1939)

354
del Priore, —. Modificazioni nella pressione sanguigna e nell'accrescimento somatico dei conigli in seguito ad inezioni d'estratto di pineale, Note psichiat., Pesaro, 7 (series 3): 445–454 (1914). Also published as: Modifications dans la pression sanguine et dans l'accroissement somatique des lapins à la suite d'injections d'extrait de glande pinéale, Arch. ital. biol. 63: 122–128 (1915)

355
Raab, W. Das hormonal-nervöse Regulationssystem des Fettstoffwechsels, Verh. Ges. Verdauungskr. 5: 102–104 (1925)

356
Reiss, M., Badrick, F. E., and Halkerston, J. M. The influence of the pituitary on phosphorus metabolism of brain, Biochem. J. 44: 257–260 (1949). Abstracted as: The uptake of radioactive tracers by the pineal gland, J. Anat. 83: 81 (1949)

357
Renton, A. D., and Rusbridge, H. W. Late effects of pinealectomy in rats, Proc. Soc. Exp. Biol. 30: 766 (1933)

358
Rihara, T. Vitamin B_1 kajō-tōyo no kato naibunpi sho-zōki ni oyobosu eikyō ni kan-suru jikken-teki kenkyū; fukujin, nōkasuitai, oyobi shōka-sen ni tsuite (Experimental studies on the effect of overdoses of vitamin B_1 on all the endocrine organs of the rabbit; the adrenals, the pituitary, and the pineal gland), Chōsen igakkai zasshi 33: 249–263 (1943)

359
Robinson, M. R., and Zondek, B. Experimental attempts to promote uterine growth, Am. J. Obst. 8: 83–99 (1924)

360
Romeis, B. Der Einfluss innersekretorischer Organe auf Wachstum und Entwicklung von Froschlarven, Naturwissenschaften 8: 860–868 (1920)

361
Romodanowskaja, S. A.   Das Gewicht der innersekretorischen Drüsen des Menschen und ihre wechselseitigen Gewichtskorrelationen, Arch. russ. anat. 15 (fasc. 3): 149–154 (1936)

362
Rossini, R., and Cavalca, G. G.   Gli estratti epifisari in terapia neuropsichiatrica; la loro influenza sull'eliminazione dei 17-chetosteroidi, Riv. neur. 21: 445–455 (1951)

363
Roux, P.   La glande pinéale ou épiphyse. Rennes: Oberthur, 1937.

364
Rowntree, L. G.   Further studies on the thymus and the pineal glands, Pennsylvania M. J. 39: 603–606 (1936)

365
Rowntree, L. G., Clark, J. H., and Steinberg, A.   The biological effects of pineal extract (Hanson); accruing retardation in growth and accruing acceleration in development in successive generations of rats under continuous treatment with pineal extract, Endocrinology 20: 348–357 (1936)

366
Rowntree, L. G., Clark, J. H., Steinberg, A., and Hanson, A. M.   Biologic effects of pineal extracts (Hanson); amplification of effects in the young resulting from the treatment of successive generations of parent rats, J. Am. Med. Ass. 106: 370–373 (1936)

367
Rowntree, L. G., Clark, J. H., Steinberg, A., Einhorn, N. H., and Hanson, A. M.   The role of the thymus and pineal glands in growth and development, N. York State J. M. 36: 1277–1283 (1936)

368
Rowntree, L. G., Clark, J. H., Steinberg, A., Hanson, A. M., Einhorn, N. H., and Shannon, W. A.   Further studies on the thymus and on the pineal gland, Ann. Int. M. 9: 359–375 (1935)

369
Ruggeri, E.   Modificazioni del contenuto lipo-mitocondriale delle cellule della pineale dopo ablazione completa degli organi genitali, Riv. pat. nerv. 19: 649–659 (1914)

370
Sai, S.   Yū-sei dōbutsu no kyosei-go ni okeru kaku-naibunpi-zōki no henka ni kan-suru jikken-teki kenkyū; yōjaku dōbutsu ni okeru jikken (Experimental studies on changes in each endocrine organ after castration of male animals; experiments on immature animals), Chōsen igakkai zasshi 29: 171–181 (1939)

[143]

371
Sai, S. Yū-sei dōbutsu no kyosei-go ni okeru kaku-naibunpi-zōki no henka ni kan-suru jikken-teki kenkyū; seijuku dōbutsu ni oite tanki keika-go no henka ni kan-suru jikken (Experimental studies on changes in each endocrine organ after castration of male animals; experiments on mature animals, and changes during a short time after castration), Chōsen igakkai zasshi 29: 132–157 (1939)

372
Sai, S. Yū-sei dōbutsu no kyosei-go ni okeru kaku-naibunpi-zōki no henka ni kan-suru jikken-teki kenkyū; seijuku dōbutsu ni oite chōki keika-go no henka ni kan-suru jikken (Experimental studies on changes in each endocrine organ after castration of male animals; experiments on mature animals, and changes during a long time after castration), Chōsen igakkai zasshi 29: 158–170 (1939)

373
Sakurane, T. Shōka-sen tekishutsu to iwayaru dainō-kasuitai zen-yō hormone chūsha to ni yoru dan-sei seishoku-sen no jikken-teki kenkyū (Experimental studies on the male gonads by means of pinealectomy and injection of the so-called hormones of the anterior pituitary), Ōsaka igakkai zasshi 34: 69–97 (1935)

374
Sander, G., and Schmid, S. Ueber die Wirkung von Epiphysenimplantationen und Epiphysenextrakten bei menschlichen malignen Tumoren, Wien. klin. Wschr. 64: 505–508 (1952)

375
Sanjust, L. Sui rapporti fra epifisi ed apparato sessuale, Atti e memorie della Società lombarda di ostetricia e ginecologia 2: 137–157 (1934)

376
Saphir, W. Concerning the function of the pineal body, Endocrinology 18: 625–628 (1934)

377
Sarteschi, U. La sindrome epifisaria macrogenitosomia precoce ottenuta sperimentalmente nei mammiferi, Pathologica, Genova, 5: 707–710 (1913). Also published in: Ancora sugli effetti prodotti della asportazione della glandola pineale, Atti Cong. Soc. ital. neur., Roma, 4: 138–139 (1914)

378
Scaglione, —. La ghiandole pineale in gravidanze, Soc. tosc. di ostet. e ginec., Siena. Published in: Riv. ostet., Milano, 4: xv–xviii (1922)

379
Scharrer, E. Die Lichtempfindlichkeit blinder Elritzen (Untersuchungen

über das Zwischenhirn der Fische), Zschr. vergleich. Physiol. 7: 1–38 (1928)

380
Schopper, A. Zur Behandlung der Nymphomanie der Stuten und der hypersexuellen Temperamentfehler der Hengste mit Epiphysan G. Richter, Wien. tieraerztl. Mschr. 38: 41–42 (1951)

381
Selye, H. Textbook of Endocrinology (ed. 2). Montreal: Acta Endocrinologica, 1949

382
Sevringhaus, E. L. Personal communication.

383
Shellabarger, C. J. Pinealectomy vs. pineal injection in the young cockerel, Endocrinology 51: 152–154 (1952)

384
Shellabarger, C. J. Studies on the Pineal Body in the White Leghorn Cockerel; Part IV—Observations on the Pineal in the White Leghorn Capon and Cockerel, Ph.D. Thesis, Department of Zoology, Indiana University, 1952.

385
Shellabarger, C. J. Personal communication.

386
Shellabarger, C. J., and Breneman, W. R. The effects of pinealectomy on young white Leghorn cockerels, Proc. Indiana Acad. Science 59: 299–302 (1950)

387
Shioya, H. Die Zirbeldrüse und ihre Silberreaktion bei der Funktionstörungen der anderen endokrinen Organe, Hokkaido igaku zasshi 7: 1097–1107 (1929)

388
Silberstein, F., and Engel, P. Ueber das vorkommen einer östrogenen Substanz in der Epiphyse, Klin. Wschr. 12: 908–910 (1933)

389
Simian, I. Le traitement par l'épiphyse dans la puberté précoce, Bull. Soc. roumain. endocr. 5: 302–306 (1939). Also published as: Ueber die Behandlung der Pubertas praecox mit Zirbeldrüsenextrakt, Wien. med. Wschr. 91: 788–789 (1941)

389A
Simonnet, H. Personal communication.

390
Simonnet, H., and Sternberg, J.   Le rôle endocrinien de l'épiphyse; I—
L'épiphyse et le métabolisme du phosphore, Revue canad. biol. 9: 407–
421 (1951)

391
Simonnet, H., and Thieblot, L.   Action de l'épiphyse sur différentes
glandes endocrines, J. physiol. path. gen. 42: 726–729 (1950)

392
Simonnet, H., and Thieblot, L.   Recherches expérimentales sur la physiologie de la glande pinéale, Acta endocr. Copenhagen 7: 306–320 (1951)

393
Simonnet, H., Thieblot, L., and Melik, T.   Influence de l'épiphyse sur
l'ovaire de la jeune rate, Ann. endocr. 12: 202–205 (1951)

394
Simonnet, H., Thieblot, L., Melik, T., and Segal, V.   Régulation hormonale de l'activité génitale femelle; influence de l'épiphyse sur la luteini-
sation, Rev. path. comp. 52: 144–148 (1952)

395
Simonnet, H., Thieblot, L., and Segal, V.   Action de l'épiphyse sur la
teneur des surrénales en cholestérol et en acide ascorbique chez le rat
blanc male ou femelle, Ann. endocr. 12: 198–202 (1951)

396
Simonnet, H., Thieblot, L., Segal, V., and Melik, T.   Modifications du
tractus génital femelle consecutives à l'épiphysectomie, J. physiol., Paris,
43: 864–866 (1951)

397
Sisson, W. R., and Finney, J. M. T.   Effect of feeding the pineal body
upon the development of the albino rat, J. Exp. Med. 31: 335–346 (1920)

398
Spiegel, E. A., and Saito, S.   Beiträge zum Studium des vegetativen
Nervensystems; IV—Ueber die hormonale Erregbarkeit vegetativer Zen-
tren, Arb. neur. Inst. Wien. 25: 247–260 (1924)

399
Starzinger, F.   Epiphysan G. Richter bei Tetanus, Wien. tieraerztl.
Mschr. 37: 419–420 (1950)

400
Steffens, —.   Zur Behandlung nymphomaner Stuten und rauschiger Sauen
mit Zirbeldrüsenextrakt "Epiphysan," Deut. tieraerztl. Wschr. 55: 56–58
(1948)

401
Steinberg, A. A new and improved method for the preparation of pineal extract, Endocrinology 24: 219–220 (1939)

402
Sturm, A., and Schöning, W. Nachweis des thyreotropen Hormons in nicht-hypophysären Geweben (Zugleich ein Beitrag zur Frage des Tropismus in der Endokrinologie), Endokrinologie 16: 1–8 (1935)

403
Sullens, W. E., and Overholser, M. D. Pinealectomy in successive generations of rats, Endocrinology 28: 835–839 (1941)

404
Swingle, W. W. The relation of the pars intermedia of the hypophysis and the pineal gland to pigmentation changes in anuran larvae, Proc. Am. Ass. Anat., Anat. Rec. 21: 87 (1921)

405
Swoboda, F. K. A quantitative method for the determination of vitamine in connection with determination of vitamine in glandular and other tissues, J. Biol. Chem. 44: 531–551 (1920)

406
Tachibana, K. Shōka-sen tekishutsu-hō (Methods of pinealectomy), Shika geppō 7: 39–42 (1927)

407
Taddei, A. L'epifisi cerebrale, durante la gravidanza, in Bos taurus L., Monit. zool. ital. 58: 66–71 (1950)

408
Takacs, L. A tobozmirigy befolyasa a novekedesre (The influence of the pineal on growth), Orv. hetil. 79: 828–829 (1935). Also published as: Der Einfluss der Zirbeldrüse auf das Wachstum, Zschr. ges. exp. Med. 97: 204–206 (1936)

409
Takagi, J. Calcium-ketsubō-shoku kakei ni okeru jikken-teki kenkyū; naibunpi-zōki no byōri-soshikigaku-teki henka (Experimental studies on fowls on a calcium-free diet; histopathological changes in the endocrine organs), Chōsen igakkai zasshi 32: 325–338 (1942)

410
Tarkhan, A. A. Zur Frage der hormonalen Wirkung der Zirbeldrüse, Endokrinologie 18: 234–242 (1937)

411
Teruyama, N. Hito no shōka-sen no kaibō oyobi byōri (Anatomy and pathology of the human pineal gland), Naibunpitsugakkai zasshi 1: 593–

623 (1925). Abstracted as: Zur Pathologie der Epiphyse des Menschens, Tr. Soc. path. jap. 15: 186–187 (1925)

412
Thieblot, L. Action correctrice des greffes épiphysaires chez les rats épiphysectomisés, Ann. endocr. 6: 220–221 (1945)

413
Thieblot, L. Sur les fonctions glandulaires de l'épiphyse, J. physiol. path. gen. 39: 321–330 (1947)

414
Thieblot, L., Naudascher, J., and LeBars, H. Modifications histologiques de l'épiphyse à la suite d'excitation électrique du ganglion cervical supérieur chez le chat, Ann. endocr. 8: 468–469 (1947)

415
Thieblot, L., Naudascher, J., and LeBars, H. Modifications de la structure épiphysaire à la suite d'injections répétées d'hormones sexuelles, Ann. endocr. 8: 469–472 (1947)

416
Thieblot, L., Naudascher, J., and LeBars, H. Modifications histologiques de l'épiphyse à la suite d'injections d'hormones gonadotropes, Ann. endocr. 10: 192–194 (1949)

417
Tokumitsu, Y. Naibunpi-zōki ketsuraku shōkō no kenkyū, koto-ni shōkasen tekishutsu-go no sōjuku no byōri-hassei ni tsuite (Deficiency syndromes after removal of ductless glands, especially pathogenesis of the precocity after pinealectomy), Nippon byōrigakkai kaishi 40: 393–394 (1951). Abstracted as: Shōka-sen tekishutsu-go no sōjuku no byōri-hassei (Pathological development of early maturity after pinealectomy), Nippon naibunpigakkai zasshi 27: 211 (1951)

418
Tomorug, E. Le traitement épiphysaire (intrarachidien) dans la schizophrénie, Bull. Soc. roumain. endocr. 7: 92–107 (1941)

419
Tomorug, E. Die Zirbeldrüse und die Keimdrüsen; I—Der Einfluss des Zirbeldrüsenextraktes auf den Brunstzyklus bei Ratten und die Befruchtung bei Ratten und Hunden, Acta endocr. Bucarest 8: 27–37 (1942)

420
Tomorug, E. Zirbeldrüsentherapieversüche in der Kinderpsychiatrie, Acta endocr. Bucarest 8: 177–192 (1942)

421
Tomorug, E., and Hussar, M. Un cas d'excitation sexuelle, chez une

femme châtrée, traitée avec de l'épiphyse, Bull. Soc. roumain. endocr. 7: 34–39 (1941)

422
Tomorug, E., and Hussar, M. Modifications biochimiques chez des malades traités avec des extraits épiphysaires, Bull. Soc. roumain. endocr. 7: 187–189 (1941)

423
Tomorug, E., and Hussar, M. Die Zirbeldrüse und die Keimdrüsen; Part III—Der Einfluss des Zirbeldrüsenextractes auf die Keimdrüsen bei Ratten, Meerschweinchen und Hunden (makroscopisch), Acta endocr. Bucarest 8: 245–252 (1942)

424
Tomorug, E., and Hussar, M. Le traitement épiphysaire (intrarachidien et souscutane) dans la manie; bref aperçu sur la thérapie employée jusqu'à présent, Bull. Acad. méd. Roumanie 7: 308–322 (1942)

425
Tomorug, E., and Hussar, M. L'action de l'épiphyse sur la fécondation, Revista stiintellor medicale 31: 483–493 (1942)

426
Tomorug, E., Hussar, M., and Petrescu, C. Les psychoses hallucinatoires post-malariques (onirisme malarique) chez des malades de paralysie générale, traitées avec de l'épiphyse; contributions à l'étude de la pathogénie, Bull. Soc. roumain. endocr. 7: 54–64 (1941)

427
Tomorug, E., and Orbesteanu, D. Syndrome skizophrénique avec ménorragie heureusement influencé par le traitement épiphysaire, Bull. Soc. roumain. endocr. 5: 136–140 (1939)

428
Traina, S. Influenza della pineale sulla laringe e sulla siringe, Ann. laring. 33: 155–172 (1933)

429
Trautmann, A. Anatomie und Histologie der Epiphysis cerebri thyreopriver Ziegen; zugleich ein Beitrag zur gegenseitigen Beeinflussung bzw. Abhängigkeit der Drüsen mit innerer Sekretion, Zschr. ges. Neur. Psychiat. 94: 742–780 (1925)

430
Trautmann, A. Die Wirkung der Zirbeldrüsenpräparates "Epiphysan" auf die Germinalen und akzidentallen Geschlechtsmerkmalle juveniler Tiere, Deut. tieraerztl. Wschr. 45: 669–671 (1937)

431

Tsion, I. *See* von Cyon, E., ref. 61

432

Tsuchimoto, S. Naibunpi-sen to shi-sei sei-shūki to no kankei; nōkasuitai, kyōsen, kōjōsen, fukujin, shōka-sen seibun no shi-sei sei-shūki narabi-ni sei-shokki ni oyobosu eikyō (The relation of the endocrine glands to the estrus cycle; the effect of the constituents of the hypophysis cerebri, the thymus, the thyroid, the adrenal glands and the pineal gland on the estrus cycle and the female genital organs), Jikken igaku zasshi 17: 1194–1229 (1933)

433

Tsuji, A. Hormon no kato ishu gyōshūso-ka ni oyobosu eikyō; shōka-sen kōtai chūsha, fukujin-hishitsu kōtai chūsha, narabi-ni kanzō kōtai chūsha no eikyō (The effect of hormones on the heterologous agglutinin value in the rabbit; the effect of injection of pineal gland antibodies, of adrenal cortex antibodies, and of liver antibodies), Nagasaki ika daigaku hōigaku kyōshitsu gyōhō 6: 20–45 (1934)

434

Uemura, S. Zur normalen und pathologischen Anatomie der Glandula pinealis des Menschen und einiger Haustiere, Frankf. Zschr. Path. 20: 381–488 (1917). Abstracted as: Hito oyobi kachiku dōbutsu ni okeru shōka-sen no seiri-teki kōzō oyobi byō-teki henka ni tsuite (Physiological structure and pathological changes in the pineal gland in man and in domestic animals), Kanpō, no. 1944: 382 (1919). Also abstracted in: Tr. Soc. path. jap. 7: 38–40 (1917)

435

Urechia, C. I., and Elekes, N. L'épiglandol dans un cas de maladie d'Addison, Rev. fr. endocr. 2: 281–283 (1924)

436

Urechia, C. I., and Gregoriu, —. L'extirpation de la glande pinéale et son influence sur l'hypophyse, C. rend. Soc. biol. 87: 815–816 (1922)

437

Urechia, C. I., and Groza, I. L'influence des injections d'extraits hypophysaire et épiphysaire sur la formule leucocytaire, C. rend. Soc. biol. 96: 1462 (1927)

438

Vecchi, G. Sulle consequenze dell'estirpazione della epifisi cerebrale nei ratti albini, Arch. sc. med. 56: 309–340 (1932)

439

Vegna, I. Considerazioni su di un caso di ninfomania curatto con estratto di ghiandola pineale, Rass. med., Milano, 27: 96–98 (1950)

440

Vegna, I., and Gandolfo, G. A proposito dell'attività antigonadotropa di un estratto di ghiandola pineale, Boll. Soc. ital. biol. sper. 26: 19–22 (1950)

441

Vercellana, G. L'epifisi ed i suoi rapporti con le ghiandola sessuale, Ateneo parmense 4: 593–680 (1932). Also published as: Ricerche istologiche sulla epiphysis cerebri di animale interi e castrati, Boll. Soc. ital. biol. sper. 7: 1244–1248 (1932)

442

Vialli, M. Ricerche sulla metamorfosi degli anfibi; ii—Innesti di epifisi in urodeli neotenici, Boll. Soc. ital. biol. sper. 6: 1052–1053 (1931)

443

Viñals, E. Influencia de la epifisis sobre la acción gonadotropa de la orina, Actas Congr. nac. med., B. Aires, 3: 287–289 (1934). Also published as: Renforcement de l'action gonadotrope de l'urine de la femme gravide, par association avec la glande épiphysaire, C. rend. Soc. biol. 119: 259–261 (1935)

444

Vintila, G. D., and Milco, S. M. L'extrait d'épiphyse dans le post-partum, Bull. Soc. roumain. endocr. 6: 73–76 (1940)

445

Vollmer, H. Beitrag zur Wirkung der Hormone, Arch. exp. Path. 96: 352–371 (1923)

446

Wade, N. J. Studies on the function of the pineal gland, Endocrinology 21: 681–683 (1937)

447

Wakida, K. Shōka-sen naibunpi ni kan-suru jikken kenkyū (Experimental studies on the internal secretion of the pineal gland), Tōkyō iji shinshi, no. 3053: 2660–2661 (1937)

448

Wakida, K. Shōka-sen tekishutsu-hō to yōjaku Ratte ni oyobosu eikyō; fu, shōka-sen extract to zen-yō Hormon to no kikkō sayō ni tsuite (Method of pinealectomy and effect on the immature rat; supplement, antagonism of pineal extract and anterior lobe pituitary hormone), Tōkyō iji shinshi, no. 3186: 1115 (1940). Also published in: Dōsō geppō (Tō-Dai Sanfujinka), no. 30: 2 (1939)

449

Wakida, K. Shōka-sen chūshutsu-eki no shi-Ratte, -Maus ni oyobosu eikyō (The effect of pineal extract on the female rat and the female mouse), Dai 39-kai Nippon Fujinkagakkai sōkai mokuroku: 48–49 (1941)

450
Wakida, K.   Shōka-sen ni kan-suru jikken-teki narabi-ni rinshō-teki kenkyū; shōka-sen no tekishutsu ni kan-suru kenkyū (Experimental and clinical studies on the pineal gland; Part 2—Studies on pinealectomy), Nippon fujinkagakkai zasshi 38: 835–849 (1943)

451
Wakida, K.   Shōka-sen ni kan-suru jikken-teki narabi-ni rinshō-teki kenkyū; shōka-sen Hormon no chūshutsu ni kan-suru kenkyū (Experimental and clinical studies on the pineal gland; studies on the extraction of the pineal gland hormone), Nippon fujinkagakkai zasshi 38: 849–867 (1943). Also published as: Kakushu chūshutsu sōsa ni yoru shōka-sen-ext. no Ratte, Maus no sei-shūki ni oyobosu eikyō (Effects of pineal extract obtained by various methods on the sexual cycle of the rat and the mouse), Nippon igaku oyobi kenko hoken, no. 3249: 2262–2264 (1941). Abstracted in: Dōsō geppō (Tō-Dai San-fujinka) 51: 3–4 (1940)

452
Wakida, K.   Shōka-sen ni kan-suru jikken-teki narabi-ni rinshō-teki kenkyū; shōka-sen hormone no seibutsugaku-teki kenkyū (Experimental and clinical research on the pineal gland; Part 4—Biological studies on the pineal gland hormone), Nippon fujinkagakkai zasshi 39: 433–450 (1944)

453
Wakida, K.   Shōka-sen ni kan-suru jikken-teki narabi-ni rinshō-teki kenkyū; shōka-sen Hormon no rinshō ōyō (Experimental and clinical studies on the pineal gland; the clinical use of pineal gland hormone), Nippon fujinkagakkai zasshi 39: 451–454 (1944)

454
Warstadt, A.   Epiglandol bei Schizophrenie? Psychiat. neur. Wschr. 32: 205–208 (1930)

455
Waysbaum-Moschkowski, —.   Action d'extraits de la glande pinéale sur l'ovarie de cobayes et de rats, C. rend. Soc. biol. 139: 1069–1070 (1945)

456
Weinberg, S. J., and Doyle, A. F.   Effects of injected extracts of fresh pineal glands of the cow on growth of immature white mice, Proc. Soc. Exp. Biol. 28: 322–323 (1930)

457
Weinberg, S. J., and Fletcher, R. V.   Effects of injected extracts of fresh pineal glands of the young calf on growth of immature white mice; effects on sexual apparatus, Proc. Soc. Exp. Biol. 28: 323 (1930)

458
Weinstein, L.   The prophylaxis of experimental anthrax infection with various hormone preparations, Yale J. Biol. 11: 369–392 (1939)

459
Wislanski, K.   Szyszynka jako gruczol wydzielania wewnetrznego i proby zastosowania leczniczych jej wlasnosci w poloznictwie i w chorobach kobiecych (The pineal as an endocrine gland; experiments in the application of its therapeutic qualities in childbirth and female diseases), Gin. polska 13: 110–136 (1934). Summarized in: Gin. polska 11: 396–403 (1932)

460
Wislanski, K.   Szyszynka jako gruczol wydzielania wewnetrznego i proby zastosowania leczniczych jej wlasnosci w poloznictwie i w chorobach kobiecych (The pineal as an endocrine gland; experiments in the application of its therapeutic qualities in childbirth and female diseases), Gin. polska 13: 263–295 (1934). Summarized in: Gin. polska 11: 396–403 (1932)

461
Wislanski, K.   Szyszynka jako gruczol wydzielania wewnetrznego i proby zastosowania leczniczych jej wlasnosci w poloznictwie i w chorobach kobiecych (The pineal as an endocrine gland; experiments in the application of its therapeutic qualities in childbirth and female diseases), Gin. polska 13: 533–553 (1934). Summarized in: Gin. polska 11: 396–403 (1932)

462
Wislocki, G. B., and Dempsey, E. W.   The chemical histology and cytology of the pineal body and neurohypophysis, Endocrinology 42: 56–72 (1948)

463
Wislocki, G. B., and Leduc, E. H.   Vital staining of the hematoencephalic barrier by silver nitrate and trypan blue, and cytological comparisons of the neurohypophysis, pineal body, area postrema, intercolumnar tubercle and supraoptic crest, J. Comp. Neur. 96: 371–413 (1952)

464
Witebsky, E., and Reichner, H.   Die serologische Spezifität der Epiphyse, Zschr. Immunforsch. 79: 335–347 (1933)

465
Wolf, K.   Zirbeldrüsenextrakt in der Geburtshilflichen Landpraxis, Deut. med. Wschr. 39: 1557 (1913)

466
Wolfshaut, C.   Le traitement des troubles de la ménopause avec l'extrait de glande pinéale, Acta endocr. Bucarest 12: 156–158 (1946)

467
Woodruff, L. L., and Swingle, W. W.   The effects of thyroid and some other endocrine products on paramecium, Am. J. Physiol. 69: 21–34 (1924)

468
Wykes, U.   The control of photopigmentary responses in eyeless catfish, J. Exp. Biol. 15: 363–370 (1938)

469
Wyman, L. C.   The reactions of the melanophores of embryonic and larval fundulus to certain chemical agents, J. Exp. Zool. 40: 161–180 (1924)

470
Yamazaki, S., and Iwamiya, M.   Shōka-tai to tō-taisha; yohō (The pineal body and sugar metabolism; preliminary report), Okayama igakkai zasshi 63: 262 (1951)

471
Yokoo, A.   Experimentale Untersuchungen über die Doppelexstirpation der Epiphyse und der Keimdrüse, Zschr. ges. exp. Med. 55: 349–370 (1927). Also published as: Shōka-sen oyobi kōgan no chōfuku-tekishutsu ni yoru jikken-teki kenkyū (Experimental research by means of extirpation of both the pineal gland and the testicles), Naibunpigaku zasshi 1: 927–962 (1926)

472
Yoshimoto, M.   The action of extracts of endocrine glands upon motor nerve and skeletal muscle, Q. J. Exp. Physiol. 13: 5–40 (1922)

473
Yoshizumi, Y.   Kato no shōka-sen tekishutsu-go gai-dōbutsu no taijū, seishokki oyobi seishoku-sen no henka ni tsuite (The effect of pinealectomy on body weight, sexual organs, and gonads in the rabbit), Fukuoka ikadai-gaku zasshi 24: 1035–1036 (1931)

474
Young, J. Z.   The photoreceptors of lampreys; II—The functions of the pineal complex, J. Exp. Biol. 12: 254–270 (1935)

475
Zephiroff, P., and Dobrovolskaia-Zavadskaia, N.   Sur une substance anti-sexuelle isolée de l'urine d'une fillette de quatre ans, C. rend. Soc. biol. 133: 405–407 (1940)

476
Zephiroff, P., and Dobrovolskaia-Zavadskaia, N.   Le rôle probable de l'âge dans le fonctionnement de l'épiphyse, C. rend. Soc. biol. 134: 57–59 (1940)

477
Zephiroff, P., and Dobrovolskaia-Zavadskaia, N.   Quelques données supplémentaires concernant la substance antisexuelle isolée de l'urine d'une fillette de quatre ans, C. rend. Soc. biol. 134: 77–79 (1940)

478
Zoia, C. *See* Foa, C., ref. 120.

479
Zsigmond, A., and Kiss, E.   Epiphysan es Ambesid az allatorvosi gyakorlatban, Allatorv. lap. 60: 388–391 (1937)

480
Zuddas, G.   Il quadro istologico della ghiandola pineale in equini interi e castrati, Boll. Soc. ital. biol. sper. 13: 1153–1155 (1938)

Clinical Correlations

481
Abe, A.   Shōka-sen shuyō no ni rei (Two cases of tumor of the pineal gland), Tōhoku igaku zasshi 39: 178–180 (1949)

482
Adie, W. J.   Pineal syndrome (ocular palsies and sexual precocity in a boy, aged 10), Brain 52: 544–545 (1929)

483
Adie, W. J.   Specimen of pineal tumour, Brain 52: 545–546 (1929)

484
Akamatu, H.   Ein Fall von primären Pinealom der Hypothalamus-Infundibulumgegend, Gann 33: 135–139 (1939). Also published by: Akazaki, K., Shikyū-kabu rōto fukin ni genpatsu-seru Pinealom no ichi rei (A case of primary pinealoma that developed near the infundibulum hypothalamium), Tōkyō iji shinshi 63 (no. 3121): 390–391 (1939)

485
Akazaki, K.   See Akamatu, H., ref. 484.

486
Alajouanine, T., Bertrand, I., Castaigne, P., and Blatrix, C.   Pinéaloblastome avec envahissement méningé et radiculaire diffus, Rev. neur. 83: 268–275 (1950)

487
Alajouanine, T., Hornet, T., and Thurel, R.   Pinéalome avec métastases multiples (Dissémination par le liquide céphalorachidien), Rev. neur. 68: 793–806 (1937)

488
Alajouanine, T., La Grange, —, and Baruk, —.   Tumeur de la glande pinéale diagnostiquée chez l'adulte (constatations radiographiques), Bull. Soc. méd. hôp. Paris, 49 (series 3): 1309–1314 (1925). Also published as: Alajouanine, T., and Gilbert, P.   Tumeur de la région des tubercles quadrijumeaux et de la glande pinéale traitée par la radiothérapie profonde; guérison depuis un an avec persistance seulement d'une séquelle motrice oculaire (paralysie de l'élévation des yeux), Rev. neur. 1: 108–111 (1927)

489
Alajouanine, T., Thurel, R., and Oberling, C. Étude séméiologique et évolutive d'un syndrome de Parinaud mésocephalique; neurospongiome de la région pinéale avec métastases médullaires, Rev. neur. 1: 227–232 (1934)

490
Albornoz Medina, C., and Romero, T. Un caso de tumor de pineal, Rev. colomb. pediat. 9: 15–23 (1950)

491
Albrecht, K. Röntgenbefunde bei cerebralen Kalkherden mit einer Bemerkung zur röntgenologischen Hirndiagnostik mit aufsteigenden Jödolen, Mschr. Psychiat. 68: 1–20 (1928)

492
Algranati Mondolfo, A. Osservazioni sulle cisti della pineale, Riv. sper. freniat. 58: 165–182 (1934)

493
Allen, E. P. Pineal localization: a rapid direct method, Brit. J. Radiol. 13: 102–104 (1940)

494
Allen, S. S., and Lovell, H. W. Tumors of the third ventricle, Arch. Neur. Psychiat. 28: 990–1006 (1932)

495
Almeida Dias, A. Ueber einen Pineal tumor mit multiplen Gliomen, Mschr. Psychiat. Neur. 76: 9–37 (1930)

496
Althausen, N. N. Znachenie obyzvestvlennoi shishkovidnoi zhelezy v topicheskoi diagnostike opukholei mozga (Significance of pineal calcification in topical diagnosis of cerebral tumors), Nevropat. i psikhiat. 7 (no. 5): 89–95 (1938)

497
Altmann, F. Ueber ein Dermoid der Zirbeldrüse, Wien. klin. Wschr. 43: 108–111 (1930)

498
Alvarez Fuertes, G. Tumores de la glandula pineal, algunos datos sobre la estructura histologica de los pinealomas, An. Esc. nac. cienc. biol., Mexico, 5: 149–166 (1948)

499
Amano, T. Pinealom ni kan-suru kōsatsu (Observations on pinealoma), Seishin-shinkeigaku zasshi 41: 436 (1937)

500
Amodei, P.   Due casi di struma adenomatoso cistico della epiphysis cerebri, Ann. clin. med., Palermo, 15 (new series): 431–442 (1925)

501
Angeli, L.   Glandola pineale tartarosa, Oss. med. prat. e chir. di val. clin. ital., Imola, 1: 27–29 (1793)

502
[Anon.]   Extract of a letter, written from Paris, containing an account of some effects of the transfusion of blood; and of two monstrous births, etc., Philos. Tr., R. Soc., London, 2–3: 479–480 (1667–1669)

503
Apert, M., and Porak, R.   Tumeur de la glande pinéale chez une obèse: atrophie mécanique de l'hypophyse: reviviscence du thymus, Rev. neur. 21: 388–390 (1911)

504
Araki, C.   Meningioma in the pineal region; a report of two cases, removed by operation, Arch. jap. Chir. 14: 1181–1192 (1937)

505
Arend, R., and Schusterowna, H.   Gruczolak zlosliwy szyszynki (A malignant tumor of the pineal gland), Polska gaz. lek. 9: 381–385 (1930)

506
Arnold, T.   Observations on the Nature, Kinds, Causes and Prevention of Insanity, Lunacy or Madness, vol. 2. London: G. Ireland, 1786

507
Askanazy, M.   Teratom und Chorioepitheliom der Zirbel, Verh. deut. path. Ges. 10: 58–76 (1906). Also published in: Zbl. allg. Path. 17: 872 (1906)

508
Askanazy, M.   Demonstration de quatre tumeurs de la région pinéale, Rev. méd. Suisse rom. 56: 590–592 (1936)

509
Askanazy, M., and Brack, W.   Sexuelle Frühreife bei einer Idiotin mit Hypoplasie der Zirbel, Virchows Arch. 234: 1–11 (1921)

510
Austregesilo, F., and Ribe Portugal, J.   Pinealoma; caso clinico, Arch. brasil. med. 32: 93 (1942)

511
Baar, H.   Makrogenitosomia praecox–Zirbeltumor, Zschr. Kinderh. 27: 143–152 (1920)

512
Bagenstoss, A. H., and Love, J. G.   Pinealomas, Arch. Neur. Psychiat. 41: 1187–1206 (1939). Reported briefly in: Proc. Mayo Clin. 14: 72–74 (1939)

513
Bailey, P.   Pinealoma, Am. J. Clin. Path. 13: 491–492 (1943)

514
Bailey, P., Buchanan, D. N., and Bucy, P. C.   Intracranial Tumors of Infancy and Childhood. Chicago: University of Chicago Press, 1939

515
Bailey, P., and Jelliffe, S. E.   Tumors of the pineal body with an account of the pineal syndrome; the report of a case of teratoma of the pineal and abstracts of all previously recorded cases of pineal tumor, Arch. Int. M. 8: 851–880 (1911)

516
Bailey, P., and Murray, H. A.   A case of pinealoma with symptoms suggestive of compulsion neurosis; a case report, Arch. Neur. Psychiat. 19: 932–945 (1928)

517
Baker, G. S., and Rucker, C. W.   Metastatic pinealoma involving the optic chiasm, J. Neurosurg. 7: 377–378 (1950)

518
Balado, M.   Tumores de la epifisis, Arch. argent. neur. 1: 10–38 (1927)

519
Balado, M., and Carrillo, R.   Rigidez decerebrada por quiste de epifisis, Bol. Inst. clin. quir., B. Aires, 5: 171–207 (1929). Also published in: Arch. argent. neur. 4: 167–203 (1929)

520
Barbacci, B.   Eunuchoidismo pineale e reperto radiologico, Endocr. pat. cost. 4: 237–246 (1929)

521
Barnett, H. J., and Hyland, H. H.   Tumours involving the brain-stem; a study of 90 cases arising in the brain-stem, fourth ventricle, and pineal tissue, Q. J. Med. 21: 265–284 (1952)

522
Barratt, J. O.   Cyst formation in the pineal gland, J. Path. Bact. 8: 213–227 (1903)

523
Barthelmes, J.   Ueber die verkalkte Zirbeldrüse, Inaug. Diss., Würzburg, 1936

[159]

524
Bartlett, F. K. A case of acromegaly and polyglandular syndrome with special reference to the pineal gland, Arch. Int. M. 12: 201 (1913)

525
Baudouin, A., Lhermitte, J., and Lereboullet, J. Un cas de pinéalome; absence de macrogénitosomie précoce; le problème de la cachexie hypophysaire, Rev. neur. 1: 388–403 (1932)

526
Bayon, —. Hypophysis, Epiphysis und peripherische Nerven bei einem Fall von Cretinismus, Neur. Zbl. 24: 146–150 (1905)

527
Bell, H. H. Hyperplasia of the pineal body, J. Nerv. Ment. Dis. 44: 481–494 (1916). Abstracted in: J. Missouri M. Ass. 13: 239 (1916)

528
Benaim, J. Pinealomas; consideraciones sobre dos casos, Dia med. 20: 430–440 (1948)

529
Benecke, E. Ueber die funktionelle Bedeutung der Zirbelgeschwülste, Virchows Arch. 297: 26–39 (1936)

530
Benedek, L. Az agyvelonek autochton pinealis dysembriomairol (pinealomak); a kombinalt encephalo-stereoarteriographianak korjelzestani jelentosegevel kapcsolatban (Autochthonous pineal dysembryoma of the brain; diagnostic importance of combined encephalo-stereoarteriography), Orvoskepzes 26 (appendix 1): 1–8 (1936). Also published as: Ueber die autochthonen pinealen Dysembriome (Pinealome) des Gehirns, in Verbindung mit der diagnostischen Bedeutung der Encephalo-Stereoarteriographie, Zschr. ges. Neur. Psychiat. 156: 677–693 (1936)

531
Benedek, L., and Angyal, L. Posttraumas latotelep es tobozmirigytünet együttes esete (Post-traumatic syndrome involving the optic tract and pineal), Orv. hetil. 83: 149–151 (1939). Also published as: Ueber einen Fall von post-traumatischen Thalamus- und Epiphysen-syndrom, Deut. Zschr. Nervenh. 148: 196–204 (1939)

532
Berblinger, W. Zur Frage der genitalen Hypertrophie bei Tumoren der Zirbeldrüse und zum Einfluss embryonaler Geschwülstgewebes auf die Drüsen mit innere Sekretion, Virchows Arch. (supplement) 227: 38–88 (1920)

533
Berblinger, W. Zur Kenntnis der Zirbelgeschwülste (Zirbelcarcinom mit metastasen), Zschr. ges. Neur. Psychiat. 95: 741–761 (1925)

534
Berblinger, W. Hypophysentuberkulose als Todesursache; die Tuberkulose der endokrinen Organe; ı–Hypophyse, Zirbel, Schweiz. med. Wschr. 20: 1217–1220 (1939)

535
Berblinger, W. Zur Kenntnis der Pinealocytome nebst Bemerkungen über die cerebrogene Frühreife, Schweiz. Zschr. allg. Path. 7: 107–128 (1944)

536
Bergmann, G. H. Anatomisch-pathologische Untersuchungen über Hirnwassersucht, Drehkrankheit der Schaafe und dieser ähliche Erscheinungen bei Menschen, Nasse's Zschr. Anthrop., pp. 126–179 (1825)

537
Bergmann, G. H. Jahres-Bericht über die in der Heilanstalt im Michaeliskloster im Jahre 1836 vorgekommenen Krankheitsfälle, nebst einigen allgemeinen psycho-pathologischen Bemerkungen und besonderen Krankheits- und Sektions-Berichten, Hannoversche Annalen für die gesammte Heilkunde 3: 485–556 (1838)

538
Bergmann, G. H. Krankheits- und Sektions-Bericht; Verrücktheit; Mord, veranlasst durch Hallucinationen-Malacie der Nebennieren, Verwachsung der Zirbel und der Hinterbörner, Allg. Zschr. Psychiat. Psych. gericht. Med. 1: 182–194 (1844)

539
Bergmann, W. The Calcified Pineal Gland. Assen: van Gorcum, 1940

540
Bienstock, —. Ueber einen Tumor der Zirbeldrüse, Schweiz. med. Wschr. 7: 502–505 (1926). Also published as: Sur une tumeur de glande pinéale, Strasbourg-méd. 8 (part 2): 4–8 (1926)

541
Bilek, F. Epilepsie a hypergenitalismus pri poruse glandulae pinealis, Arch. neur. psychiat. ceske 4: 24–28 (1941)

542
Blane, G. Case of a tumor found in the situation of the pineal gland, Tr. Soc. Improve. M. and Chir. Knowl., London, 2: 198–207 (1800)

543
Blanquinque, P. Tumeur de la glande pinéale; épanchement abondant;

hernies du cerveau à travers la dure-mère, Gaz. hébd. de méd., Paris, 8 (series 2): 532–533 (1871)

544
Boas, E. P., and Scholz, T.   Calcification in the pineal gland, Arch. Int. M. 21: 66–72 (1918)

545
Bochner, S. J., and Scarff, J. E.   Teratoma of the pineal body: classification of the embryonal tumors of the pineal body; report of a case of teratoma of the pineal body presenting formed teeth, Arch. Surg. 36: 303–329 (1938)

546
Boehm, E.   Zirbeldrüsenteratom und genitale Frühreife, Frankf. Zschr. Path. 22: 121–146 (1919)

547
Boix Barrios, J.   El sindrome pineal, Pediat. espan. 25: 71–83 (1936)

548
Bolten, G. C.   Een geval van gezwel der glandula pinealis, Geneesk. gids. 14: 435–441 (1936)

549
Bond, H.   Case of diseased brain, N. Amer. Med. and Surg. J. 5: 65–72 (1828)

550
Bonnin, M., and Simpson, O. A.   Parinaud's syndrome: a report of two cases, Med. J. Australia 2: 333–335 (1950)

551
Borchardt, L.   Pubertas praecox epiphysären Ursprungs ohne Teratombildung, Deut. med. Wschr. 54: 1252–1253 (1928)

552
Bouchut, M.   Kyste séreux du troisième ventricule avec hydrocephalie des ventricules latéraux—atrophie des nerfs optiques, Gaz. hôp. 45: 353–355 (1872)

553
Brandenburg, E.   Morphologische Beiträge zur Frage der endokrinen Funktion der Epiphyse, Endokrinologie 4: 81–96 (1929)

554
Bronner, H.   Die Verkalkung des Corpus pineale im Röntgenbild, Fortschr. Röntgenstrahl. 35: 277–281 (1926)

555
Brunner, –, and Rohrschach, H.   See Rorschach, H., ref. 905

556
Brusa, P. Contributo allo studio dei tumori del corpo pineale, Riv. clin. pediat. 22: 73–97 (1924)

557
del Buono, G. Studi per la determinazione della sede normale della pineale sul craniogramma normale, Radiol. med., Torino, 37: 997–1002 (1952)

558
del Buono, P. Sui processi di calcificazione della pineale, Boll. ed atti dell'Accademia pugliese di Scienze 6: 253–266 (1931)

559
Businco, A. Neuroglioma cistico della pineale (considerazioni sui tumori epifisari), Tumori, Roma, 7: 173–199 (1919)

560
de Busscher, J. Tumeur épiphysaire; envahissement des ventricules cérébraux, J. belge neur. psychiat. 36: 375–385 (1936). Also published in: Tr. Inst. Bunge, Anvers, 2 (no. 3): 1–11 (1938)

561
de Busscher, J., and Thomas, F. Tératome de la région pinéale avec macrogénitosomia praecox chez un garçon de 5 ans et demi, J. belge neur. psychiat. 44–46: 79–119 (1946)

562
Bustamente Zuleta, E. Yodoventriculografia, diagnostico de un tumor de la pineal, Bol. clin., Medellín, 9: 67–73 (1947)

563
Cahana, M. G., and Cahana, T. Le rôle de l'épiphyse dans certaines psychoses; étude anatomo-clinique d'un cas de psychose maniaque avec macropénis et masturbation, Ann. méd. psychol., Paris, 99: 152–161 (1941)

564
Camauër, A. G., and Mortola, G. Quiste glial de la epifisis o glandula pineal; hipertensión arterial; eclampsia hipertensiva, Prensa med. argent. 16: 487–493 (1929)

565
Camp, J. D. Intracranial calcification and its roentgenologic significance, Am. J. Roentg. 23: 615–624 (1930)

566
Campbell, A. W. Notes of two cases of dilatation of the central cavity or ventricle of the pineal gland, Tr. Path. Soc., London, 50: 15–18 (1898–1899)

567
Carr, J. L.   Cystic hydrops of the pineal gland; report of six cases, J. Nerv. Ment. Dis. 99: 552–572 (1944)

568
Castleman, B., Editor.   Case records of the Massachusetts General Hospital; case 38521, N. England J. M. 247: 1036–1040 (1952)

569
Charlton, H. H.   A tumor of the pineal organ with cartilage formation in the mackerel, Scomber scombrus, Anat. Rec. 43: 271–276 (1929)

570
Chiba, M., and Yamada, M.   About the calcification of the pineal gland in the Japanese, Folia psychiatrica et neurologica japonica 2: 301–303 (1948)

571
Chirone, P.   I tumori della glandula pineale, Med. ital. Napoli 5: 141–143, 161–168 (1907)

572
Chor, H., and Barth, E. E.   Roentgen study of the skull in epilepsy, Am. J. Roentg. 39: 534–547 (1938)

573
Christ, A.   Zur Kasuistik der nucleären Ophthalmoplegie, Deut. Arch. klin. Med. 46: 497–510 (1890)

574
Church, –.   Cancer of the dura mater and calvaria, with similar disease scattered through most of the organs of the body, Tr. Path. Soc., London, 20: 325–330 (1869)

575
Cignolini, P.   Aspetti diversi delle concrezioni saline della ghiandole pineale, Radiol. med. 14: 1000–1005 (1927)

576
Cignolini, P.   Étude radiologique et clinique sur les concrétions calcaires de la pinéale et leurs rapports avec les états hypogénitaux, Rev. fr. endocr. 5: 324–338 (1927). Also published as: Le concrezioni della pineale ed i loro rapporti cogli stati ipogenitali, Endocr. pat. cost. 2: 317–319 (1927)

577
Cleghorn, R. A., Hyland, H. H., Mills, J. R. F., and Linell, E. A.   Hypogonadism associated with invasion of the mid-brain and hypothalamus by a pineal tumor, Q. J. Med. 7 (new series): 183–209 (1938)

578
Clemente, G.   Contributo allo studio della glandola pineale nell'uomo

e in alcuni animali, Endocr. pat. cost. 2: 44–47 (1923). Also published in: Rendic. R. Accad. naz. Lincei, Roma, 32: 47–51 (1923)

579
Clemente, G.   Contributo allo studio della glandola pineale nell'uomo e in alcuni mammiferi, Gior. biol. med. sper. 1: 76–80 (1923)

580
Coats, J.   An adenoid carcinoma with cartilage originating in the pineal gland, Tr. Path. Soc., London, 38: 44–52 (1887)

581
Collins, S. A.   Of the glandula pinealis, in: The Parts of the Middle and Highest Apartment of Man's Body; Systeme of Anatomy, Treating of the Body of Man, vol. 2, pp. 1020–1021. London: Newcomb, 1685

582
Cooper, E. R. A.   The human pineal gland and pineal cysts, J. Anat. 67: 28–46 (1932)

583
Corbetta, S.   Pinealoma ectopico con malformazione del corpo pineal, Riv. anat. pat. 3: 430–447 (1950)

584
Crichton, A.   An Inquiry into the Nature and Origin of Mental Derangement; Comprehending a Concise System of the Physiology and Pathology of the Human Mind and a History of the Passions and Their Effects, vol. 2, pp. 413–419. London: Cadell & Davies, 1798

585
de Crinis, M., and Rüsken, W.   Bestimmung und diagnostische Verwertung der Lageveränderungen des Epiphysen- (Zirbeldrüsen-) Schattens im seitlichen Röntgenbild, Fortsch. Röntgenstrahl. 59: 401–407 (1939)

586
Cuneo, H. M., and Rand, C. W.   Brain Tumors of Childhood. Springfield, Mass.: Thomas, 1952

587
Daly, E. O.   (i) A case of recurring attacks of transient aphasia and right hemiplegia; (ii) A case of tumour of the pineal gland, Brain 10: 233–236 (1887–1888)

588
Dana, C. L., and Berkeley, W. N.   The functions of the pineal gland; with report of feeding experiments by H. H. Goddard and W. S. Cornell, Med. Rec. 83: 835–847 (1913)

589

Dandy, W. E. Operative experience in cases of pineal tumor, Arch. Surg. 33: 19–46 (1936)

590

David, M., Mahoudeau, D., Askenasy, H., and Brun, M. Sur le diagnostic des tumeurs de la région épiphysaire ne se manifestant que par des signes d'hypertension intracranienne; de l'importance de la ventriculographie en pareil cas; interpretation délicate de certains ventriculogrammes, Rev. neur. 63: 571–580 (1935)

591

Davidoff, L. M. The endocrinologic aspects of tumors of the pineal gland, Surgery 16: 306–314 (1944). Also published in: Endocrinology of Neoplastic Diseases, pp. 376–385. New York: Oxford Univ. Press, 1947

592

Davidson, H. S. A case of pineal tumor, J. M. Soc. N. Jersey 24: 308–310 (1927)

593

Deimler, —. Neubildung in der Zirbeldrüse, Berl. u. Münch. tieraerztl. Wschr. 57: 7 (1941)

594

Delay, —. Un cas de gigantisme épiphysaire, Praxis 17 (no. 2): 3 (1928)

595

Dercum, F. X. Probable diagnosis of tumor of the pineal gland, J. Nerv. Ment. Dis. 44: 147–150 (1916)

596

Derman, G. L., and Kopelowitsch, M. A. Zur Kenntnis der Zirbeldrüsengewächse (Ein seltener Fall von Neuroglioma ependymale embryonale gl. pinealis), Virchows Arch. 273: 657–662 (1929)

597

Deshayes, —. Syndrome épiphysaire guéri par les injections d'extrait hypophysaire, Bull. Soc. pediat. Paris 19: 236–239 (1921)

598

Dietrich, A. Mangel der Zirbeldrüse mit Hirsutismus, Zbl. allg. Path. 48: 209–212 (1930)

599

Dimolescu, A., Arama, O., Stroescu, G., and Olteanu, I. Studiu clinic si fiziopatologic asupra tumorilor glandei pineale (Pinealome), Spitalul 60: 79–85 (1940)

600
Djoerup, —. Et tilfaelde af svulst og degeneration af glandula pinealis, Ugeskr. laeger 2: 378–383 (1840)

601
Dolmetsch, H. Ueber ein Teratom der Zirbeldrüse bei einem 14-jährigen Knaben ohne Frühreife, Inaug. Diss., Zürich, 1926

602
Drewes, H. G. Die Lageänderung der verkalkten Zirbeldrüse auf dem Röntgenbild bei gerichteter intrakranieller Schrumpfung nach offenen Gehirnverletzungen, Fortschr. Röntgenstrahl. 77: 77–80 (1952)

603
Dublin, W. B. Pinealoma with report of a case, Northwest M. 44: 86–87 (1945)

604
Duffin, A. B. Case of cerebral tumour, Tr. clin. Soc., London, 9: 183–187 (1876). Also published in: Lancet 1: 888 (1876)

605
Duges, —. Mémoire sur les altérations intra-utérines de l'encéphale et de ses enveloppes, Ephémérides médicales de Montpellier 1: 296–336 (1826). Also found in: Lallemand, F., Recherches anatomico-pathologiques sur l'encéphale et ses dépendances, 3: 267–270, Bechet: Paris, 1834. Article 40—Idiotée congénitale, hémiplégie à droite

606
Dyes, O. Verlagerungen der verkalkten Zirbeldrüse auf dem seitlichen Röntgenbild des Schädels, Nervenarzt 9: 11–14 (1936)

607
Dyke, C. G. Indirect signs of brain tumor as noted in routine roentgen examinations, Am. J. Roentg. 23: 598–606 (1930)

608
Ehni, G. Pineal teratoma; report of a case, J. Neurosurg. 3: 86–94 (1946)

609
Elkington, J. Calcified pineal tumor, Proc. R. Soc. M. 25 (part 2): 1533–1534 (1932)

610
Engelberg, K. Verlagerung der verkalkten Zirbeldrüse und ihre Bedeutung für die röntgenologische Diagnostik von Hirntumoren, Inaug. Diss., Würzburg, 1937

611
Ernst, M.   Die diagnostiche Bedeutung der Zirbeldrüsenverlagerung bei intrakranieller Druckänderung, Deut. Zschr. Chir. 250: 224–233 (1938)

612
Faeli, C.   Das Zirbeldrüsensymptom bei Hypogenitalismus unter besonderer Berücksichtigung der sogenannten Sexualneurasthenie, Endokrinologie 7: 189–198 (1930)

613
Falkson, R.   Ein Chondrocystosarcom im dritten Ventrikel, Virchows Arch. 75: 550–553 (1879)

614
Farina, C.   Pinealoma associato a carcinoma uterino, Ateneo parmense 12: 313–322 (1940)

615
Fassbender, F.   Ueber einen Fall von Praecositas somo-psycho-genitalis bei einem 7½ Jahre alten Mädchen, Zschr. Kinderh. 54: 642–656 (1933)

616
Feilchenfeld, L.   Ein Fall von Tumor cerebri (Gliosarcom der Zirbeldrüse), Neur. Zbl. 4: 409–412 (1885)

617
Fein, A.   Ein Fall von kindlichem Riesenwuchs mit vorzeitiger Geschlechtsreife (Erkrankung der Zirbeldrüse), Münch. med. Wschr. 70: 772–773 (1923). Also published as: Zwei Fälle von Erkrankung der Zirbeldrüse und der Hypophyse, Med. Korbl. Württemberg 93: 87–88, 99–100 (1923)

618
Floris, V., and Agostini, L.   Tumore della pineale decorso unicamente con sindrome chiasmatica e con particolari risposte vestibolo-oculari, Riv. neur. 21: 181–195 (1951)

619
Foerster, —.   Fall von Markschwamm mit ungewöhnlichen vielfacher metastatischer Verbreitung, Virchows Arch. 13: 271–274 (1858)

620
Fracassi, T., Babbini, R. J., Marelli, F. L., and Castane Decoud, A.   Ependimoma de la región pineal, Rev. argent. neur. psiquiat. 4: 66–74 (1939)

621
Frada, G., and Micale, G.   Studio clinico-radiologico sulle calcificazioni pineali in gravidanza, Radiologia medica 28: 209–218 (1941). Abstracted in: Ormoni 3: 111–112 (1941)

622

Frank, —. Epiphysentumor bei einem 20 jährigen Mann, Verein deut. Aerzte, Prague. Published in: Berl. klin. Wschr. 57: 888 (1920)

623

Frank, M. Veränderungen an den endokrinen Drüsen bei Dementia praecox, Zschr. angew. Anat. 5: 23–46 (1920)

624

Frank, M. Pubertas praecox, Münch. med. Wschr. 68: 29 (1921). Autopsy presented by: Huebschmann, —, Pubertas praecox, Münch. med. Wschr. 68: 220 (1921)

625

Frank, M. Ein Beitrag zu den Mischtumoren der Zirbeldrüse, Zschr. angew. Anat. 8: 65–78 (1922)

626

von Frankl-Hochwart, L. Ueber Diagnose der Zirbeldrüsentumoren, Deut. Zschr. Nervenh. 37: 455–465 (1909). Also published in: Deut. Zschr. Nervenh. 38: 309–310 (1910) and in: Wien. med. Wschr. 60: 506–508 (1910)

627

Fray, W. W. A study of the effect of skull rotation on roentgenological measurements of the pineal gland, Radiology 27: 433–441 (1936)

628

Fray, W. W. Roentgenologic study of orientation of the pineal body; i—Comparison of the proportional and the graphic method in absence of tumor of the brain, Arch. Neur. Psychiat. 38: 1199–1207 (1937)

629

Fray, W. W. A roentgenological study of pineal orientation; iii—A comparison of methods used in pineal orientation, Am. J. Roentg. 39: 899–907 (1938)

630

Fray, W. W. A roentgenological study of pineal orientation; ii—A comparison of the graphic and proportional methods in proven cases of brain tumor, Radiology 30: 579–587 (1938)

631

Fray, W. W. Methods for determining pineal position with analysis of their errors, Am. J. Roentg. 42: 490–497 (1939)

632

Friedman, N. B. Germinoma of the pineal; its identity with germinoma (seminoma) of the testes, Cancer Res. 7: 363–368 (1947). Published in part in: Tompkins, W. N., Haymaker, W., and Campbell, E. H., Metastatic pineal tumors; a clinico-pathological report of two cases, J. Neurosurg. 7: 159–169 (1950)

633
Friedmann, E. D., and Plaut, A. Tumor of the pineal gland (pinealocytoma) with meningeal and neural metastases, Arch. Neur. Psychiat. 33: 1324–1341 (1935). Abstracted in: Tr. Am. Neur. Ass. 60: 119–123 (1934)

634
Friedmann, R., and Scheinker, J. Ein Fall von Neuroepitheliom der Zirbeldrüse, Mschr. Psychiat. 89: 81–96 (1934)

635
Friedreich, N. Psammoma kystomatosum haemorrhagicum der Glandula pinealis in Combination mit Medullasarkom, Virchows Arch. 33: 165–167 (1865)

636
Fujita, H. Bōken ni yorite kakunin-shi etaru shōka-sen shuyō ni kitareru gai-chokkin-mahi no ichi rei (A case of paralysis of the musculus rectus oculi lateralis caused by a pineal tumor verified at autopsy), Jikken ganka zasshi, no. 20: 41–46 (1920)

637
Fukuo, Y. Ueber die Teratome der Glandula pinealis, Inaug. Diss., München (1914)

638
Gabriel, P. Les pinéalomes, Thesis, Paris, 1936

639
Gagel, O. Zur Klinik und Pathologie der Pinealome, Wien. klin. Wschr. 55: 597–598 (1942). Also published in: Wien. med. Wschr. 92: 168–169 (1942)

640
Garm, C. A study on bovine nymphomania, Acta endocr., Copenhagen, Supplement 3: 120–126 (1949)

641
Garrod, A. E. Pineal cyst, Tr. Path. Soc., London, 50: 14–15, 1899

642
Gauderer, L. Zur Kasuistik der Zirbeldrüsentumoren (Teratoma glandulae pinealis), Inaug. Diss., Giessen, 1889

643
Gautier, P., Jentzer, A., and de Morsier, G. Syndrome infundibulaire avec atrophie optique bilatérale chez l'enfant; pinéalome développé dans le troisième ventricule, Rev. otoneur., Paris, 10: 407–408 (1932)

644

van Gehuchten, P. Un cas de tumeur de l'épiphyse, J. belge neur. psychiat. 36: 69–72 (1936)

645

van Gehuchten, P., and Callewaert, P. Trois cas de tumeur de la région épiphysaire, J. belge neur. psychiat. 37: 283–291 (1937)

646

van Gehuchten, P., Morelle, J., and Dereymaker, A. Un cas de tumeur perlée de la région épiphysaire, J. belge neur. psychiat. 40: 134–139 (1940)

647

Gerstley, J. R., Kasanin, J., and Lowenhaupt, E. Teratoma of the pineal body, J. Pediat. 17: 512–520 (1940). Also reported in: Gerstley, J. R., Anorexia of perplexing origin, Med. Clin. N. America 25: 147–154 (1941); and in: Kasanin, J., Defense reactions in anxiety states of central origin, Psychoanal. Q. 11: 493–502 (1942)

648

Ghirardi, L., and Davini, V. Metodi e significato diagnostico della localizzazione della pineale calcificata nell'indagine radiologica diretta del cranio, Sistema nerv. 3: 284–291 (1951)

649

Giebel, W. Ueber primäre Tumoren der Zirbeldrüse, Frankf. Zschr. Path. 25: 176–190 (1921)

650

Glaser, M. A. Tumours of the pineal, corpora quadrigemina and third ventricle, their inter-relationship of their syndromes and their surgical treatment, Brain 52: 226–261 (1929)

651

Glass, R. L., and Culbertson, C. G. Teratoma of the pineal gland with choriocarcinoma and rhabdomyosarcoma, Arch. Path. 41: 552–555 (1946)

652

Globus, J. H. Pinealoma, Arch. Path. 31: 533–568 (1941). Published in part as: Pinealoma with supratentorial extension and manifestations of disrupted temperature regulation; clinicopathological study of two cases, Libman Anniv. Vols. 2: 491–505 (1932)

653

Globus, J. H., and Silbert, S. Pinealoma, Arch. Neur. Psychiat. 25: 937–985 (1931). Also published as: Globus, J. H., Tumors of the quadrigeminate plate; a clinico-anatomic study of seven cases, Arch. Opth. 5: 418–444 (1931)

654
Goldzieher, M.   Ueber eine Zirbeldrüsengeschwülst, Virchows Arch. 213: 353–365 (1913)

655
Gordon, M. B.   Morphological changes in the endocrine glands in Mongolian idiocy with report of two cases, Endocrinology 14: 1–5 (1930)

656
Gowers, W. R.   Cases of cerebral tumor illustrating diagnosis and localization, Lancet 1: 363–365 (1879)

657
Greding, J. E.   Vermischte medizinische und chirurgischen Schriften, pp. 179–186. Altenburg: Richterische Buchhandlung, 1781

658
Grevstad, J.   Pinealisskyggen i skallerontgenogrammer, Med. rev., Bergen, 50: 551–554 (1933)

659
Groff, R. A.   The dissemination of glioma by extension at a distance, Am. J. Cancer 29: 651–658 (1937)

660
Günz, J. G.   Pr indicit, ac simul lapillos glandulae pinealis in quinque mente alienatis inventos proponit. Leipzig: Langenheim, 1753

661
Guillain, G.   Étude anatomo-clinique sur un cas de pinéalome, Vol. jubilaire Marinesco, Bucarest, pp. 281–292 (1933)

662
Guillain, G., Mollaret, P., and Bertrand, I.   Contribution à l'étude du diagnostic des pinéalomes; forme oculaire tonico-myoclonique simulant l'encéphalite épidémique, Bull. Soc. med. hôp. Paris, pp. 984–993, July 7, 1933

663
Guinzbourg, E.   Développement sexuel prémature, Rev. fr. endocr. 13: 372–385 (1935)

664
Gutzeit, R.   Ein Teratom der Zirbeldrüse, Inaug. Diss., Königsberg, 1896

665
Haldemann, K. O.   Tumors of the pineal gland, Arch. Neur. Psychiat. 18: 724–754 (1927)

666
von Haller, A.   Elementa physiologiae corporis humani; Tomus quartus—Cerebrum, Nervi, Musculi, pp. 64–66 and 343. Lausanne: Grassett, 1762

[172]

667

Handley, J.   Pineal cysts, with report of two cases, J. Ment. Sc. 76: 250–253 (1930)

668

Harris, W., and Cairns, H.   Diagnosis and treatment of pineal tumors with report of a case, Lancet 1: 3–9 (1932)

669

Hart, C.   Ein Fall von Angiosarkom der Glandula pinealis, Berl. klin. Wschr. 46 (part 2): 2298–2299 (1909). Also published in: Veröff. Hufeland. Ges. (1909), Berl., 2: 37–42 (1910)

670

Haslam, J.   Observations on Madness and Melancholy, including Practical Remarks on Those Diseases; Together with Cases and an Account of the Morbid Appearance on Dissection. 2nd ed. London: J. Callow, 1809

671

Hawes, L. E., and Mead, S.   Posterior displacement of the calcified pineal gland in subtentorial brain tumors, Radiology 40: 367–370 (1943)

672

Healey, C. E., and Guy, C. C.   Pseudohermaphroditismus masculinus externus associated with suprarenal hyperplasia and vascular hypertension; report of a case, Arch. Path. 12: 543–561 (1931)

673

Hedenius, I., and Henschen, F.   Ett fall af tumor i glandula pinealis, Hygeia, Stockholm, 75: 226–240 (1913)

674

Hegnelius, T.   Psykos av corpus callosumtyp vid pinealom, Nord. med. 20: 2217–2219 (1943)

675

van der Heide, C. C.   Les tumeurs de l'épiphyse, Gaz. hôp. 86: 1383 (1913)

676

van der Heide, C. C.   Tumor glandulae pinealis sive epiphysis cerebri, Ned. mschr. verlosk. 3: 253–260 (1914)

677

van der Heide, C. C.   Gezwel van de glandula pinealis sive epiphysis cerebri, Ned. tschr. geneesk. 58: 1021 (1914)

678

Hekman, J.   Een geval van gezwel van epiphyse, Ned. tschr. geneesk. 64: 1891–1893 (1920)

[173]

679
Hempel, H. K.   Ein Beitrag zur Pathologie der Glandula Pinealis, Inaug. Diss., Leipzig, 1901

680
Herren, R. Y.   A note on the reliability of roentgenographically determined pineal gland shift in brain tumors, Surgery 8: 478–479 (1940)

681
Herrera, J. M.   Un caso de pinealoma; breves consideraciones sobre los tumores de la región epifisaria, Bol. As. med. nac. Panama 14: 171–182 (1951)

682
Heubner, O.   See Oestreich, R., and Slawyk, —, ref. 864

683
Heuer, G. J., and Dandy, W. E.   Roentgenography in the localization of brain tumor based upon a series of one hundred consecutive cases, Bull. Johns Hopkins Hosp. 26: 311–322 (1916)

684
Hijmans van den Bergh, A. A., and van Hasselt, J. A.   Tumor glandulae pinealis, sive epiphysis cerebri, Ned. tschr. geneesk. 57 (part 1): 1271–1287 (1913)

685
Hirafuku, —.   Shōka-sen fukin ni miraretaru kikeishu (Teratoma discovered in the region of the pineal gland), Rinshō igaku 30: 1281–1282 (1942)

686
Hirata, M.   Pinealoma no ichi rei (A case of pinealoma), Acta Soc. ophth. jap. 48: 693–701 (1944)

687
Hishiki, T.   Byōsō kettei no goshin rei; shōka-sen-bu shuyō (Cases of mistaken diagnosis of the focus of infection; tumor in the pineal region), Rinshō Nippon igaku 5: 1626–1628 (1936)

688
von Hoesslin, R.   Tumor der Epiphysis cerebri, Münch. med. Wschr. 43: 292 (1896)

689
Holzhaüer, R.   Zur Kasuistik der Gehirntumoren im Kindesalter, Inaug. Diss., Berlin, 1903

690
Horrax, G.   Studies on the pineal gland; clinical observations, Arch. Int. M. 17: 627–645 (1916)

691
Horrax, G.   Differential diagnosis of tumors primarily pineal and primarily pontile, Arch. Neur. Psychiat. 17: 179–192 (1927)

692
Horrax, G.   Further observations on tumors of the pineal body, Arch. Neur. Psychiat. 35: 215–228 (1936)

693
Horrax, G.   Extirpation of a huge pinealoma from a patient with pubertas praecox: a new operative approach, Arch. Neur. Psychiat. 37: 385–397 (1937)

694
Horrax, G.   Treatment of tumors of the pineal body; experience in a series of twenty-two cases, Arch. Neur. Psychiat. 64: 227–242 (1950)

695
Horrax, G., and Bailey, P.   Tumors of the pineal body, Arch. Neur. Psychiat. 13: 423–470 (1925)

696
Horrax, G., and Bailey, P.   Pineal pathology; further studies, Arch. Neur. Psychiat. 19: 394–414 (1928)

697
Horrax, G., and Daniels, J. T.   The conservative treatment of pineal tumors, Surg. Clin. N. America 22: 649–659 (1942)

698
Horrax, G., and Wyatt, J. P.   Ectopic pinealomas in the chiasmal region; report of three cases, J. Neurosurg. 4: 309–326 (1947)

699
Howell, C. M. H.   Tumours of the pineal body, Proc. R. Soc. M., London, 3 (part 2): 65–78 (1909–10)

700
Huebschmann, —.   See Frank, M., ref. 624

701
Hückel, R.   Ein Fall von Sarkom der Zirbeldrüse, Virchows Arch. 269: 76–82 (1928)

702
Hueter, —.   Teratom der Zirbeldrüse, Altonaer Aerztlicher Verein, Münch. med. Wschr. 60 (part 1): 895 (1913)

703
Ikuta, H.   Histopathologie der menschlichen Zirbeldrüse; Mitteilung II, Tr. Soc. path. jap. 24: 471–478 (1934)

704
Ikuta, H.   Histopathologie der menschlichen Zirbeldrüse; Mitteilung III,
Tr. Soc. path. jap. 25: 613–617 (1935)

705
Ikuta, H.   Hito no shōka-sen no soshiki-byōri (Histopathology of the
human pineal gland), Keiō igaku 16: 1883–1997 (1936)

706
Ikuta, H.   Hyōhon shisetsu; I—Pinealom no ichi bōken rei (Specimen
demonstration lectures; I—An autopsy case of pinealoma), Tōkyō iji shinshi 63 (no. 3116): 68 (1939)

707
Imai, T.   Aku-sei shōka-sen shuyō wo heiyū-seru shōka-sen kikeishu no
ichi rei (A case of teratoma of the pineal gland accompanied by pinealoma
malignum), Seishin shinkeigaku zasshi 39: 303–317 (1935)

708
Irizawa, T., and Sō, T.   See Uehara, K., and Sō, T., ref. 985

709
Ishizaki, C.   Macrogenitosomia praecox (shintai seishokki-sōki-hatsuiku-
shō) wo tomonaeru shōka-sen shuyō no ichi rei (A case of tumor of the
pineal gland accompanied by macrogenitosomia praecox), Ōsaka igakkai
zasshi 29: 1147–1158 (1930)

710
Iwakawa, K.   Shōni-ki ni okeru shintai seishokki ijō-hattatsu-shō ni tsuite
(Macrogenitosomia praecox in childhood), Hokuetsu igakkai zasshi 33:
578 (1918)

711
Jacobi, W.   Beitrag zur Kenntnis der Epiphysentumoren, Deut. Zschr.
Nervenh. 71: 350–357 (1921)

712
Jaensch, P. A.   Doppelseitige Trochlearisparese als einzige Motilitäts-
störung bei Zirbeldrüsentumor, Zschr. Augenh. 75: 58–68 (1931)

713
Jedlicka, J., and Jedlicka, V.   Vznik mnohonasobnych blastomu cerebral-
nich a pluriglandularniho syndromu na basi konstitucionalni disposice
(The origin of multiple cerebral blastomas and pluriglandular syndrome
on the basis of constitutional disposition), Cas. lek. cesk. 59: 2–6, 27–31,
45–48 (1920)

714
Jedlicka, V.   Macrogenitosomia praecox, Cas. lek. cesk. 66: 973–981
(1927)

714 A
Jen Yi-ming. *See* Yi-ming Jen, ref. 1021

715
Jingu, R. Ein Fall von Zyste der Zirbeldrüse bei einer Lepraleiche, Jap. J. Derm. Urol., Transactions and Abstracts 40: 165 (1936)

716
Jo, S. Shōka-sen-shu no ichi bōken rei (An autopsy case of tumor of the pineal gland), Tōhoku igaku zasshi 46: 299–300 (1952)

717
Johan, B. Corpus pineale–daganat okozta korai pubertas, egyeb belso secretios mirigyek elvaltozasaival (Early puberty caused by pineal tumor with changes in the other endocrines), Orv. hetil. 66: 369–372, 380–382 (1922). Also published in: Steiner, B., Adatok a corpus pineale physiologiajahoz e pathologiajahoz (Physiological and pathological data on the pineal), Orv. hetil. 66: 367–369 (1922)

718
Joukovsky, V. Hydrocéphalie et tumeur congénitale de la glande pinéale chez un nouveau-né, Rev. mens. mal. enfance 19: 197–217 (1901)

719
Kahn, E. A. Surgical treatment of pineal tumor, Arch. Neur. Psychiat. 38: 833–842, 1937. Also published as: The surgery of pineal tumors: a preliminary report, Univ. Hosp. Bull., Ann Arbor, 2: 57 (1936)

720
Kalm, H., and Magun, R. Beitrag zur Klinik und pathologischen Anatomie der Pinealome, Deut. Zschr. Nervenh. 164: 453–468 (1950)

721
Kaminski, R. Missbildung und Geschwulst der Pinealis, Inaug. Diss., Berlin, 1937

722
Kaneko, T. X-sen shōmei ni yoru shōka-sen shōmei no hindo oyobi kyōmi-aru shōka-sen ijō sekkai chinchaku no ichi rei (Frequency of appearance of the pineal gland in x-ray shadowgrams, and a case of peculiar symptoms due to abnormal calcification of the gland), Keiō igaku 17: 261–265 (1937)

723
Kasahara, M., and Fujii, S. Seishokki sōki hatsuiku-shō (Macrogenitosomia praecox), Jikken ihō 14: 1386–1389 (1928)

724
Kasanin, J. *See* Gerstley, J. R., Kasanin, J., and Lowenhaupt, E., ref. 647

725
Katahira, S.   *See* Uehara, K., and Sō, T., ref. 985

726
Katō, M.   Basedow-shi-byō ni okeru kyōsen, fukujin, nōkasuitai, shōka-sen shoken (Observations on the thymus, the adrenals, the hypophysis cerebri, and the pineal gland in Basedow's disease), Nippon gekagakkai zasshi 20: 112–113 (1919)

727
Katsurashima, T.   Shōka-sen shuyō no ichi rei (A case of pineal gland tumor), Tōhoku igaku zasshi 11: 307–317 (1928)

728
Kawamura, M.   Kōgan ruihyōhi-shu wo tomonaeru shōka-sen kikeishu no rei (A case of epidermoid of the testicle accompanying pineal tera-toma), Jūzenkai zasshi 46: 2438–2446 (1941)

729
Kerckringius, T.   Observatio xxxv: Lapis in cerebro repertus; Opera om-nia anatomica spicilegium anatomicum, osteogeniam foetuum, nec non anthropogenae ichnographiam. 2nd ed. Leyden: Boutesteyn, 1717. Also published as: Spicilegium anatomicum continens observationum anato-micarum rariorum centuriam unam. Amsterdam: Frisius, 1670. (Bound with: Malphigius, M., Opera posthuma . . . . , Amsterdam, 1698)

730
Kessel, F. K.   Art und Häufigkeit endokriner Störungen bei intrakrani-ellen Geschwülsten, Nervenarzt 9: 620–624 (1936)

731
Kikuchi, H., and Akiyasu, S.   Shōka-sen kikei-shu no ni rei (Two cases of teratoma of the pineal gland), Nō to shinkei 4: 24–25 (1952)

732
King, E.   A relation of a petrified glandula pinealis lately found in the dissection of a brain, Phil. Tr., Royal Soc., London, no. 185: 228–231 (1686). Also published as: A stone in the glandula pinealis, Abridged Phil. Tr. Royal Soc. 1700, London, 3: 157–158 (1731)

733
Kinoshita, R., and Satō, J.   Shōka-sen shuyō (Tumor of the pineal gland), Ōsaka iji shinshi 13: 1210–1216 (1942)

734
Kitamura, E.   X-sen ni yori shōka-sen sekkai-kaku oyobi kyūjō-ryūki fukin ni sekkai-ei wo shimeshitaru kōdo no nōmaku hensei (A high degree of degeneration of the retina, in which there were observed by means of roentgen rays calcified nodes in the pineal gland and calcium shadows in

[178]

the meninges near the arciform process), Nippon gankagakkai zasshi 42: 759–765 (1938)

735

Kitaoka, S.   Hinketsu narabi-ni shinkō-sei mahi-yō shōjō wo tei-suru shoka-senshu no ichi rei (One case of tumor of the pineal gland, showing symptoms of anemia and progressive paralysis), Nippon naikagakkai zasshi 40: 604 (1952)

736

Klapproth, W.   Teratom der Zirbel, kombiniert mit Adenom, Zbl. allg. Path. 32: 617–630 (1921–1922)

737

Klien, H.   Ueber Lipodystrophie nebst Mitteilung eines Fälles, Münch. med. Wschr. 68: 206–208 (1921)

738

Klippel, M., Weil, M. P., and Minvielle, M.   Un cas de tumeur épiphysaire, Rev. neur. 36: 1202–1205 (1920). Also reported in: Lereboullet, P., Pathologie de l'épiphyse chez les enfants, Progr. méd., Paris, 36: 75–77 (1922)

739

Kny, E.   Fall von isoliertem Tumor der Zirbeldrüse, Neur. Zbl. 8: 281–285 (1889)

740

Koenig, E.   Ueber ein Psammosarkom der Zirbeldrüse, Inaug. Diss., München, 1894

741

Kornblueth, W.   Transient abolition of the pupillary reaction to convergence in the presence of intact convergence and accommodation and normal pupillary reaction to accommodation in a case of tumor of the pineal gland, Am. J. Ophth. 35: 1815–1820 (1952)

742

Korniansky, G. P.   Oshibki v diagnostike ipukholej shishkovidnoi zhelezy (Errors in diagnosis of tumors of the pineal gland), Vopr. nevrokhir. 4: 32–44 (1940)

743

Krabbe, K. H.   La sclérose tubéreuse du cerveau (Maladie de Bourneville) et l'hydrocéphalie dans leurs relations avec la puberté précoce, Encéphale 17: 281–289, 437–444, 496–506 (1922)

744

Krabbe, K. H.   Un cas de tératome dans la glande pinéale, guéri par intervention opératoire, Acta psychiat. neur. 19: 233–245 (1944)

745
Krayenbühl, H., and Zollinger, H. U.   Malignes metastasierendes Pinealocytom mit dem klinischen Bild der Dystrophia adiposo-genitalis, Schweiz. Arch. Neur. Psychiat. 51: 77–98 (1943)

746
Kubo, H.   Shōka-sen-syu no ichi rei (A case of pineal tumor), Gann 27: 293–306 (1933)

747
Kucherenko, B. P.   Obizmeneniach shishkovidnoi zhelezy pri zlokachestvennych novoobrazvaniach (Changes in the pineal gland in malignant tumors), Probl. endokr., Moskva, 6 (no. 1): 131–135 (1941)

748
Kuligowski, Z. W.   Tératome de l'épiphyse et macrogénitosomie précoce, Rev. neur. 2: 482 (1933)

749
von Kup, J.   Frühzeitiges Altern als Folge einer Epiphysencyste, Frankf. Zschr. Path. 48: 318–322 (1935). Also published as: Kup, G., Adatok az epiphysis korelettanahoz a felnött korban (Data on the pathophysiology of the pineal in adults), Gyogyaszat 75: 428–429 (1935)

750
von Kup, J.   Ein Beitrag zur Kenntnis der konstitutionellen Veränderungen des endokrinen Drüsensystems bei Tuberkulösen, Beitr. klin. Tuberk. 88: 533–538 (1936)

751
von Kup, J.   Zusammenhang zwischen Makroorchie und Zirbeldrüsenhypoplasie, Beitr. path. Anat. 97: 385–390 (1936). Also published as: Kup, G., Adatok a makroorchia es epiphysis hypoplasia összefuggesehez (Data on the interrelation of macroorchia and pineal hypoplasia), Orv. hetil. 82: 175–176 (1938)

752
von Kup, J.   Ein neuer Beitrag zur Frage des Zusammenhanges zwischen Zirbel und Nebennierenrinde, Beitr. path. Anat. 100: 137–148 (1937)

753
von Kup, J.   Die Häufigkeit der Erscheinungen von Seiten der Zirbel bei Basedow und Thyreotoxikosen, Deut. med. Wschr. 65: 1587–1590 (1937). Also published as: Kup, G., Tobozmirigy-tunetek elofordulasa es gyakorisaga Basedowkorban es thyreotoxicosis-ban (Occurrence and frequency of epiphyseal symptoms in exophthalmic goiter and thyrotoxicosis), Orv. hetil. 81: 1176–1178 (1937)

754
von Kup, J. Beiträge zum Zusammenhang zwischen Epiphyse und Eierstocken, Frankf. Zschr. Path. 50: 20–25 (1937)

755
von Kup, J. Der Zusammenhang zwischen der Zirbel und den anderen endokrinen Drüsen, Frankf. Zschr. Path. 50: 152–189 (1937)

756
von Kup, J. Zur Frage der Funktion der Zirbel (Beobachtungen bei einem Fall von Makrogenitosomia praecox), Frankf. Zschr. Path. 51: 12–17 (1937–1938). Also published as: Kup, G., Adatok a tobozmirigy muködesehez makrogenitosomia praecox dementias alakja kapcsan (The relation of pineal function to the demential form of macrogenitosomia praecox), Orv. hetil. 83: 36–37 (1939)

757
von Kup, J. Ein Beitrag zur Funktion der Zirbel bei Cushing'scher Krankheit, in einem Falle von basophilem Adenom der Hypophyse, Münch. med. Wschr. 84: 1542–1544 (1937)

758
Kutscherenko, P. Tumor glandulae pinealis, Zbl. allg. Path. 37: 490–495 (1926)

759
Kux, E. Ueber ein bösartiges Pinealom und ein bösartiges fötales Adenom der Hypophyse, Beitr. path. Anat. 87: 59–70 (1931)

760
Kyū, U. F. Shōka-sen-nōsyu ni yoru nainō-suishu no ichi rei ni tsuite (A case of internal hydrocephalus caused by a pineal cyst), Taiwan igakkai zasshi 35: 1–9 (1936). Preliminary report in: Taiwan igakkai zasshi 34: 136 (1935). Abstracted in: Nippon naibunpigakkai zasshi 12: 768 (1936)

761
Laignel-Lavastine, M. Anatomie pathologique de la glande pinéale, Encéphale 16: 225–239, 289–296, 361–367, 437–449 (1921)

762
Laignel-Lavastine, M. Anatomie pathologique de la glande pinéale, Arch. internat. neur., Paris, 1 (series 15): 76 (1922)

763
Lallemand, F. See Duges, –, ref. 605

764
Landauer, W. Untersuchungen über Chondrodystrophie; III–Die His-

tologie der Drüsen mit innerer Sekretion von chondrodystrophischen Hühnerembryonen, Virchows Arch. 271: 534–545 (1929)

765
Lange-Cosack, H. Verschiedene Gruppen der hypothalamischen Pubertas praecox; Mitteilung II—Sexuelle Frühreife bei verschiedenen hypothalamischen Krankheitsprozessen (mit Ausnahme der hyperplastischen Missbildung) und bei Zirbeltumoren, Deut. Zschr. Nervenh. 168: 237–266 (1952)

766
Langelaan, —. Een patient met vermoed. vergrooting van de glandula pinealis, Psychiat. neur. bl., Amsterdam, 19: 292 (1915)

767
Lanz, W. Ueber einen Fall von Teratom der Zirbeldrüse, Inaug. Diss., Lausanne, 1926

768
Laszlo, F. Beiträge zur pathologischen Anatomie und Histologie der Zirbel, Deut. tieraerztl. Wschr. 42: 685–689 (1934)

769
Laszlo, F. Weitere Beiträge zur vergleichenden pathologischen Anatomie der Zirbel, Deut. tieraerztl. Wschr. 43: 245–247 (1935)

770
Laszlo, F. A toboztest korbonctana elettani es kortani vonatkozasai (Pathological, biological and physiological relations of the pineal), Allatorv. lap. 61: 19–22 (1938)

771
Laurinsich, A. Contributo allo studio delle sindromi epifisarie, Pediatria, Napoli, 31: 817–833 (1923)

772
Lawrence, T. W. P. Tumor of the pineal body, Tr. Path. Soc., London, 50: 12–14 (1898–1899)

773
Lereboullet, P. See Klippel, M., Weil, M. P., and Minvielle, M., ref. 738

774
Lereboullet, P., Maillet, —, and Brizard, —. Un cas de tumeur de l'épiphyse, Bull. Soc. pédiat. Paris 19: 116–120 (1921). Autopsy reported in: Lereboullet, P., and Brizard, —, Tumeur de l'épiphyse; autopsie, Bull. Soc. pédiat. Paris 19: 324–328 (1921). Also reported in: Lereboullet, P., Pathologie de l'épiphyse chez les enfants, Progr. méd. Paris 36: 75–77 (1922)

775
Leri, A., and Layani, F. Sur la calcification de la glande pinéale, Bull. Soc. méd. hôp. Paris 49 (series 3): 1329 (1925)

776
Ley, R. Tumeur de la pinéale, J. belge neur. psychiat. 25: 698–707 (1925)

777
Lhermitte, J., de Martel, –, and Guillaume, –. Sur un cas de tumeur de la pinéale avec hydrocéphalie irreductible traité par la section de la lame sus-optique, Rev. neur. 66: 547–550 (1936)

778
Liber, A. F. Cystic hydrops of the pineal gland, Arch. Path. 25: 594–595 (1938). Also published in: J. Nerv. Ment. Dis. 89: 782–794 (1939)

779
Lichtenstein, B. W. Teratoma of the pineal body; a clinico-pathologic report, Arch. Neur. Psychiat. 44: 153–161 (1940)

780
Liebert, –. Ueber Epiphysentumoren, Deut. Zschr. Nervenh. 108: 101–116 (1929)

781
Lilja, B. On the localization of calcified pineal bodies under normal and pathological conditions, Acta radiol. 15: 659–667 (1934)

782
Lilja, B. Displacement of the calcified pineal body in roentgen pictures as an aid in diagnosing intracranial tumors, Acta radiol., Supplement 37: 1–183 (1939)

783
Lilja, B. The tentorial pressure cone; its significance and its diagnosis through dislocation of the calcified pineal body, Acta radiol. 30: 129–151 (1948)

784
Löwenthal, K. Zur Pathologie der Zirbeldrüse; epiphysäre Fettsucht bei geschwülstförmiger Entartung des Organs, Beitr. path. Anat. 67: 207–219 (1920)

785
Lo Giudice, P. La calcificazione della pineale nelle radiografie del cranio, Arch. radiol. 3: 944–962 (1927)

786
Lord, J. R. The pineal gland; its normal structure; some general remarks

on its pathology; a case of syphilitic enlargement, Tr. Path. Soc., London, 50: 18–21 (1898–1899)

787
Lorenz, R.   Zur Lagebestimmung der verkalkten Glandula pinealis im Röntgenbild, Fortsch. Röntgenstrahl. 61: 338–348 (1940)

788
Luce, H.   Zur Diagnostik der Zirbelgeschwülste und zur Kritik der cerebralen Adipositas, Deut. Zschr. Nervenh. 68–69: 187–210 (1921)

789
Luce, H.   Weiterer Beitrag zur Pathologie der Zirbeldrüse, Deut. Zschr. Nervenh. 75: 356–369 (1922)

790
Lyssunkin, I. I.   Contributo allo studio clinico e anatomo-patologico dei tumori cerebrali con particolare riguardo alle anomalie della ghiandola pineale, Riv. neur. 8: 56–73 (1935)

791
Madonick, M. J., and Oljenick, I. W.   Displacement of the pineal gland with extradural hemorrhage, Arch. Neur. Psychiat. 53: 311–312 (1945)

792
Magarey, F. R., and Wolfe, H. R. I.   Pinealoma with a solitary spinal metastasis, J. Neur. Neurosurg. Psychiat., London, 12: 155–159 (1949)

793
Magni, L.   Considerazioni anatomo-cliniche intorno ad un tumore teratologico dell'epifisi cerebrale, Riv. pat. nerv. 19: 872–897 (1924)

794
Mallory, T. B., Editor.   Case records of the Massachusetts General Hospital; case 25302, N. England J. M. 221: 151–155 (1939)

795
Mallory, T. B., Editor.   Case records of the Massachusetts General Hospital; case 25481, N. England J. M. 221: 863–866 (1939)

796
Mallory, T. B., Editor.   Case records of the Massachusetts General Hospital; case 32271, N. England J. M. 235: 25–28 (1946)

797
Mallory, T. B., Editor.   Case records of the Massachusetts General Hospital; case 32292, N. England J. M. 235: 91–95 (1946)

798
Manca, C.   Su di un teratoma paraepifisario, Arch. ital. anat. pat. 6: 371–394 (1935)

[184]

799
Mankowsky, B. N., and Smirnow, L. I.   Ein Beitrag zur Klinik und pathologischen Anatomie der Geschwülste der Zirbeldrüse, Zschr. ges. Neur. Psychiat. 121: 641–681 (1929)

800
Marburg, O.   Zur Kenntnis der normalen und pathologischen Histologie der Zirbeldrüse; die Adipositas cerebralis, Arb. neur. Inst. Wien. 17: 217–279 (1909)

801
Marburg, O.   Die Adipositas cerebralis; ein Beitrag zur Kenntnis der Pathologie der Zirbeldrüse, Deut. Zschr. Nervenh. 36: 114–121 (1909)

802
Martin, J., and Davis, L.   Syndrome of destruction of the pineal gland; experimental and clinical observations, Arch. Int. M. 67: 1119–1128 (1941)

803
Maschke, E. G.   Ueber ein Spongioblastom der Zirbel, Inaug. Diss., Würzburg, 1934

804
Maspes, P. E.   Pinealomi e tumori della regione pineale, Minerva chir. 4: 317–337 (1949)

805
Massobrio, E., and Boccuzzi, G.   Complessa sindrome iperpituitarica da ipopinealismo per probabile tumore della pineale associata a malformazioni congenite, Gior. Accad. med. Torino 101 (part 2): 412–422 (1938). Also published as: Tumore (teratome?) della pineale associato a malformazioni scheletriche come causa di pubertà precoce e sindrome iperpituitarica tipo Cushing, Endocr. pat. cost. 14: 86–112 (1939)

806
Massot, M.   Note sur un cas de tumeur cérébrale avec polyurie, Lyon méd. 10: 373–383, 413–422 (1872)

807
Matano, I., and Matsuzawa, K.   See Matsuzawa, K., and Matano, I., ref. 808

808
Matsuzawa, K., and Matano, I.   Shōka-sen shuyō no ichi rei (One case of pineal tumor), Shinkeigaku zasshi 26: 65–78 (1926). Also published as: Matano, I., and Matsuzawa, K., Ein Fall von Epiphysentumor, Tr. Soc. path. jap. 15: 295 (1925)

[185]

809
Mayer, W.   Ueber hypophysäre und epiphysäre Störungen bei Hydrocephalus internus, Zschr. ges. Neur. Psychiat. 44: 101–105 (1918)

810
McAlpine, D., and Ascroft, P. B.   Pineal tumor with invasion of quadrigeminal plate; unusual type of paresis of reflex ocular movements, treated by subtemporal decompression and radiotherapy, Proc. R. Soc. M., London, 32: 214–215 (1938–1939)

811
McCartney, J. L.   Dementia praecox as an endocrinopathy with clinical and autopsy reports, Endocrinology 13: 73–87 (1929)

812
McGovern, V. J.   Tumours of the epiphysis cerebri, J. Path. Bact. 61: 1–9 (1949)

813
McLean, A. J.   Pineal teratomas; with report of a case of operative removal, Surg. Gyn. Obst. 61: 523–533 (1935). Reported briefly as: Case of parapineal tumor, Northwest M. 33: 216 (1934)

814
Meckel, J. F.   Beträchtliche Vergrösserung der Zirbeldrüse, Deut. Arch. Physiol. 1: 644–646 (1815)

815
Mehrtens, H. G., and Newell, R. R.   Displacement of the pineal gland in head injury; report of a case, J. Neur. Psychopath. 6: 198–200 (1925–1926)

816
Mendenhall, E. N.   Tumor of the pineal body with high insulin resistance, Indiana State M. J. 43: 32–36 (1950)

817
Merlini, A.   La sindrome epifisaria di macrogenitosomia precoce, Minerva med. 5: 239–246 (1925)

818
Mesquita Sampaio, J. A., and Gama, C.   Estudo clinico-cirurgico de um caso de macrogenitosomia com puberdade precoce, por tumor da região de glandula pineal, Pediat. prat., S. Paulo, 14: 321–326 (1943)

819
de Mesquita Sampaio, J. A., and Gama, C.   Puberdade precoce por tumor da região pineal e por tumor da suprarenal, Pediat. e puericult., Bahía, 16: 87–130 (1947)

820

Meyer, A.   Adenoma of the pineal gland, occluding the aqueduct of Sylvius, with escape of the cerebro-spinal fluid through the nose and perforation of the frontal horn of the right lateral ventricle, Proc. N. York Neur. Soc., J. Nerv. Ment. Dis. 32: 464–465 (1905). Also published in: Med. Rec. 67: 315 (1905)

821

Meyer, O.   Demonstration einiger seltener Präparate von Hirntumoren und Erkrankungen der Hypophysengegend; ı–Teratom der Zirbeldrüse bei einem 11-jährigen Knaben mit Zeichen pathologischer Frühreife, Allg. Zschr. Psychiat. 74: 521–529 (1918)

822

Meyers, E. S.   Intracranial calcification, probably in a tumor in the region of the pineal body, Med. J. Australia 2: 275–276 (1924)

823

Mitsuno, T.   Shōka-sen shuyō rei no geka-teki keiken (Surgical experience with cases of pinealoma), Nō to shinkei 1: 340 (1949)

824

Miyake, H.   Bōken zufu; shōka-sen shuyō no ichi rei (Dissection illustration; a case of tumor of the pineal gland), Rinshō igaku 24: 689–690 (1936)

825

Miyamura, H.   Ruikangan-shō, tōnyōbyō, shōka-sen ketsujo wo tomonaeru tasen-sei naibunpi-kinō fuzen no byōri-soshikigaku-teki kenkyū (Patho-histological studies on the endocrine insufficiency of many glands, accompanying eunuchoidism, diabetes mellitus, and pineal deficiency), Jūzenkai zasshi 39: 1469–1489 (1933)

826

Mompo Alino, L.   Pinealoma y macrogenitosomia, correlación neuroendocrina de la epifisis, Med. espan. 3: 522–534 (1940)

827

de Monchy, S. J. R.   Rhythmical convergence spasm of the eyes in a case of tumour of the pineal gland, Brain 46: 179–188 (1923)

828

de Monchy, S. J. R.   Gezwellen van de epiphysis cerebri, Ned. tschr. geneesk. 67: 853–854 (1923)

829

Moniz, E.   Tumores da glandula pineal; diagnostico angiografico, Actas españ. neur. psiquiat. 2: 3–14 (1941)

830
Moniz, E., Pinto, A., and Lima, A.   Tumeur de la glande pinéale irriguée par un seul des groupes sylviens; diagnostic par l'épreuve encéphalographique, Rev. neur. 37 (part 2): 51–54 (1930). Also published as: Moniz, E., Aspectos arteriográficos num caso da glandula pineal e tuberculos quadrigemeos, Lisboa med. 7: 368–380 (1930)

831
Moore, W. D.   Important case of medullary fungus of the pineal gland in the brain with relatively trifling phenomena during life, Dublin Medical Press 1 (series 2): 255–256 (1860). Translated from: [Anon.] Belangrijk geval van fungus medullaris der glandula pinealis in de hersenen met betrekkelijk geringe verschijnselen in het leven, Geneeskurdige Courant voor het Koningrijk der Nederlanden 13 (no. 52): 2–3 (December 25, 1859)

832
Morabito, F.   Sulle sindromi pineali nell'infanzia, Pediatria 37: 911–932 (1929)

833
Morgagni, J. B.   De sedibus et causis morborum per anatomen indagitis. Ebrodunum, Helvetia, 1779

834
Mori, S.   Shōka-sen shuyō no ni rei (Two cases of tumor of the pineal gland), Nippon naikagakkai zasshi 30: 420 (1942)

835
Mori, S.   See Ogata, T., and Mitamura, T., ref. 867

836
Morquio, L.   Tumor de la glandula pineal, simulando una meningitis tuberculosa, Arch. lat. amer. pediat. 13: 119–126 (1919)

837
Morse, J. L.   A case of abnormal physical and sexual development in an infant of two years, probably due to a tumor of the pineal gland, Arch. Pediat. 30: 179–190 (1913)

838
Müller, R., and Wohlfart, G.   Om tumörer i corpus pineale, Nord. med. 33: 15–21 (1947)

839
Münzer, F. T.   Beiträge zur Pathologie und Pathogenese der Dementia Praecox (Schizophrenie), Zschr. ges. Neur. Psychiat. 103: 73–132 (1926)

840
Muneuchi, T.   Jōhi-shōtai narabi-ni shōka-sen no rai-sei henka (Changes

due to leprosy in the parathyroid glands and the pineal gland), Hifuka-hinyōkika zasshi 38: 131–132 (1935)

841
Muneuchi, T.   Shōka-sen no rai-sei henka ni tsuite (Changes in the pineal gland in leprosy), Lepra 7: 131 (1936)

842
Naffziger, H. C.   A method for localization of brain tumors—the pineal shift, Surg. Gyn. Obst. 40: 481–484 (1925)

843
Nagaoka, Y., and Ushijima, H.   Shōka-sen no shuyō (Tumors of the pineal body), Gann 39: 129–131 (1948)

844
Nagata, M., and Ueki, Y.   Shōka-sen shuyō no kanzen tekishutsu seikō rei (Cases of successful total removal of the pineal gland), Nō to shinkei 5: 99–100 (1953)

845
Nagaya, K.   Shōka-sen shuyō no ichi rei (A case of tumor of the pineal gland), Hokuetsu igakkai zasshi 58: 785–794 (1943). Also published in: Hokuetsu igakkai zasshi 52: 926–928 (1937)

846
Nagayo, M.   Shōka-sen no byōri (Pathology of the pineal gland), Shin-keigaku zasshi 18: 1–47 (1919). Also published as: Shōni-ki ni okeru seishokki ijō-hatsuiku ni tsuite; shōka-sen shuyō ni tsuite (Macrogenito-somia in childhood; tumor of the pineal gland), Jika zasshi, no. 213: 158–167 (1918); and: Shōka-sen shuyō no ni rei (Two cases of tumor of the pineal gland), Shinkeigaku zasshi 16: 315–319 (1917). Abstracted as: Beiträge zur Pathologie der Zirbeldrüse, Tr. Soc. path. jap. 7: 41–46 (1917)

847
Nakajima, M.   Shōka-sen-shu (Pinealoma), Rinshō ganka 3: 32–36 (1949). Abstracted as: Pinealom, hyōhon kyōran (Pinealoma, discussion of a specimen), Ganka rinshō ihō 44: 209 (1950)

848
Nakamura, H.   Sagara-shi no kisai-seru nyōhōshō rei no byōri-kaibōgaku-teki kenkyū, koto-ni shōka-sen oyobi kannō-tei-bu no henka ni tsuite (Patho-anatomical studies on the case of diabetes insipidus described by Sagara, especially the changes in the pineal gland and the base of the diencephalon), Jūzenkai zasshi 27: 169–183 (1922)

849
Nakata, M., and Tanaka, K.   Shōka-sen shuyō (Pinealoma) no geka (Surgery for pinealoma), Nippon gekagakkai zasshi 39: 635–636 (1938)

850
Nassetti, F.   Contributo allo conoscenza delle cisti della ghiandola pineale, Riv. sper. freniat. 38: 291–308 (1912). Also published as: Cisti della ghiandola pineale; considerazioni ed esperienze sulla possibilità di un intervento chirurgico, Tr. Internat. Cong. Med. (1913); Sect. vii–Surgery, part 2, pp. 239–246. London, 1914

851
Neale, A. V.   Precocious puberty with a report on a case of pineal syndrome, Arch. Dis. Childhood 13: 241–248 (1938)

852
Neumann, M.   Zur Kenntnis der Zirbeldrüsengeschwülste, Mschr. Psychiat. 9: 337–367 (1901)

853
Neumann, P.   Ein neuer Fall von Teratom der Zirbeldrüse, Inaug. Diss., Königsberg, 1900

854
New England Deaconess Hospital.   Pinealoma, Radiogr. Clin. Photogr. 12 (no. 2): 22 (1936)

855
Niccolai, N.   Contributo clinico allo studio delle sindromi epifisarie e funzione endocrine, Riv. crit. clin. med. 15: 241–247, 257–263 (1914)

856
Nieden, —.   Fall von Tumor (hydrops cysticus) glandulae pinealis, Zbl. Nervenh. 2: 169–171 (1879)

857
Nishimatsu, A., and Akiyama, Y.   Pinealoma no ichi bōken rei (An autopsy case of pinealoma), Gann 37: 229–231 (1943)

858
Nishino, Y.   Chūnō oyobi kannō wo kohan-i ni shin seru Pinealom no ichi rei, toku-ni rinshō shōjō to kaibōgaku-teki shoken to no kankei (A case of pinealoma with wide invasion of the di- and mesencephalon, especially the relation of clinical symptoms to anatomical observations), Hokuetu igakkai zasshi 55: 879–920 (1940)

859
Noguer-More, S., and Corachan Llort, M.   Las formas incompletas de la enfermedad de Bourneville (Adenomas sebaceos simetricos de la cara, ataques epileptiformes, formaciones calcareas intracraneales), Actas dermo-sif., Madrid, 32: 632–638 (1941)

860
Nothnagel, H.   Topische Diagnostik der Gehirnkrankheiten, pp. 206–207. Berlin: Hirschwald, 1879

861
Odermatt, W.   Zur Diagnostik der Zirbeldrüsentumoren, Inaug. Diss., Zürich, 1915

862
Odermatt, W.   Die epiphysäre Frühreife, Schweiz. med. Wschr. 6: 474–478, 1925

863
Ody, F.   Hémangioblastome de la région épiphysaire avec prolongement thalamique droit et prolongement cérébelleux gauche; intervention; guérison, Chirurgie, Lausanne, 4: 230–241 (1942)

864
Oestreich, R., and Slawyk, —.   Riesenwuchs und Zirbeldrüsengeschwülst, Virchows Arch. 157: 475–484 (1899). Also published in: Heubner, O., Tumor der Glandula pinealis, Deut. med. Wschr. 24 (part 2): 214–215 (1898); and Fall von Tumor der Glandula pinealis mit eigenthümlichen Wachsthumsanomalien, Verh. Ges. deut. Naturforsch. 70 (part 2): 220–221 (1898) and Allg. med. Zentr. Ztg. 68: 89 (1899)

865
Ogata, T., and Mitamura, T.   Bōken shisetsu; . . . shōka-sen-shu . . . (Autopsy lecture; . . . tumor of the pineal gland . . .), Iji eisei 8: 1480 (1938)

866
Ogata, T., and Mitamura, T.   Byōri-kaibō wa nani wo oshieta ka? Shōka-sen shuyō (What does pathological anatomy teach us? Tumor of the pineal gland), Nippon iji shinpō, no. 1023: 1015 (1942)

867
Ogata, T., and Mitamura, T.   Byōri-kaibō wa nani wo oshieta ka? Shōka-sen shuyō; pinealom (What does pathological anatomy teach us? Tumor of the pineal gland; pinealoma), Nippon iji shinpō, no. 1059: 126 (1943). Also reported by: Mori, S., Shōka-sen shuyō no nirei (Two cases of tumor of the pineal gland), Nippon naikagakkai zasshi 30: 420 (1942)

868
Ogle, C.   (1) Sarcoma of pineal body, with diffused melanotic sarcoma of the surface of cerebrum; (2) Tumor of pineal body in a boy, Tr. Path. Soc., London, 50: 4–12 (1898–1899)

869
Ohmura, S.   Shōka-sen no byōri (Pathology of the pineal gland; Part 1), Shinkeigaku zasshi 29: 297–298 (1928)

870
Ohmura, S.   Nippon-jin shōka-sen no kaibōgaku-teki, soshikigaku-teki, narabi-ni byōrigaku-teki kenkyū (Anatomical, histological, and pathologi-

cal study of the pineal gland of the Japanese), Nippon ika daigaku zasshi 2: 30–68, 139–202 (1931)

871
Ohno, S. Bōken shisetsu; shōka-sen shuyō (Autopsy lecture; tumor of the pineal gland), Jitchi ika to rinshō 19: 862–863 (1942)

872
Ohno, Y. See Takeya, H., ref. 961

873
Okamoto, H. Shōka-sen shuyō no ichi rei (One case of tumor of the pineal gland), Shinkeigaku zasshi 16: 561–569 (1917)

874
Okamoto, R., and Ikuta, H. Histopathologie der menschlichen Zirbeldrüse, Tr. Soc. path. jap. 23: 145–152 (1933)

875
Oribe, M. F., and Prado, J. M. Teratomas de la epifisis, Arch. neurocir., B. Aires, 1: 54–66 (1944)

876
Oriya, M., and Osada, T. Pubertas praecox wo tomonaeru shōka-sen shuyō no ichi rei (A case of pineal tumor accompanied by pubertas praecox), Nagoya igakkai zasshi 58: 531–544 (1943). Preliminary report published in: Nagoya igakkai zasshi 56: 742 (1942)

877
Ortega, P., Malamud, N., and Shimkin, M. B. Metastasis to the pineal body, Arch. Path. 52: 518–528 (1951)

878
Oyake, Y. Shōka-tai no byōri-soshikigaku-teki chiken hoi (Contributions to pineal pathology), Niigata igakkai zasshi 66: 109–131 (1952). Preliminary report published as: Tumors of the pineal body, Tr. Soc. path. jap. 38: 186–188 (1949)

879
Pacaud, R. Contribution à l'étude clinique du syndrome de Pellizzi (Macrogénitosomie précoce), Thesis, Paris, 1921

880
Pässler, H. W. Beiträge zu den Erkrankungen der Epiphyse, Inaug. Diss., Königsberg, 1928

881
Page, I. H. A clinical study of malignant hypertension, Ann. Int. M. 12: 978–1004 (1939)

882
Palazzi, D.   Osservazioni istologiche su di una neoplasia della ghiandola pineale, Osp. maggiore, Milano, 39: 34–37 (1951)

883
Pappenheimer, A. M.   Ueber Geschwülste des Corpus pineale, Virchows Arch. 200: 122–141 (1910)

884
Parhon, C. I., and Fastlich, G.   Recherches histopathologiques sur l'épiphyse dans quelques cas d'aliénation mentale, Bull. et mém. de la Sect. d'endocrinol., Bucarest, 2: 265–266 (1936)

885
Parhon, C. I., and Milco, S. M.   Sur un cas de macrogénitosomie précoce avec tératome épiphysaire, Bull. Soc. roumain. endocr. 6: 84–96 (1940)

886
Parhon, C. I., and Tomorug, E.   Calcification de l'épiphyse et macropénis; dissociation rélative du développement des caractères sexuels secondaires, Bull. et mém. de la Sect. d'endocrinol., Bucarest, 4: 176–180 (1938)

887
Pastori, G.   Studi sulla epiphysis cerebri, Endocrinol. pat. cost. 2: 3–37 (1927)

888
Patti, F.   Di un raro tumore della ghiandola pineale (epifisoma), Riv. ital. neuropat. 16: 109–116 (1923)

889
Pellizzi, G. B.   La sindrome epifisaria 'macrogenitosomia precoce,' Riv. ital. neuropat. 3: 193–207, 250–272 (1910)

890
Pende, G.   Sindrome neuro-cutaneo-ipatosica su sfondo simil-settico con infiltrazione granulomatosa linfo-splenica e con pinealoma, Arch. Maragliano pat. clin. 5: 991–1017 (1950)

891
Pero, C., and Platania, S.   Le cisti colloidee del terzo ventricolo, Riv. pat. nerv. 59: 17–91 (1942)

892
Peters, J. T.   Een geval van hypopinealisme?, Ned. tschr. geneesk. 59: 1189–1193 (1915)

893
Plauchu, M., Lecuire, —, and Potton, F.   A propos d'un nouveau cas de

macro-génitosomie précoce due à une tumeur de la région épiphysaire, Sem. hôp., Paris, 28: 1503–1505 (1952)

894
Pontoppidan, K.   Ein Fall von Tumor der Zirbeldrüse, Neur. Zbl. 4: 553–555 (1885)

895
Posner, M., and Horrax, G.   Eye signs in pineal tumors, J. Neurosurg. 3: 15–24 (1946)

896
Prado, J. M.   Estudio anatomopathologico de siete tumores de epifisis y uno yuxtaepifisario, Arch. argent. neur. 22: 21–63 (1940)

897
Pratt, D. W., and Brooks, E. F.   Successful excision of a tumor of the pineal gland, Canad. M. Ass. J. 39: 240–243 (1938)

898
Puusep, L. M.   Die operative Entfernung einer Zyste der Glandula pinealis, Neur. Zbl. 33: 560–563 (1914)

899
Ragan, L.   Tumor of the pineal body; case report, Nebraska M. J. 19: 258–259 (1934)

900
Raymond, F., and Claude, H.   Les tumeurs de la glande pinéale chez l'enfant, Bull. Acad. méd. Paris 63 (series 3): 265–290 (1910)

901
Regnault, F.   Le rôle mental des sécrétions internes et le cerveau d'Anatole France, Bull. Soc. anthrop., Paris, 9: 1 (1928)

902
Reinhold, H.   Ein Fall von Tumor der Zirbeldrüse, Thesis, Leipzig, 1886

903
Röschmann, R.   Ueber intrakranielle Verkalkungen unter besonderer Berücksichtigung der Zirbeldrüse, Inaug. Diss., Würzburg, 1931

904
Romodanowskaja, S. A.   Das Gewicht der innersekretorischen Drüsen des Menschen und ihre wechselseitigen Gewichtskorrelationen, Arch. russ. anat. 15 (fasc. 3): 149–154 (1936)

905
Rorschach, H.   Zur Pathologie und Operabilität der Tumoren der Zirbeldrüse, Beitr. klin. Chir. 83: 451–474 (1913). Reported briefly by: Brunner, —, and Rohrschach, H., Ueber einen Fall von Tumor der

Glandula pinealis cerebri, Correspond.-Bl. f. schweiz. Aerzte 41: 642–643 (1911)

906
Rosenfeld, M. Symptomatologie der Mittelhirnerkrankungen, Münch. med. Wschr. 76: 307 (1929)

907
Rosenthal, S. R. Spongioblastoma of the pineal gland, in: Jaffe, R. H., Pathological Conferences, pp. 391–393. Chicago: Chicago Medical Book Co., 1940

908
Rothmann, H. Die Häufigkeit des röntgenologischen Nachweises der Zirbeldrüse und seine diagnostische Bedeutung, Med. Klin. 25: 1205–1206 (1929)

909
Rückart, F. Zur Röntgendiagnose des Krankheitsbildes der allgemeinen Frühreife bei Hirngeschwülsten, Röntgenpraxis 4: 718–720 (1932)

910
Russell, A. E. Cysts of the pineal body, Tr. Path. Soc., London, 50: 15 (1898–1899)

911
Russell, D. S. The pinealoma: its relationship to teratoma, J. Path. Bact. 56: 145–150 (1944)

912
Russell, W. O., and Sachs, E. Pinealoma; a clinico-pathologic study of seven cases with a review of the literature, Arch. Path. 35: 869–888 (1943). Corrected in: Arch. Path. 36: 126 (1943)

913
Saitō, F. Seishokki sōki-hatsuiku-shō no ichi rei (A case of macrogenitosomia praecox), Jika zasshi, no. 340: 1626–1627 (1928)

914
Saitō, M. Shōka-sen shuyō ni tsuite (Pineal tumor), Nippon gakujutsu kyōkai hōkoku 14: 355–360 (1939)

915
Salman, A. J. Oshibki v diagnostike i khirurgicheskom lechenii opucholei shishkovidnoi zhelezy (Mistakes in the diagnosis and surgical treatment of pineal tumors), Nov. khir. arkh. 39: 416–432 (1937)

916
Sanada, Y. Shōka-sen shuyō (Tumor of the pineal gland), Tōhoku igaku zasshi 17 (suppl. 2): 187–188 (1934)

917
Sanada, Y.   Shōka-sen shōjō to kōdō no bonyō to wo tomonaeru nō-shuyō no ichi rei (A case of cerebral tumor accompanied by pineal symptoms and a high degree of oliguria), Tōhoku igaku zasshi 19: 291–310 (1936)

918
Sasaki, K., and Ishimaru, Y.   Shōka-sen shuyō no ichi bōken rei (An autopsy case of pineal tumor), Jika zasshi 44: 1771–1777 (1938). Preliminary report in: Jika zasshi 44: 659 (1938)

919
Sasaki, M., and Daita, S.   Shōka-sen shuyō no ichi rei (A case of pinealoma), Gann 42: 298–300 (1951)

920
Sato, H.   Ein Sektionsfall von Pinealom, Gann 35: 351–353 (1941)

921
Satō, T.   Shōka-sen nōshu no ni rei (Two cases of pineal cyst), Taiwan igakkai zasshi 36: 2835–2836 (1937). Also published in: Taiwan igakkai zasshi 37: 1118–1127 (1938)

922
Satomi, M., and Kuriaki, H.   Sōhatsu-sei shintai-seishokki hatsuiku-kyo-dai-sho wo tomonatta shōka-sen shuyō no bōken rei (An autopsy case of tumor of the pineal gland accompanying macrogenitosomia praecox), Jika shinryō 15: 245–246 (1952)

923
Schaeffer, H., de Martel, —, and Guillaume, —.   Les tumeurs de la glande pinéale sans signes focaux de localisation, Rev. neur. 65: 346–351 (1936). Published in part by: Schaeffer, H., Tumeur gliale de la glande pinéale; contribution anatomo-clinique à l'étude de ces tumeurs, Clinique, Paris, 30: 58–60 (1935)

924
Schlotthauer, C. F., and Kernohan, J. W.   A glioma in a dog and a pinealoma in a silver fox (Vulpes fulvus), Am. J. Cancer 24: 350–356 (1935)

925
Schmid, G.   Ueber latente Hirnherde, Virchows Arch. 134: 71–117 (1893)

926
Schmidt, P.   Enormites glandulae pinealis, Med. Ztg., Berlin, 6: 33–34 (1837)

927
Schmincke, —.   Ueber die Teratome der Zirbeldrüse, Münch. med. Wschr. 61: 2043–2044 (1914)

928
Schmincke, A. Zur Kenntnis der Zirbelgeschwülste; ein Ganglioneurom der Zirbel, Beitr. path. Anat. 83: 279–288 (1929)

929
Schnepf, —. Idiotie; altération de la glande pinéale, C. rend. Soc. biol. 2: 167–169 (1850). Also published in: Gaz. méd. Paris 5 (series 3): 894–895 (1850)

930
Schuller, —. Ueber intrakranielle Verkalkungsherde, Wien. klin. Wschr. 26: 642 (1913)

931
Schultze, —. Erweichung der Glandula pinealis und Knorpel in der Lunge, Med. Ztg., Berlin, 17: 108 (1848)

932
Schulz, R. Tumor der Zirbeldrüse, Neur. Zbl. 5: 439–445 (1886)

933
Sevitt, S., and Schorstein, J. A case of pineal cyst, Brit. M. J. 2: 490–491 (1947)

934
Shearer, G. Enlargement of the pineal gland and sclerosis of the brain in a case of chronic epilepsy with amentia and aphasia, Edinb. M. J. 21: 297–299 (1875)

935
Shepherd, G. R., and Delp, M. H. Case report from the University of Kansas Medical Center Clinical Pathological Conference, J. Kansas M. Soc. 53: 346–351 (1952)

936
Shereshevski, N. A. A syndrome of endocrine origin, Am. Rev. Soviet Med. 1: 337–339 (1943–1944)

937
Shimamoto, M. Pinealom wo tomonaeru shōka-sen kikeishu no bōken rei (An autopsy case of pineal teratoma accompanied by pinealoma), Byōrigaku zasshi 3: 75–76 (1944)

938
Shimizu, K., Mayumi, M., Okazaki, K., and Ishizaki, S. Shōka-sen shuyō ni tsuite (Tumor of the pineal gland), Tōzai igaku taikan 32 (group 2, no. 5): 213–250 (1930)

939
Sicard, —, and Hagenau, —. Virilisme épiphisaire, Rev. neur. 27: 858–861 (1914)

940
Simian, I., and Constantinesco, P. Puberté précoce avec macrogénito-somie, Bull. Soc. roumain. endocr. 5: 169–172 (1939)

941
Simon, E. Hémorragie de la glande pinéale, Bull. Soc. anat. Paris 34: 306 (1859)

942
Skoog, A. L. Pineal gland neoplasms; report of a case studied clinically and pathologically, N. York M. J. 107: 1199–1200 (1918)

943
Smith, H. Case of sudden coma and paralysis; partial recovery of consciousness and power; rapid death; hydatids of pineal gland, liver, and peritoneum, Lancet 1: 48–49 (1878)

944
Snyder, G. A. C. Two cases of pineal tumor, Northwest M. 33: 216–217 (1934)

945
Soemmerring, S. T. De acervulo cerebri, in: Ludwig, C. F., Scriptores neurologici minores selecti, vol. III, pp. 322–338. Leipzig: J. F. Junius, 1793

946
Sosman, M. C. Radiology as an aid in the diagnosis of skull and intra-cranial lesions, Radiology 9: 396–404 (1927)

947
Spalding, O. B. The pineal shadow—a diagnostic landmark, U. S. Nav. M. Bull. 26: 302–308 (1928)

948
Spolverini, L. M. Contributo allo studio dell'insufficienza della ghiandola pineale nei bambini, Riv. clin. pediat. 12: 848–857 (1914)

949
Stalpart van der Wiel, C. Steen in de pynappelklier en saadt-vaten gevonden, in his: Hond. seldz. aanmerk., pp. 43–48. Amsterdam: J. ten Hoorn, 1682. Published in Latin in: Obs. rar. med. anat. chir., pp. 53–61. Leyden: P. van der Aa, 1687

950
Stanley, S. S. Dropsy of the pineal gland, Lancet 1: 935–936 (1837–1838)

951
Stanton, N. B. Three brain tumors, Proc. N. York Path. Soc. 21: 77–82 (1921)

952
Starck, —. Tumor der Glandula pinealis und des Hypophysisgebietes, Zbl. ges. Neur. Psychiat. 48: 72–73 (1928)

953
Steiner, B. *See* Johan, B., ref. 717

954
Stoll, W. S. Pinealzytom, Schweiz. med. Wschr. 26: 908–912 (1945)

955
Stowell, R. E., Sachs, E., and Russell, W. D. Primary intracranial chorionepithelioma with metastases to the lungs, Am. J. Path. 21: 787–800 (1945)

956
Straub, H. Zur Kenntnis der Zirbeldrüsengeschwülste (der sogenannten 'Pinealome'), Frankf. Zschr. Path. 42: 250–260 (1931)

957
Stringer, S. W. Diabetes insipidus associated with pinealoma transplant in the tuber cinereum, Yale J. Biol. 6: 375–383 (1933–1934)

958
Ström, S. Ueber die Röntgendiagnostik intrakranieller Verkalkungen, Fortsch. Röntgenstrahl. 27: 577–601 (1919–1921)

959
Takagi, —. Shōka-sen shuyō no ichi rei (A case of tumor of the pineal gland), Rinshō igaku 30: 925–926 (1942)

960
Takatsu, S. Shōka-sen kikeisyu ni tsuite (Teratoma of the pineal gland), Gun-idan zasshii (Zschr. mil. Aerzte, Tokyo) 24: 760–775 (1919)

961
Takeya, H. Shōka-sen no shikkan (Diseases of the pineal gland), Nisshin igaku 3: 319–348 (1913). Also published as: Shindan shiete bōken ni yori kore wo tashikametaru shōka-sen shuyō no ichi rei (A case of pineal tumor), Shinkeigaku zasshi 12: 463–468 (1913). Also published by: Ohno, Y., Ein Fall von Epiphysentumor, Tr. Soc. path. jap. 4: 133–134 (1914); and: Shōka-sen kikei-shu (Pineal teratoma), Fukuoka ika daigaku zasshi 8: 1–26 (1914)

962
Tamura, O. Shōka-sen shuyō no ichi rei (A case of tumor of the pineal gland), Okayama igakkai zasshi, no. 352: 385–392 (1919). Also published as: Shōka-sen no shuyō ni tsuite (Tumor of the pineal gland), Okayama igakkai zasshi, no. 346: 1080 (1918)

963

Tanaka, T.   Shunjō shukuhatsu-byō no ichi rei ni tsuite; fu, shōka-sen shuyō no ichi rei (A case of pubertas praecox; supplement, a case of tumor of the pineal gland), Rinshō igaku 8: 929–944, 1012–1022 (1920)

964

Tarozzi, G.   Sulla sindrome epifisaria, macrogenitosomia precoce (Pellizzi), Note psichiat., Pesaro, 13 (series 3): 275–295 (1925)

965

Taubenhaus, M.   Ueber einen Fall von multipler Blutdrüsenerkrankung mit Beteiligung der Zirbeldrüse, Endokrinologie 11: 324–334 (1932)

966

Teruyama, N.   Basedow-shi-byō ni okeru naibunpi-zōki no byōrigaku-teki kenkyū (Pathological studies on the endocrine organs in Basedow's disease), Nippon iji shuhō, no. 1510: 13–29, no. 1511: 3–12, no. 1512: 4–15 (1924)

967

Teruyama, N.   Hito no shōka-sen kaibō oyobi byōri (Anatomy and pathology of the human pineal gland), Kyōto igaku zasshi 22 (supplement): 28–29 (1925). Also published as: Zur Pathologie der Epiphyse des Menschens, Tr. Soc. path. jap. 15: 186–187 (1925)

968

Teruyama, N.   Hito no shōka-sen no kaibō oyobi byōri (Anatomy and pathology of the human pineal gland), Naibunpitsugakkai zasshi 1: 593–623 (1925)

969

Thiem, C.   Verschlimmerung einer Zirbeldrüsengeschwülst als Unfallfolge, Mschr. Unfallh. 21: 320–322 (1914)

970

Thurel, R.   Tumeurs de la région pinéale: fréquence et polymorphisme clinique; traitement combiné, chirurgical (incision de la lame sus-optique) et radiothérapeutique, Rev. neur. 73: 97–107 (1941)

971

Thurel, R., Pedrono, J., and Gruner, J.   Thrombophlébite de la veine de Galien: hemorragies des noyaux gris centraux et de l'épiphyse, Rev. neur. 86: 55–57 (1952). Also published in: Arch. fr. pédiat. 9: 746–747 (1952) and Sem. hôp., Paris, 29: 17–19 (1953)

972

Timme, W.   Progressive muscular dystrophy as an endocrine disease, J. Nerv. Ment. Dis. 19: 79–104 (1917)

973
Tobioka, M. Nyōhōshō no ichi bōken rei (One autopsy case of diabetes insipidus), Nippon byōrigakkai kaishi 38: 156–157 (1949)

974
Tolosa Colmer, E. Conducta terapeutica ante los tumores de la region pineal, An. med., Barcelona, 33: 492–497 (1946)

975
Tolosa, E. Conducta terapeutica ante los tumores de la region pineal, Medicina, Madrid, 15 (part 2): 271–277 (1947)

976
Tompkins, V. N., Haymaker, W., and Campbell, E. H. *See* Friedman, N. B., ref. 632

977
Toussaint, —. Deux cas de calcification de la glande pinéale, Arch. méd. belg. 83: 462–463 (1930)

978
Trizzino, E. Sopra un caso di voluminoso struma della epifisi, Arch. ital. anat. pat. 8: 355–380 (1938)

979
Troland, C. E., and Brown, C. A. Precocious puberty of intracranial origin, J. Neurosurg. 5: 541–555 (1948)

980
Tsuchida, U. Shōka-sen shuyō no ichi rei (A case of tumor of the pineal gland), Shinkeigaku zasshi 17: 62–65 (1918)

981
Tsukamoto, M. Shōka-sen shuyō-shō no ichi rei (A case of pineal tumor), Jūzenkai zasshi 27: 627–628 (1922)

982
Turner, F. C. Spindle-cell sarcoma of the pineal body, containing glandular and carcinomatous structures, Tr. Path. Soc., London, 36: 27–35 (1884–1885)

983
Uchida, K. Shōka-sen bui ni okeru iwayuru aku-sei shinkei-kōshu ichi rei (A case of the so-called malignant neuroglioma in the pineal gland region), Nippon gankagakkai zasshi 20: 1143–1152 (1916)

984
Uchimura, S., and Ohguma, T. Sōhatsu seishun-ki ni tsuite (Concerning pubertas praecox), Nō to shinkei 4: 181–189 (1952)

985
Uehara, K., and Sō, T.   Shōka-sen shuyō (Pineal tumor), Rinshō igaku
12: 136–149, 227–254 (1924). Preliminary reports published as follows:
Shōka-sen shuyō no kanja kyōran (Demonstration of a patient with pineal
tumor), Nippon naikagakkai zasshi 10: 359–360 (1922); and: Shōka-sen
shuyō no hyōhon kyōran (Demonstration of a specimen of pineal tumor),
Nippon naikagakkai zasshi 10: 639 (1922). Also published by: Irizawa,
T., and Sō, T., Shōka-sen shuyō; shinchō, taijū no kyūsoku zōka to seishokki no ijō-hattatsu (Pineal gland tumor; abnormal development of the
sexual organs and rapid increase in height and weight), Jikken ihō 13:
994–1002 (1927); and by: Katahira, S., Shōka-sen shuyō-shō no ichi rei
(A case of pineal tumor), Taiwan igakkai zasshi, no. 221: 124–128 (1922)

986
Uemura, S.   Zur normalen und pathologischen Anatomie der Glandula
pinealis des Menschen und einiger Haustiere, Frankf. Zschr. Path. 20:
381–488 (1917). Abstracted as: Hito oyobi kachiku dōbutsu ni okeru
shōka-sen no seiri-teki kōzō oyobi byō-teki henka ni tsuite (Physiological
structure and pathological changes in the pineal gland in man and in
domestic animals), Kanpō, no. 1944: 382 (1919). Also abstracted in:
Tr. Soc. path. jap. 7: 38–40, 46–48 (1917)

987
Uesaka, K.   Shintai hatsuiku no ichijirushiku chien-seru ichi shitai no
shōka-sen ni tsuite (The pineal gland in a cadaver in which bodily development had been greatly retarded), Okayama igakkai zasshi, no. 385:
101 (1922)

988
Ulrich, —.   Verkalkung der Glandula pinealis im Röntgenbild, Klin.
Wschr. 7: 2130 (1928)

989
Urechia, C. I.   Pinéalome dans la région des tubercles quadrijumeaux,
Rev. neur. 70: 511–513 (1938)

990
Uyama, Y.   Jin-chū shō-hin; shōka-sen shuyō (Short accounts from an
army camp; tumor of the pineal gland), Ōsaka iji shinshi 9: 1126–1127
(1938)

991
Uyama, Y.   Shōka-sen shuyō (Tumor of the pineal gland), Rinshō ganka
3: 125–127 (1949)

992
Vanek, J.   Primarni chorionepitheliom epifysy a generalisovany chorionepitheliom z nevelkeho nekrotickeho primarniho novotvaru varlete (A

primary chorionepithelioma of the pineal and a generalized chorionepithelioma from a small necrotic primary tumor of the testes), Cas. Lek. cesk. 89: 340–344 (1950)

993
Vastine, J. H. The pineal body—roentgenological considerations, Am. J. Roentg. 30: 145–155 (1933)

994
Vastine, J. H., and Kinney, K. K. The pineal shadow as an aid in localization of brain tumors, Am. J. Roentg. 17: 320–324 (1927)

995
Verger, —. Glio-sarcome développé au niveau de la glande pinéale, J. méd. Bordeaux 37: 216 (1907)

996
Vermeulen, H. A. Epiphyse und Epiphysentumoren bei Tieren, Berl. tieraerztl. Wschr. 41: 717–719 (1925)

997
Vincent, C., and Rappoport, —. Contribution à l'étude des pinéalomes, Rev. neur. 1: 517–525 (1933)

998
Virchow, R. Die krankhaften Geschwülste, vol. ii, pp. 148–149. Berlin: Hirschwald, 1863

999
Vryman, L. H. Ueber einen Fall von Thyreohypoplasie, Endokrinologie 4: 9–25 (1929)

1000
van Wagenen, W. P. A surgical approach for the removal of certain pineal tumors, Surg. Gyn. Obst. 53: 216–220 (1931)

1001
Wakeley, C. P. G. Medulloblastoma of the pineal, Tr. M. Soc., London, 59: 85 (1936)

1002
Wakeley, C. P. G. The surgery of the pineal organ, Brit. J. Surg. 25: 561–591 (1938)

1003
Walter, F. K. Zur Histologie und Physiologie der menschlichen Zirbeldrüse, Zschr. ges. Neur. Psychiat. 74: 314–330 (1922)

1004
Walter, F. K. Weitere Untersuchungen zur Pathologie und Physiologie der Zirbeldrüse, Zschr. ges. Neur. Psychiat. 83: 411–463 (1923)

1005
Walton, K. Teratomas of the pineal region and their relationship to pinealomas, J. Path. Bact. 61: 11–21 (1949)

1006
Warren, L. F., and Tilney, F. Tumor of the pineal body with invasion of the mid-brain, thalamus, hypothalamus, and pituitary body, J. Nerv. Ment. Dis. 45: 74–75 (1917)

1007
Warren, S. Studies on tumor metastasis; vii–Metastasis to the pineal gland, Am. J. Cancer 28: 713–719 (1936)

1008
Weigert, C. Zur Lehre von den Tumoren der Hirnanhänge; Teratom der Zirbeldrüse, Virchows Arch. 65: 212–226 (1875)

1009
Weinberg, E. Untersuchungen über die Veränderungen der menschlichen Epiphyse in Abhängigkeit vom Alter und einigen pathologischen Prozessen, Fol. neuropath. eston. 6: 57–82 (1926)

1010
Werner, T. Ein Pinealom mit diffuser Metastasierung in die Meningen, Zbl. Neurochir. 4: 155–160 (1939)

1011
Weygandt, W. Epiphysenstörungen, Med. Welt. 4: 12–14 (1930)

1012
Wirth, W. Ueber sexuelle Frühreife, Zschr. angew. Anat. 15: 477–491 (1931)

1013
Wörner, E. Die Bedeutung der Verlagerung der verkalkten Glandula pinealis, insbesondere in Hinsicht auf die röntgenologische Diagnostik der Hirntumoren, Fortsch. Röntgenstrahl. 49: 499–512 (1934)

1014
Worms, M. G. Calcification de la glande pinéale; calcification symétrique des plexus choroïdes, Rev. otoneur., Paris, 11: 35–36 (1933)

1015
Wurm, H. Die Missbildungen der Epiphyse, in: Schwalbe, E., Morphologie der Missbildungen des Menschen und der Tiere, part 3, section 3, pp. 564–574. Jena: Fischer, 1927

1016
Yamada, J. Shōka-sen shuyō no ichi bōken rei (One autopsy case of pineal tumor), Jika zasshi, no. 340: 1631 (1928)

1017
Yamamoto, S., and Takeuchi, T.   Shōka-tai shuyō no san rei (Three cases of tumor of the pineal gland), Nō to shinkei 4: 241–242 (1952)

1018
Yamanaka, T.   Shōka-sen shuyō no ichi rei (A case of tumor of the pineal gland), Chuo ganka ihō 14: 161 (1922)

1019
Yano, K.   Nō shuyō no kenkyū; kōtai-sei gankyū-shintō, jōhō-bekken-mohi, oyobi Bell-genshō shōshitsu wo tai-seru shōka-sen-shu (Pinealom) no ichi rei (Studies on brain tumor; a case of pinealoma, with retrogressive nystagmus, upward-glance paralysis, and disappearance of Bell's phenomenon, as symptoms), Kitano Byōin gyōseki hōkoku 2: 2–23 (1938)

1020
Yasutake, K.   Kyōmi-aru shōka-sen nōshu no ichi rei (An interesting case of cystoma of the pineal gland), Okayama igakkai zasshi, no. 414: 601–603 (1924)

1021
Yi-ming Jen.   Der Habitus als diagnostisches Hilfsmittel zur klinischen Diagnose von Zirbeltumoren, Inaug. Diss., Göttingen, 1927

1022
Yoshimatsu, K.   Shōka-sen shuyō ni yoru nō-suishu no ichi rei ni tsuite (A case of hydrocephalus caused by pineal tumor), Shinkeigaku zasshi 31: 714 (1930)

1023
Young, S., Wu, C. P., and Chen, C. S.   Pinealoma; a report of a case, Chin. M. J. 68: 261–262 (1950)

1024
Zagnoni, C.   Intorno alle emorragie della pineale, Friuli med. 1: 269–276 (1946)

1025
Zandren, A.   A contribution to the study of the function of glandula pinealis, Acta med. scand. 54: 323–335 (1921)

1026
Zeitlin, H.   Tumors in the region of the pineal body; report of 3 cases, Arch. Neur. Psychiat. 34: 567–586 (1935)

1027
Zenner, P.   A case of tumor of the pineal gland, Alienist and Neur. 13: 470–475 (1892)

1028
Zülch, K. J.   Häufigkeit, Vorzugssitz und Erkrankungsalter bei Hirngeschwülsten, Zbl. Neurochir. 9: 115–128 (1949)

Appendices to Bibliography

I. PINEAL ANATOMY, EMBRYOLOGY, AND HISTOLOGY

II. REVIEWS AND RELATED PAPERS

Pineal Anatomy, Embryology, and Histology

1
Achucarro, N.   La estructura secretora de la glandula pineal humana, Bol. Soc. espan. biol. 2: 83–88 (1913)

2
Achucarro, N.   La estructura secretora de la glandula pineal humana, Rev. clin. Madrid 10: 410–415 (1913)

3
Achucarro, N., and Sacristan, J. M.   Sobre la histología de la glandula pineal humana, Rev. clin. Madrid 8: 336–340 (1912)

4
Achucarro, N., and Sacristan, J. M.   Investigaciones histologicas y histopatologicas sobre la glandula pineal humana, Trab. Laborat. invest. biol., Univ. Madrid, 10: 185–208 (1912)

5
Achucarro, N., and Sacristan, J. M.   Zur Kenntnis der Ganglienzellen der menschlichen Zirbeldrüse, Trab. Laborat. invest. biol., Univ. Madrid, 11: 1–9 (1913)

6
Adelmann, H. B.   Experimental studies on the development of the eye; III—The effect of the substrate "Unterlagerung" on the heterotopic development of median and lateral strips of the anterior end of the neural plate of Amblystoma, J. Exp. Zool. 57: 223–281 (1930)

7
Agduhr, E.   Ueber ein zentrales Sinnesorgan (?) bei den Vertebraten, Zschr. Anat. Entw. 66: 223–360 (1922)

8
Ahlborn, F.   Untersuchungen über das Gehirn der Petromyzonten, Zschr. wiss. Zool. 39: 191–294 (1883)

9
Ahlborn, F.   Ueber die Bedeutung der Zirbeldrüse (Glandula pinealis; Conarium; Epiphysis cerebri), Zschr. wiss. Zool. 40: 331–337 (1884)

10
Alexander, A. Zur Frage der Existenz eines Parietalorganrudiments, Arb. neur. Inst. Wien. 34: 252–265 (1932)

11
Algranati Mondolfo, A. Die alcuni ricerche sulla pineale, Arch. ital. anat. pat. 4: 149–189 (1933)

12
Amprino, R. Transformazioni della struttura della ghiandola pineale in rapporto all'età, Monit. zool. ital. 43 (suppl.): 147–149 (1932)

13
Amprino, R. Transformazioni della ghiandola pineale dell'uomo e degli animali nell'accrescimento e nella senescenza, Arch. ital. anat. 34: 446–485 (1935)

14
Anglade, –. La pinéale de quelques vertèbres, Gaz. hebd. sc. méd. Bordeaux 41: 21 (1920)

15
Anglade, –. La pinéale de quelques vertèbres, J. méd. Bordeaux 47: 185 (1920)

16
Anglade, –, and Ducos, –. Note préliminaire sur l'anatomie et la physiologie de la glande pinéale, Bull. Soc. anat. physiol. Bordeaux 29: 287–288 (1908)

17
Anglade, –, and Ducos, –. Considérations sur la glande pinéale, Gaz. hebd. sc. méd. Bordeaux 30: 22 (1909)

18
Anglade, –, and Ducos, –. Note préliminaire sur l'anatomie et la physiologie de la glande pinéale, J. méd. Bordeaux 39: 152–153 (1909)

19
Anglade, –, and Ducos, –. Sur les pédoncules de la glande pinéale, J. méd. Bordeaux 42: 772 (1912)

20
Anglade, –, and Ducos, –. Les plaques et les formations lacunaires dans la glande pinéale, J. méd. Bordeaux 42: 772–773 (1912)

21
Antonow, A. Zur Frage von dem Bau der Gl. pinealis, Anat. Anz. 60: 21–31 (1925–1926)

22
Antonow, A. The structure of gl. pinealis in man and animals, Zoologicheski Zhurnal 6 (no. 1): 129–138 (1936)

23
Ariens Kappers, J.   Preliminary data on the function of the paraphysis cerebri in Urodela, Experientia 5: 162–164 (1949)

24
Auersperg, A.   Beobachtungen am menschlichen Plexus chorioideus der Seitenventrikel, Arb. neur. Inst. Wien. 31: 55–95 (1929)

25
Ayers, H.   Concerning vertebrate cephalogenesis, J. Morph. 4: 221–245 (1890)

26
Azuma, T.   Kakushu mubi-ryōseirui ni okeru shōka-sen no hikaku-hassei-gaku-teki kenkyū (Studies on the pineal glands of all kinds of tailless amphibians from the standpoint of comparative genetics), Ōsaka igakkai zasshi 41: 1439–1451 (1942)

27
Baginski, S.   Sur la nature des cellules lipopigmentaires dites de "Ciaccio," Bull. histol. appl., Lyon, 4: 173–179 (1927)

28
Baginski, S.   Recherches histochimiques sur les cellules lipopigmentaires dites de "Ciaccio," C. rend. Soc. biol. 96: 537–539 (1927)

29
Bauer-Jokl, M.   Ueber das sogenannte Subkommissuralorgan, Arb. neur. Inst. Wien. 22: 41–79 (1917–1919)

30
Beard, J.   The parietal eye in fishes, Nature 36: 246–248 (1887)

31
Beard, J.   The parietal eye of the cyclostome fishes, Q. J. Micr. Sc. 29: 55–73 (1889)

32
Benoit, W.   Ueber die histologischen Färbemethoden der Zirbel, in: Abderholden, E., Handb. biol. Arbeitsmeth. 8²: 1575–1586. Berlin: Urban & Schwarzenberg, 1935

33
Beraneck, E.   Ueber das Parietalauge der Reptilien, Jena. Zschr. Naturwiss. 21: 374–410 (1887)

34
Beraneck, E.   Sur le nerf de l'œil pariétal (64ᵉ Sess. Soc. helv. sc. nat.), Bibliothèque universelle; Arch. sc. phys. nat. 26 (series 3): 589–594 (1891)

35

Beraneck, E.   Sur le nerf pariétal et la morphologie du troisième œil des vertèbres, Anat. Anz. 7: 674–689 (1892)

36

Beraneck, E.   L'individualité de l'œil pariétal; Réponse à M. de Klinckowstroem, Anat. Anz. 8: 669–677 (1892–1893)

37

Beraneck, E.   Contribution à l'embryogénie de la glande pinéale des amphibiens, Rev. suisse zoöl., Geneva, 1: 255–288 (1893)

38

van den Bergh, —.   Les vestiges du troisième œil considérés comme siège de l'instinct du retour, Gaz. hebd. sc. méd. Bordeaux 10: 150–153 (1889)

39

Bergmann, W.   The calcified pineal gland. Assen: van Gorcum, 1940

40

Bernard, H. M.   An attempt to deduce the vertebrate eyes from the skin, J. Micr. Sc. 39: 343–370 (1896–1897)

41

Biondi, G.   Histologische Beobachtungen an der Zirbeldrüse, Zschr. ges. Neur. Psychiat. 9: 43–50 (1912)

42

Biondi, G.   Studi sulla ghiandola pineale, Riv. ital. neuropat. 9: 251–258, 269–300, 303–321 (1916)

43

Bizzozero, G.   Sul parenchima della ghiandola pineale, Rendic. R. Ist. lombardo sc. lett., Milano, 1 (series 2): 588–594 (1868). Also published in: Gazz. med. lomb., Milano, 1 (series 6): 257–258 (1868)

44

Bizzozero, G.   Sulla struttura del parenchima della ghiandola pineale umana, Rendic. R. Ist. lombardo sc. lett., Milano, 4 (series 2): 324–326 (1871)

45

Bizzozero, G.   Beitrag zur Kenntnis des Baues der Zirbeldrüse; Vorläufige Mittheilung, Zbl. med. Wiss. 9: 722–724 (1871)

46

Blanc, H.   Sur le développement de l'épiphyse et de la paraphyse chez la Salamandra atra, C. rend., 83e Sess. Soc. helv. sc. nat., pp. 64–66 (1900). Also published in: Bibliothèque universelle; Arch. sc. phys. nat. 10 (series 4): 571–572 (1900)

47
Bochenek, A.   Ueber die Nervendigungen in den Plexus chorioidei des Frosches, Bulletin internationale de l'Académie des sciences de Cracovie; Comptes rendus des séances de l'année 1899, pp. 346–348

48
Born, G.   Ueber das Scheitelauge, Jahrber. Schles. Ges. vaterl. Cult. (1889), Breslau, 67: 14–17 (1890)

49
Bozza, G.   Contributo alla conoscenza dello sviluppo della regione epifisaria in alcuni Mammiferi compreso l'uomo, Arch. ital. anat. 24: 532–626 (1927)

50
Braem, F.   Epiphysis und Hypophysis von Rana, Zschr. wiss. Zool. 63: 433–439 (1898)

51
Brandenburg, E.   Morphologische Beiträge zur Frage der endokrinen Funktion der Epiphyse, Endokrinologie 4: 81–96 (1929)

52
Bratiano, S., and Giugariu, D.   Les processus histophysiologiques d'involution de l'épiphyse humaine adulte, Arch. anat. micr. 29: 261–284 (1933)

53
Bugnion, E.   Recherches sur le développement de l'épiphyse et de l'organ pariétal chez les Reptiles (Iguana, Lacerta, Coluber), C. rend. Schweiz. naturf. Ges., 80: 56 (1937)

54
Burckhardt, R.   Die Zirbel von Ichthyophis glutinosus und Protopterus annectens, Anat. Anz. 6: 348–349 (1891)

55
Burckhardt, R.   Untersuchungen am Hirn und Geruchsorgan von Triton und Ichthyophis, Zschr. wiss. Zool. 52: 369–403 (1891)

56
Burckhardt, R.   Die Homologien des Zwischenhirndaches und ihre Bedeutung für die Morphologie des Hirns bei niederen Vertebraten, Anat. Anz. 9: 152–155 (1893–1894)

57
Burckhardt, R.   Die Homologien des Zwischenhirndaches bei Reptilien und Vögeln, Anat. Anz. 9: 320–324 (1893–1894)

58

Burckhardt, R.   Der Bauplan des Wirbeltiergehirns, Morph. Arb. 4: 131–150 (1895)

59

Cajal (Ramon y), –.   Apuntes para el estudio del bulbo raquideo, cerebelo y origen de los nervios encefalicos, An. Soc. espan. hist. nat. 24: 5–118 (1895)

60

Calvet, J.   Étude du chondriome dans les cellules épiphysaires de quelques mammifères, C. rend. Soc. biol. 113: 300–301 (1933)

61

Cameron, J.   On the origin of the pineal body as an amesial structure deduced from the study of its development in amphibia, Anat. Anz. 23: 394–395 (1903). Also published in: Proc. Scot. Micr. Soc., London and Edinburgh, 3: 340–349 (1899–1903)

62

Cameron, J.   On the origin of the epiphysis cerebri as a bilateral structure in the chick, Proc. R. Soc., Edinburgh, 25: 160–167 (1903)

63

Cameron, J.   On the origin of the epiphysis in Amphibia as a bilateral structure, Rep. Brit. Ass. Adv. Sci. 73: 689–690 (1903)

64

Cameron, J.   On the presence and significance of the superior commissure throughout the Vertebra, J. Anat. Physiol. 38: 275–292 (1904)

65

Carriere, J.   Neuere Untersuchungen über das Parietalorgan, Biol. Zbl. 9: 136–149 (1889–1890)

66

Casajaghy, M.   Beitrag zur Phylogenese und Ontogenese sowie zur Funktion der Epiphyse, Zschr. ges. Neur. Psychiat. 168: 624–643 (1940)

67

Castigli, G.   Sulla presenza e sulla natura delle formazioni a rosetta nell' epifisi del coniglio, Boll. Soc. ital. biol. sper. 16: 86–89 (1941)

68

Castigli, G.   Osservazioni sopra le particolari formazioni a "Rosetta" nella epifisi del coniglio, Riv. biol. 31: 164–185 (1941)

69

Cattie, J. T.   Recherches sur la glande pinéale (Epiphysis cerebri) des Plagiostomes, des Ganoïdes et des Téléostéens, Arch. Biol., Paris, 3: 101–194 (1882)

70

Cattie, J. T.   Ueber das Gewebe der Epiphyse von Plagiostomen, Ganoiden und Teleostieren; zur Verteidigung, Zschr. wiss. Zool. 39: 720–722 (1883)

71

Cattie, J. T.   De beteekenis der epiphyse bij de gewervelde dieren, Handel, 1e Ned. natuur geneesk. congr., Harlem (1887), p. 183

72

Chiarugi, G.   Di un organo preepifisario nella Cavia, Monit. zool. ital. 30: 34–42 (1919)

73

Chiarugi, G.   L'organo subcommissurale in un embrione di marsupiale, petrogale (Macropus) penicillata, Monit. zool. ital. 42 (suppl.): 66–70 (1932)

74

Chiodi, V.   Sullo sviluppo dell'epifisi del pollo, Fol. clin. biol., S. Paulo, 2: 33–38 (1930)

75

Chiodi, V.   Sviluppo, struttura e topografia dell'epifisi, Riv. biol. 29: 237–365 (1940)

76

Christensen, K.   The morphology of the brain of Sphenodon, Univ. Iowa Studies Nat. Hist. 12: 1–29 (1927)

77

Cionini, A.   Sulla struttura della ghiandola pineale, Riv. sper. freniat. 11: 182–183 (1885)

78

Cionini, A.   Sulla struttura della ghiandola pineale, Riv. sper. freniat. 12: 364–369 (1886)

79

Cionini, A.   La ghiandola pineale e il terzo occhio dei vertebrati, Riv. sper. freniat. 14: 65–80 (1888)

80

Cisotti, F.   Sulla citoarchitettonica del corpo pineale, Rendic. R. Ist. lombardo sci. lett.; Classe sci. mat. nat. 76: 79–102 (1942–1943)

81

Citterio, V.   Sulla fine struttura dell'epifisi degli Ofidi, Arch. zool. ital. 17: 29–38 (1932)

82

Clark, W. E. L.   The nervous and vascular relations of the pineal gland, J. Anat. 74: 471–492 (1939–1940)

83

Clark, W. E. L.   The nerve of the pineal gland, Nature 145: 349–350 (1940)

84

Clarke, J. L.   Notes of researches on the intimate structure of the brain (Structure of the pineal gland), Proc. R. Soc., London, 11: 359–366 (1861)

85

Clemente, G.   Contributo allo studio della glandola pineale nell'uomo e in alcuni animali, Endocr. pat. cost. 2: 44–47 (1923). Also published in: Rendic. R. Accad. naz. Lincei, Roma, 32: 47–51 (1923)

86

Clemente, G.   Contributo allo studio della glandola pineale nell'uomo e in alcuni mammiferi, Gior. biol. med. sper. 1: 76–80 (1923)

87

Cohrs, P.   Das subfornikale Organ des dritten Hirnventrikels und seine Ontogenese, Verh. Anat. Ges., Jena, 44: 109–115 (1937)

88

Cohrs, P., and Knobloch, D.   Das subfornikale Organ des 3. Ventrikels, Zschr. Anat. Entw. 105: 491–518 (1936)

89

Collier, R.   Ueber den Feinbau der Epiphysis cerebri von Nagetieren und die Frage seiner funktionellen Veränderungen, Zschr. Zellforsch. 33: 51–67 (1943)

90

Condorelli-Francaviglia, M.   L'encefalo dell'Helmaturus dorsalis Gray, Boll. Soc. zool. ital. 4: 24–39 (1895)

91

Costantini, G.   Intorno ad alcune particolarite di struttura della glandola pineale, Pathologica, Genova, 2: 439–441 (1910)

92

Costero, I., and von Lichtenberg, F.   Sobre la estructura de la glandula pineal; Armazon neurologico, Bol. Laborat. estud. med., Mexico, 1: 63–68 (1942)

93

Creutzfeldt, H. G.   Ueber das Fehlen der Epiphysis cerebri bei einigen Säugern, Anat. Anz. 42: 517–521 (1912)

94

Cutore, G.   Di una particolare formazione prepineale nel Bos-Taurus L., Arch. ital. anat. 8: 230–236 (1909–1910)

95
Cutore, G.   Il corpo pineale di alcuni mammiferi, Arch. ital. anat. 9: 402–464, 599–659 (1910–1911)

96
Cutore, G.   A proposito del corpo pineale dei Mammiferi; risposta a G. Favaro, Anat. Anz. 40: 657–662 (1911–1912)

97
Cutore, G.   Un'ultima parola di risposta a G. Favaro, Anat. Anz. 41: 496 (1912)

98
Cutore, G.   Alcune notizie sul corpo pineale del Macacus sinicus L. e del Cercopithecus griseus viridis L., Fol. neur. biol., Leipzig, 6: 267–276 (1912)

99
Da Fano, C.   Osservazioni sulla fine struttura della nevroglia, Ricer. Laborat. anat. Univ. Roma 12: 101–176 (1907)

100
Dalcq, A.   Sur l'induction de l'épiphyse, C. rend. Soc. biol. 140: 1162–1165 (1946)

101
Dana, C. L., and Berkeley, W. N.   The functions of the pineal gland; with report of feeding experiments by H. H. Goddard and W. S. Cornell, Med. Rec. 83: 835–847 (1913)

102
Dannheimer, W.   Ueber das subfornikale Organ des dritten Ventrikels beim Menschen, Anat. Anz. 88: 351–358 (1939)

103
Darkschewitsch, L.   Zur Anatomie der Glandula pinealis, Neur. Zbl. 5: 29–30 (1886)

104
Darkschewitsch, L.   Einige Bemerkungen über den Faserverlauf in der hinteren Commissur des Gehirns, Neur. Zbl. 5: 99–103 (1886)

105
Dean, B.   The early development of Amia, Q. J. Micr. Sc. 38: 413–444 (1895–1896)

106
Deletra, J., Chavaz, G., and Curtet, W.   Les premières traces d'innervation dans l'organe pinéal chez les embryons de poulet, C. rend. Soc. phys. hist. nat., Genève, 58: 51–54 (1941)

107
Delfini, C. Ricerche sugli acervuli della ghiandola pineale coi metodi del Donaggio, Boll. Soc. ital. biol. sper. 9: 525–526 (1934)

108
Delfini, C. Ricerche sulla ghiandola pineale con i metodi del Donaggio per il connettivo, Boll. Soc. ital. biol. sper. 9: 762–765 (1934)

109
Dendy, A. On the development of the parietal eye and adjacent organs in Sphenodon (Hatteria), Q. J. Micr. Sc. 42: 111–153 (1899)

110
Dendy, A. On the parietal sense organs and associated structures in the New Zealand lamprey, Q. J. Micr. Sc. 51: 1–29 (1907)

111
Dendy, A. On the structure, development and morphological interpretation of pineal organs and adjacent parts of the brain in the Tuatara (Sphenodon punctatus), Anat. Anz. 37: 453–462 (1910)

112
Dendy, A. On the structure, development and morphological interpretation of the pineal organs and adjacent parts of the brain in the Tuatara (Sphenodon punctatus), Phil. Tr. R. Soc., London, 201 (series B): 227–331 (1910–1911)

113
Dendy, A., and Nicholls, G. E. On the occurrence of a mesocoelic recess in the human brain, and its relation to the subcommissural organ of the lower vertebrates; with special reference to the distribution of Reissner's fibre in the vertebrate series and its possible function, Anat. Anz. 37: 496–508 (1910)

114
Dexter, F. The development of the paraphysis in the common fowl, Am. J. Anat. 2: 13–24 (1902–1903)

115
Dimitrova, Z. Recherches sur la structure de la glande pinéale chez quelques mammifères, Névraxe, Louvain, 2: 257–321 (1901)

116
Dohrn, A. Studien zur Urgeschichte des Wirbeltierkörpers, Mitt. Zool. Station Neapel 4: 172–189 (1883)

117
Dollo, M. L. L'œil pinéal et les poissons placodermes du vieux grès rouge, Rev. clin. oculist., Bordeaux, 7: 213 (1887)

118
Duges, A. Mémoire sur les espèces indigènes du genre Lacerta, Ann. sc. nat., Paris, 16: 337–389 (1829)

119
Duval, M. Le troisième œil des vertèbres, J. microg., Paris, 12: 250–258, 273–279, 308–314, 336–340, 368–376, 401–405, 429–433, 459–465, 500–507, 523–527 (1888); and 13: 16–20, 42–48, 76–80 (1889)

120
Duval, M., and Kalt, —. Des yeux pinéaux multiples chez l'orvet, C. rend. Soc. biol. 41: 85–86 (1889)

121
Edinger, L. Untersuchungen über die vergleichende Anatomie des Gehirns; ii—Das Zwischenhirn der Selachier und der Amphibien, Abh. Senckenb. naturf. Ges., Frankfurt, 18: 3–55 (1892)

122
Edinger, T. Die Foramina parietalia der Säugetiere, Zschr. Anat. Entw. 102: 266–289 (1934)

123
Edwards, M. H. M. Recherches zoölogiques pour servir à l'histoire des Lezards, Ann. sc. nat., Paris, 16: 50–89 (1829)

124
Ehlers, E. Die Epiphyse am Gehirn der Plagiostomen, Zschr. wiss. Zool. 30 (suppl.): 607–634 (1878)

125
Eletto, L. Per la migliore conoscenza della fine struttura della epifisi dell'uomo; i—Lipoidi, Osp. maggiore, Milano, 26: 389–391 (1938)

126
d'Erchia, F. Contributo allo studio della volta del cervello intermedio e della regione parafisaria in embrioni di Pesci e di Mammiferi, Monit. zool. ital. 7: 75–80, 118–122, 201–213 (1896)

127
Esterley, C. O. The light recipient organs of the Copepod, Eucalanus elongatus, Bull. Mus. Comp. Zool., Harvard, 53: 1–56 (1908)

128
Eycleshymer, A. C. Paraphysis und Epiphysis in Amblystoma, Anat. Anz. 7: 215–217 (1892)

129
Eycleshymer, A. C., and Davis, B. M. The early development of the epiphysis and paraphysis in Amia, J. Comp. Neur. 7: 45–70 (1897)

130
Faivre, E.   Observations sur le conarium, C. rend. Soc. biol. 6: 195–200 (1854)

131
Faivre, E.   Études sur le conarium et le plexus choroideus chez l'homme et les animaux, Ann. sc. nat., Zool. 7 (series 4): 52–90 (1857)

132
Farina, C.   Sopra gli inclusi nucleari e sulla natura e genesi dei pigmenti della pineale umana, Boll. Soc. ital. biol. sper. 15: 1219–1221 (1940)

133
Farina, C., and Rindi, B.   Osservazioni sulle mastzellen della pineale umana, Ateneo parmense 13: 393–411 (1941)

134
Favaro, G.   Intorno al sacco dorsale del Pulvinar pineale nell'encefalo dei Mammiferi, Monit. zool. ital. 14: 275–277 (1903)

135
Favaro, G.   Le fibre nervose prepineali e pineali nell'encefalo dei Mammiferi, Arch. ital. anat. 3: 750–789 (1904)

136
Favaro, G.   Di un organo speciale della volta diencefalica in Bos Taurus L.; contributo alla morfologia comparata ed allo sviluppo del diencefalo, Monit. zool. ital. 15: 111–120 (1904)

137
Favaro, G.   Intorno ad un anomalo abbazzo di Diaphysis cerebri in Ovis aries L., Monit. zool. ital. 15: 395–396 (1904)

138
Favaro, G.   A proposito di una pubblicazione di G. Cutore dal titolo: Il corpo pineale di alcuni mammiferi, Anat. Anz. 40: 328–331 (1911–1912)

139
Fazio, C., and Perria, L.   Alcuni particolari caratteri della vascolarizzazione della pineale dell'uomo, Accad. med., Genova, 55: 194–197 (1940)

140
Fazio, C., and Perria, L.   Sulla vascolarizzazione della pineale dell'uomo, Riv. otoneuroft. 17: 63–64 (1940)

141
Fazio, C., and Perria, L.   Primo contributo allo studio della vascolarizzazione della pineale dell'uomo, Riv. pat. nerv. 56: 79–104 (1940)

142
Fazzari, I. Lo sviluppo della volta del diencefalo in Ovis ed in Vesperugo, Monit. zool. ital. 38: 181–187 (1927)

143
Ferner, H. Untersuchungen über die "zelligen Knötchen" (Epithelgranulationen) und die Kalkugeln in den Hirnhäuten der Menschen, Zschr. mikr. anat. Forsch. 48: 592–606 (1940)

144
Flesch, M. Ueber die Deutung der Zirbel bei den Säugetieren, Anat. Anz. 3: 173–176 (1888)

145
Francotte, P. Contribution à l'étude du développement de l'épiphyse et du troisième œil chez les Reptiles, Bull. Acad. roy. de Belg. 14 (series 3): 810–840 (1887)

146
Francotte, P. Recherches sur le développement de l'épiphyse, Arch. de biol. 8: 757–821 (1888)

147
Francotte, P. Note sur l'œil pariétal, l'épiphyse, la paraphyse et les plexus choroïdes du troisième ventricule, Bull. Acad. roy. de Belg. 27 (series 3): 84–112 (1894)

148
Francotte, P. Contribution à l'étude de l'œil pariétal, de l'épiphyse et de la paraphyse chez les Lacertiliens, Bull. Acad. roy. sc. Belg. 31 (series 3): 436–438 (1896)

149
Francotte, P. Contribution à l'étude de l'œil pariétal, de l'épiphyse et de la paraphyse chez les Lacertiliens, Mém. couron. Acad. roy. de sc. de Belg., Bruxelles, vol. 55, mém. iii (1896–1898)

150
von Frankl-Hochwart, L. Zur Kenntnis der Anatomie des Gehirns der Blindmans (Spalax typhlus), Arb. neur. Inst. Wien. 8: 190–220 (1902)

151
Friedrich-Freksa, H. Entwicklung, Bau und Bedeutung der Parietalgegend bei Teleostiern, Zschr. wiss. Zool. 141: 52–142 (1932)

152
Frigerio, A. Contributo alla conoscenza della ghiandola pineale, Riv. pat. nerv. 19: 499–501, 1914

153
von Frisch, —. Ueber das Parietalorgan der Fische als funktionierendes Organ, Sitzber. Ges. Morph. München 27: 16–18 (1911)

154

Froriep, E.   Beitrag zur normalen Histologie der Zirbel. Thesis, Jena, 1934

155

Fuchs, A.   Der goldene Schnitt; Geschichtliche Ergänzung zu der Arbeit von H. W. Reich, Zschr. ges. Neur. Psychiat. 111: 722–723 (1927)

156

Fujita, D.   Mouse shōka-sen ni okeru rohō ni tsuite (Follicles in the pineal gland of the mouse), Nagoya igakkai zasshi 50: 1247 (1939)

157

Fujita, D.   Mouse shōka-sen no keitai-hassei narabini soshiki-hassei-gaku-teki kenkyū (Morphogenetic and histogenetic studies on the pineal gland of the mouse), Nagoya igakkai zasshi 51: 1347–1374 (1940)

158

Fulliquette, G.   Recherches sur le cerveau du Protopterus annectens, Rec. zoöl. suisse 3: 1–130 (1886)

159

Funkquist, H.   Zur Morphogenie und Histogenese des Pinealorgans bei den Vögeln und Säugetieren, Anat. Anz. 42: 111–123 (1912)

160

Fuse, G.   Ueber die Epiphyse bei einigen wasserbewohnenden Säugetieren, Arb. anat. Inst. Univ. Sendai 18: 241–341 (1936)

161

Gage, S. P.   Comparative morphology of the brain of the soft-shelled turtle (Amyda mutica) and the English sparrow (Passer domesticus), Tr. Amer. Micr. Soc., Decatur, Illinois, 17: 185–225 (1895)

162

Galasescu, P., and Urechia, C. J.   Les cellules acidophiles de la glande pinéale, C. rend. Soc. biol. 68: 623–624 (1910)

163

Galeotti, G.   Studio morfologico e citologico della volta del diencefalo in alcuni vertebrati, Riv. pat. nerv. 2: 481–517 (1897)

164

Gardner, J. H.   Development of the pineal body in the hooded rat. Read at 62nd Sess. Amer. Assoc. Anat. Abstracted in: Anat. Rec. 103: 538–539 (1949)

165

Gargano, C.   Lo sviluppo dell'occhio pineale, Gior. internaz. di sc. med., Napoli, 31 (new series): 505–508 (1909)

166
Garman, H.   Some notes on the brain and pineal structures of Polyodon folium, Bull. Illinois State Laborat. Nat. Hist. 4: 298–309 (1892–1897)

167
Gaupp, E.   Zirbel, Parietalorgan und Paraphysis, Anat. Hefte; part 1—Ergebnisse, 7: 208–285 (1897)

168
Gerebtzoff, M. A.   Note anatomo-expérimentale sur le fornix, la corne d'Ammon et leurs relations avec diverses structures encéphaliques, notamment l'épiphyse, J. belge neur. psychiat. 41–42: 199–206 (1941–1942)

169
Gerlach, F.   Untersuchungen an der Epiphysis cerebri von Pferd und Rind, Anat. Anz. 50: 49–65 (1917–18)

170
Gersh, I.   Note on the pineal gland of the humpback whale, J. Mammal. 19: 477–480 (1938)

171
Giannelli, L.   Contributo allo studio comparative delle formazioni del tetto del cervello intermedio in base a ricerche praticate sul loro sviluppo in embrioni di Rettile (Seps chalcides) e di Mammiferi (Sus scrofa domesticus e Lepus cuniculus), Arch. ital. anat. 4: 551–592 (1905)

172
Giannelli, L.   Ancora sull'occhio parietale dei Rettili, Monit. zool. ital. 16: 4–9 (1905)

173
Gladstone, R. J., and Wakeley, C. P. G.   Development and histogenesis of the human pineal organ, J. Anat. 69: 427–454 (1934–1935)

174
Gladstone, R. J., and Wakeley, C. P. G.   The Pineal Organ. London: Bailliere, Tindall and Cox, 1940

175
Globus, J. H., and Silbert, S.   Pinealoma, Arch. Neur. Psychiat. 25: 937–985 (1931)

176
Godina, G.   Sulle fine struttura dell'epiphysis cerebri di alcuni mammiferi domestici, Arch. ital. anat. 40: 459–490 (1938)

177
Godina, G.   Sulla presenza di fibre muscolari striate nell'epiphysis cerebri dei bovini, Monit. zool. ital. 50: 39–44 (1939)

178

Godina, G.   Risposta alla nota del Prof. del Vecchio; sui reperti di fibre muscolari striate nell'epifisi cerebrale; qualche osservazione in rapporto alla nota del Dott. Godina, Monit. zool. ital. 50: 231–235 (1939)

179

de Graaf, H. W.   Bijdrage tot de Kennis van der Bouw en de ontwikkeling der Epiphyse bij Amphibien en Reptilien. Leyden: Adriani, 1886

180

de Graaf, H. W.   Zur Anatomie und Entwicklung der Epiphyse bei Amphibien und Reptilien, Zool. Anz. 9: 191–194 (1886)

181

Grandry, M.   Mémoire sur le structure de la capsule surrénale de l'homme et de quelques animeaux (troisième partie: glande pinéale), J. anat. et physiol., Paris, 4: 389–409 (1867)

182

Greving, R.   Die Innervation der Epiphyse, in: Muller, L. R., Lebensnerven und Lebenstriebe (3rd ed.), pp. 209–226. Berlin: Springer, 1931

183

Grieb, A.   Contribuzione allo studio dell'organo parietale del Podarcis muralis, Monit. zool. ital. 12: 218–221 (1901)

184

Groenberg, G.   Die Ontogenese eines medern Säugergehirns nach Untersuchungen an Erinaceus europaeus, Zool. Jahrb.; Abt. 2—Anat. 15: 261–384 (1901)

185

Gudernatsch, F.   Die Spielweite der inneren Sekretion, Zschr. Anat. Entw. 80: 750–776 (1926)

186

Hagemann, G.   Ueber den Bau des Conarium, Arch. Anat. Physiol. wiss. Med., 429–454 (1872)

187

Haller, B.   Vom Bau des Wirbeltiergehirns, Morph. Jahrb. 28: 252–346 (1900)

188

Haller, G.   Die epithelialen Gebilde am Gehirn der Wirbeltiere (i), Zschr. Anat. Entw. 63: 118–202 (1922)

189

Hammar, J. A.   Konstitutionsanatomische Studien über die Neurotisierung des Menschenembryos; iv—Ueber die Innervationsverhältnisse der

Inkretorgane und der Thymus bis in den 4. Fötalmonat, Zschr. mikr. anat. Forsch. 38: 253–293 (1935)

190
Hannitsch, R.   On the pineal eye of the young and adult Anguis fragilis, Proc. Liverpool Biol. Soc. 3: 87–95 (1888–1889)

191
Hepburn, D.   (Scottish National Antarctic Expedition).   Observations on the anatomy of the Weddel seal (Leptonychotes Weddelli); Part IV—The brain, Tr. R. Soc., Edinburgh, 48: 827–847 (1912–1913)

192
Herrick, C. J.   The membranous parts of the brain, meninges and their blood vessels in Amblystoma, J. Comp. Neur. 61: 297–346 (1935)

193
Herring, P. T.   The pineal region of mammalian brain; its morphology and histology in relation to function, Q. J. Exp. Physiol. 17: 125–147 (1927)

194
Hescheler, K., and Boveri, V.   Zur Beurteilung des Parietalauges der Wirbeltiere, Vjschr. naturf. Ges., Zurich, 68: 398–419 (1923)

195
Hett, J.   Ueber den Austritt von Kernsubstanzen in das Protoplasma, Zschr. Zellforsch. 26: 239–248 (1937)

196
Hill, C.   Development of the epiphysis in Coregonus albus, J. Morph. 5: 503–510 (1891)

197
Hill, C.   The epiphysis of Teleosts and Amia, J. Morph. 9: 237–263 (1894)

198
Hill, C.   Two epiphyses in a four-day chick, Bull. Northwestern Univ. Med. School, Chicago, 2: 513–517 (1900)

199
Hochstetter, F.   Ueber die Entwicklung der Zirbeldrüse des Menschens, Verh. Anat. Ges., Jena, 30: 193–198 (1921)

200
Holmdahl, D. E.   Ein rätselhaftes, zirbelähnliches, embryonales Organ in mittleren Teils des Daches des Rhombencephalon, Anat. Anz. 65: 428–433 (1928)

201

Holmgren, N.   Zum Bau der Epiphyse von Squalus Acanthias, Arkiv för zoologi, vol. 11, no. 23 (1917–1918)

202

Holmgren, N.   Zur Kenntnis der Parietalorgane von Rana temporaria, Arkiv för zoologi, vol. 11, no. 24 (1917–1918)

203

Holmgren, N.   Ueber die Epiphysennerven von Clupea sprattus und harengus, Arkiv för zoologi, vol. 11, no. 25 (1917–1918)

204

Holmgren, N.   Zur Frage der Epiphysennerven bei Teleostiern, Fol. neurobiol. 11: 1–16 (1918)

205

Holmgren, N.   Zur Anatomie und Histologie des Vorder- und Zwischenhirns der Knochenfische, Acta Zool. Stockholm 1: 137–315 (1920)

206

Holt, E. W. L.   Observations upon the development of the Teleostean brain with especial reference to that of Clupea harengus, Zool. Jahrb.; Abt. 2—Anat., 4: 478–504 (1891)

207

Honegger, J.   Vergleichend-anatomische Untersuchungen über den Fornix und die zu ihm in Beziehung gebrachten Gebilde im Gehirn des Menschen und der Säugetiere, Rec. zool. suisse 5: 201–434 (1892)

208

Huxley, T. H.   On Ceratodus forsteri, with observations on the classification of fishes, Proc. Zool. Soc., London, 24–59 (1876)

209

Illing, P.   Vergleichende anatomische und histologische Untersuchungen über die Epiphysis cerebri einiger Säuger. Inaug. Diss., Leipzig, 1910

210

Ishikawa, E.   Vergleichende Untersuchungen der Zirbeldrüse bei männlichen und weiblichen Tieren, Arb. neur. Inst. Wien. 29: 337–347 (1927)

211

Izawa, Y.   Studies on the pineal body; ɪ—On the postnatal growth of the pineal body of the albino rat with observations on its histology, J. Comp. Neur. 39: 1–15 (1925)

212

Johnston, J. B.   The brain of Acipenser, Zool. Jahrb.; Abt. 2—Anat. 15: 59–260 (1901)

213
Jordan, H. E. The microscopic anatomy of the epiphysis of the opossum, Anat. Rec. 5: 325–338 (1911)

214
Jordan, H. E. The histogenesis of the pineal body of the sheep, Am. J. Anat. 12: 249–270 (1911–1912)

215
Jordan, H. E. A note on the cytology of the pineal body of the sheep, Anat. Rec. 22: 275–285 (1921)

216
Josephy, H. Zur feineren Histologie der Epiphyse, Allg. Zschr. Psychiat. 76: 659–660 (1920). Also published in: Zschr. ges. Neur. Psychiat. 62: 91–119 (1920)

217
Jullien, G. Contribution à l'étude histologique de l'épiphyse. Thesis, Marseille, 1939

218
Jullien, G. Sur l'origine et la formation des vésicules closes dans l'épiphyse des gallinaces, C. rend. Soc. biol. 136: 243–244 (1942)

219
Julin, C. De la signification morphologique de l'épiphyse (Glande pinéale) des vertèbres, Extrait du Bulletin Scientifique du Departement du Nord, series 2, vol. 10 (1887). Reprint

220
Kajimoto, N. Niwatori shōka-sen ni tsuite (The pineal gland of the domestic fowl), Kaibōgaku zasshi 2: appendix 22 (1929)

221
Kajimoto, N. Shōka-sen no hasseigaku-teki kenkyū (Genetic studies on the pineal gland), Kumamoto igakkai zasshi 7: 1347–1375 (1931)

222
van de Kamer, J. C. Development of the pineal organ, in: Woerdeman, M. W., and Raven, C. P., Experimental Embryology in the Netherlands 1940–1945, pp. 121–123. New York: Elsevier, 1946

223
van de Kamer, J. C. Over de ontwikkeling, de determinatie en de betekenis van de epiphyse en de paraphyse van de amphibien. Arnhem: van der Wiel, 1949

224
Kaneko, K. Ueber das Vorkommen eines Fettgewebes an der Epiphyse einiger Beuteltiere, Arb. anat. Inst. Univ. Sendai 20: 79–86 (1937)

225
Kaneko, K. Ueber einige Entwicklungseigenheiten der Epiphyse beim buntfarbigen Gibbon, Hylobates variegatus s. agilis Desm., Arb. anat. Inst. Univ. Sendai 20: 87–96 (1937)

226
Karcher, J. B. Dissertatio anatomica de glanduli pineali lapisdescente. Strasbourg: F. Le Roux, 1733

227
Katayama, I., Okamoto, F., and Kurozu, T. Shōka-sen ni okeru shinkei-saihō ni tsuite (Nerve cells in the pineal gland), Kaibōgaku zasshi 5: 43–48 (1932)

228
Kawamura, R., and Hosono, H. Fettbefunde der innersekretorischen Organe, Tr. Soc. path. Jap. 23: 232–234 (1933)

229
King, L. S. The hematoencephalic barrier, Arch. Neur. Psychiat. 41: 51–72 (1939)

230
Kleine, A. Ueber die Parietalorgane bei einheimischen und ausländischen Anuren, Jena. Zschr. Naturwiss. 64: 339–376 (1930)

231
Klinckowstroem, A. Untersuchungen über den Scheitelfleck bei Embryonen einiger Schwimmvögel, Zool. Jahrb. 5: 177–183 (1892)

232
de Klinckowström, A. Le premier développement de l'œil pinéal, l'épiphyse et le nerf pariétal chez Iguana tuberculata, Anat. Anz. 8: 289–299 (1892–1893)

233
von Klinckowström, A. Die Zirbel und das Foramen parietale bei Callichthys (asper und littoralis), Anat. Anz. 8: 561–564 (1892–1893)

234
Klinckowstroem, A. Beiträge zur Kenntnis des Parietalauges, Zool. Jahrb.; Abt. 2–Anat. 7: 249–280 (1894)

235
von Knobloch, D. Das subfornikale Organ des dritten Hirnventrikels in seiner embryonalen und postembryonalen Entwicklung beim Hausschwein (Sus scrofa domesticus), Zschr. Anat. Entw. 106: 379–397 (1936)

236
Knowles, F. G. W. Photomechanical changes in the pineal of lampreys, J. Exp. Biol. 16: 524–529 (1939)

237
Kohn, A. Morphologie der inneren Sekretion und der Inkretorischen Organe, in: Bethe, A., and Bergmann, G. von, Handbuch der normalen und pathologischen Physiologie 16[1]: 36–41. Berlin: Springer, 1930

238
von Kölliker, —. Ueber das dritte oder Parietalauge der Wirbelthiere, Münch. med. Wschr. 34: 210 (1887)

239
Kolmer, W. Das Sagittalorgan der Wirbeltiere, Zschr. Anat. Entw. 60: 652–717 (1921)

240
Kolmer, W. Ueber Nebenzirbeln, Verh. Anat. Ges., Jena, 34: 250–252 (1925)

241
Kolmer, W. Weitere Beiträge zur Kenntnis des Sagittalorgans der Wirbeltiere, Verh. Anat. Ges., Jena, 34: 252–257 (1925)

242
Kolmer, W. Ganglienzellen als konstanter Bestandteil der Zirbel von Affen, Zschr. ges. Neur. Psychiat. 121: 423–428 (1929)

243
Krabbe, K. Sur la glande pinéale chez l'homme, N. iconog. de la Salpêtrière, Paris, 24: 257–272 (1911)

244
Krabbe, K. H. Histologiske Undersogelser over Corpus pineale, Bibl. Laeger. 107: 175–182 (1915)

245
Krabbe, K. H. Histologiske Undersogelser over Corpus pineale. Copenhagen: 1915

246
Krabbe, K. H. Histologische und Embryologische Untersuchungen über die Zirbeldrüse des Menschen, Anat. Hefte; Abt. 1–Arbeiten, 54: 187–319 (1916–1917)

247
Krabbe, K. H. Bidrag til Kundskaben om Corpus Pineale hos pattedyrene, Kgl. Danske Videnskabernes Selskab, Biologiske Meddelelser, vol. 2, no. 2 (1920)

248
Krabbe, K. H. Fortsatte Undersogelser over Corpus pineale hos pattedyrene. Kgl. Danske Videnskabernes Selskab, Biologiske Meddelelser, vol. 3, no. 7 (1921)

249
Krabbe, K. H.   Recherches sur l'existence d'un œil pariétal rudimentaire (le corpuscle pariétal) chez les mammifères, Kgl. Danske Videnskabernes Selskab, Biologiske Meddelelser, vol. 8, no. 3 (1929)

250
Krabbe, K. H.   Embryologische Untersuchungen des Hirndaches bei Tieren mit fehlender oder unentwickelter Zirbeldrüse, Verh. Anat. Ges., Jena, 41: 160–170 (1932)

251
Krabbe, K. H.   L'organe souscommissural du cerveau, Presse méd. 41^2: 1750–1752 (1933)

252
Krabbe, K. H.   Embryonal development of parietal organs in Chamaelo bitaeniatus Fischer, Psychiat. neur. bl., Amsterdam, 38: 750–760 (1934)

253
Krabbe, K. H.   Recherches embryologiques sur les organes pariétaux chez certains reptiles, Kgl. Danske Videnskabernes Selskab, Biologiske Meddelelser, vol. 12, no. 3 (1935)

254
Krabbe, K. H.   Quelques considérations sur la glande pinéale et le complexe épithalamo-épiphysaire, Rev. neur. 70: 596–603 (1938)

255
Krabbe, K. H.   Pineal body in procavia, Acta psychiat. neur. 16: 183–190 (1941)

256
Kraushaar, R.   Entwicklung der Hypophysis und Epiphysis bei Nagetieren, Zschr. wiss. Zool. 41: 79–98 (1885)

257
Kudo, T.   Dai-sansyōuo no hassei ni tsuite; nōkasuitai, zyōkasuitai oyobi hukusuitai (Development of the giant salamander; hypophysis cerebri, epiphysis cerebri and paraphyseal body), Tōkyō iji shinshi, no. 2485: 2095–2105 (1926)

258
Kuhlenbeck, H.   Ueber die Grundbestandteile des Zwischenhirnbauplanes der Anamnier, Morph. Jahrb. 63: 50–95 (1929)

259
Kunkel, B. W.   The paraphysis and pineal region of the garter snake, Anat. Rec. 9: 607–636 (1915)

260
Kupffer, —.   Ueber die Zirbeldrüse des Gehirns als Rudiment eines unpaarigen Auges (Scheitelauge), Münch. med. Wschr. 34: 205–206 (1887)

261
Kux, E.   Der sekundäre Neuroporus und der Reissnersche Faden bei Entembryonen, Zschr. mikr. anat. Forsch. 16: 141–174 (1929)

262
Landau, E.   Eine leichte Methode zur Demonstration der aus dem Kern in das Zellprotoplasma auswandernden Kernkörperchen, Zschr. wiss. Mikr. 46: 139–140 (1929)

263
Lecchini, S. I.   Contributo allo studio della struttura e dell'innervazione della ghiandola pineale nei primati, Atti Accad. fisiocr., Siena, 3 (series 11): 715–723 (1935)

264
Leduc, E. H., and Wislocki, G. B.   The histochemical localization of acid and alkaline phosphatases, non-specific esterase and succinic dehydrogenase in the structures comprising the hematoencephalic barrier of the rat, J. Comp. Neur. 97: 241–280 (1952)

265
Legge, F.   Sullo sviluppo dell'occhio pineale del Gongylus ocellatus e Forsk, Boll. Accad. med. Roma 23: 184–207 (1897–1898)

266
von Lendenfeld, R.   Die Leuchtorgane der Fische, Biol. Zbl. 7: 609–621 (1887–1888)

267
Lessona, M.   Sulla ghiandola frontale degli anfibi anuri, Atti Accad. sc., Torino, 15: 581–590 (1880)

268
Levin, P. M.   A nervous structure in the pineal body of the monkey, J. Comp. Neur. 68: 405–409 (1937–1938)

269
Leydig, F.   Ueber Organe eines sechsten Sinnes; Zugleich ein Beitrag zur Kenntnis des feineren Baues der Haut bei Amphibien und Reptilien, Verhandlungen der K. Leopoldinisch-Carolinischen Akademie der Naturforscher, vol. 34, sect. v (1868)

270
Leydig, F.   Das Parietalorgan der Wirbeltiere, Zool. Anz. 10: 534–539 (1887)

271
Leydig, F.   Das Parietalorgan der Reptilien und Amphibien kein Sinneswerkzeug, Biol. Zbl. 8: 707–718 (1888–1889)

272
Leydig, F.   Das Parietalorgan der Amphibien und Reptilien; Anatomisch-

histologische Untersuchungen, Abh. Senckenb. naturf. Ges., Frankfurt, 16: 441–552 (1890)

273
Leydig, F.   Das Parietalorgan, Biol. Zbl. 10: 278–285 (1890–1891)

274
Leydig, F.   Zur Kenntnis der Zirbel und Parietalorgane, Abh. Senckenb. Natur. Ges., Frankfurt, 19: 217–278 (1896)

275
Leydig, F.   Zirbel und Jacobson'sche Organe einiger Reptilien, Arch. mikr. Anat. 50: 385–418 (1897)

276
Lieberkühn, N.   Ueber die Zirbeldrüse, Sitzungsber. Ges. Beförd. ges. Naturwiss., Marburg, pp. 18–19 (1871)

277
Lignac, G. O. E.   Ueber die Entstehung von Sandkörnern und Pigment in der Zirbeldrüse, Beitr. path. Anat. 73: 366–376 (1925)

278
Livini, F.   Formazioni della volta del proencefalo in alcuni uccelli, Arch. ital. anat. 5: 377–417 (1906)

279
Livini, F.   Formazioni della volta del proencefalo in Salamandrina perspicillata, Monit. zool. ital. 17: 177–193 (1906)

280
Locy, W. A.   The derivation of the pineal eye, Anat. Anz. 9: 169–180 (1893–1894)

281
Locy, W. A.   The mid-brain and the accessory optic vesicles, Anat. Anz. 9: 486–488 (1893–1894)

282
Locy, W. A. The optic vesicles of elasmobranches and their serial relation to other structures on the cephalic plate, J. Morph. 9: 115–122 (1894)

283
Loewy, P.   Die Secretwege der Zirbeldrüse, Arb. neur. Inst. Wien. 20: 130–144 (1913)

284
Masse, E.   La glande pinéale et le troisième œil des vertèbres par le Dr. Peytoureau (Rev.), Gaz. hebd. sc. méd. Bordeaux 8: 397–401, 406–409 (1887)

285

Mayer, C. Beiträge zur Anatomie des Elephanten und der übrigen Pachydermen, Verhandlungen der K. Leopoldinisch-Carolinischen Akademie der Naturforscher 22: 1–88 (1847)

286

Mayer, F. Das Zentralnervensystem von Ammocoetes; ɪ–Vorder-, Zwischen- und Mittelhirn, Anat. Anz. 13: 649–657 (1897)

287

Mayer, F. J. C. Ueber den Bau des Gehirns der Fische in Beziehung auf eine darauf gegründete Eintheilung dieser Thierklasse, Verhandlungen der K. Leopoldinisch-Carolinischen Akademie der Naturforscher, vol. 30, sect. ᴠɪ (1864)

288

Mazzucchelli, B. Osservazioni sulla innervazione della epifisi cerebrale, Boll. Soc. ital. biol. sper. 25: 772–773 (1949)

289

Mazzucchelli, B. Osservazioni sulla struttura e sulla innervazione della epifisi cerebrale dei mammiferi, Riv. pat. nerv. 71: 185–189 (1950)

290

McKay, W. J. The development and structure of the pineal eye in Hinulia and Grammatophora, Proc. Linnean Soc., New South Wales, 3 (series 2): 876–889 (1888)

291

McKay, W. J. On the development and structure of the pineal eye in Hinulia and Grammatophora, Rep. Australas. Ass. Adv. Sc. (1888), Sydney, 1: 332–334 (1889)

292

Meckel, F. Observations anatomiques sur la glande pinéale, sur l'origine du nerf de la septième paire, Histoire, Akademie der wissenschaften, Berlin, 21: 91–101 (1765)

293

Meckel, F. Observationes anatomicae de glandula pineali, septo lucido, et origine paris septimi nervorum cerebri, in: Ludwig, C. F., Scriptores neurologici minores selecti, vol. ɪᴠ, pp. 9–10. Leipzig: I. F. Inium, 1795

294

von Meduna, L. Die Entwicklung der Zirbeldrüse im Säuglingsalter, Zschr. Anat. Entw. 76: 534–547 (1925)

295

Melchers, F. Ueber rudimentäre Hirnanhangsgebilde beim Gecko (Epi-, Para- und Hypophyse), Zschr. wiss. Zool. 67: 139–166 (1899)

296

de Mennato, M.   Per una più esatta conoscenza degli acervuli e di altri inclusi dell'epiphysis cerebri, Rass. stud. psichiat. 16: 263–285 (1927)

297

de Mennato, M.   Pour une connaissance plus exacte des Acervules et d'autres corps inclus dan l'épiphysis cerebri, Arch. ital. biol. 79: 113–118 (1928)

298

de Mennato, M.   Ancora sulla genesi delle alterazioni degenerative del corpo pineale e dei plessi caroidei, Rass. stud. psichiat. 17: 648–655 (1928)

299

Meyer, R.   Ueber den morphologisch fassbaren Kernstoffwechsel der Parenchymzellen der Epiphysis cerebri des Menschen, Zschr. Zellforsch. 25: 83–98 (1936–1937)

300

Meyer, R.   Das verhalten mehrer nucleolärer Blasen im Kernstoffwechsel der Pinealzellen des Menschen und die Entstehung der Kernfalten, Zschr. Zellforsch. 25: 173–180 (1936–1937)

301

Meyer, R.   Die Entstehung des Parenchympigments in der menschlichen Epiphysis cerebri, Zschr. Zellforsch. 25: 605–613 (1936–1937)

302

von Mihalkovics, V.   Entwickelung der Zirbeldrüse; Vorläufige Mittheilung, Zbl. med. Wiss. 12: 241–242 (1874)

303

Mikami, S.   Kachiku no shōka-tai no saihōgaku-teki narabi-ni soshiki-kagaku-teki kenkyū (Cytological and histochemical studies on the pineal gland of the domestic animals), Igaku to seibutsugaku 21: 203–206 (1951)

304

Minot, C. S.   On the morphology of the pineal region, based on its development in Acanthias, Am. J. Anat. 1: 81–98 (1901–1902)

305

Möller, J.   Einiges über die Zirbeldrüse des Chimpanse, Verh. naturf. Ges., Basel, 8: 755–760 (1890)

306

Müller, W.   Ueber Entwicklung und Bau der Hypophysis und des Processus infundibuli cerebri, Jena. Zschr. Naturwiss. 6: 354–425 (1871)

307
Murie, J. On the form and structure of the manatee, Tr. Zool. Soc., London, 8: 127–202 (1874)

308
Murie, J. Researches upon the anatomy of the Pinnipedia; III—Descriptive anatomy of the sea-lion (Otaria jubata), Tr. Zool. Soc., London, 8: 501–582 (1874)

309
Nassar, T., and Shanklin, W. M. Staining pineal parenchyma by a modified Hortega method after paraffin embedding, Stain Techn. 25: 35–38 (1950)

310
Neumayer, L. Studie zur Entwicklungsgeschichte des Gehirns der Säugetiere, in: Festschrift zum 70. Geburtstag von Carl von Kupffer, pp. 455–486. Jena: G. Fischer, 1899

311
Nicholls, G. E. The function of Reissner's fibre and the ependymal groove, Nature 82: 217 (1909)

312
Nicholls, G. E. An experimental investigation on the function of Reissner's fibre, Anat. Anz. 40: 409–432 (1911–1912)

313
Nicolas, A. Note sur la présence de fibres musculaires striées dans la glande pinéale de quelques mammifères, C. rend. Soc. biol. 52: 876–877 (1900)

314
Nowikoff, M. Ueber die Augen und die Frontalorgane der Branchiopoden, Zschr. wiss. Zool. 79: 432–464 (1905)

315
Nowikoff, M. Ueber das Parietalauge von Lacerta agilis und Anguis fragilis, Biol. Zbl. 27: 364–370, 405–414 (1907)

316
Nowikoff, M. Ueber die Rückensinnesorgane der Placophoren nebst einigen Bemerkungen über die Schale derselben, Zschr. wiss. Zool. 88: 153–186 (1907)

317
Nowikoff, M. Ueber den Bau des Medianauges der Ostracoden, Zschr. wiss. Zool. 91: 81–92 (1908)

318
Nowikoff, M. Zur Frage über die Paarigkeit der Epiphyse und des Parietalauges der Saurier, Biol. J., Moskva, 1: 161–166 (1910)

319
Nowikoff, M. Untersuchungen über den Bau, die Entwicklung und die Bedeutung des Parietalauges von Sauriern, Zschr. wiss. Zool. 96: 118–207 (1910)

320
Ochoterena, I. Estudios neurologicos; la región epifisaria y la epifisis, Mem. Soc. cient. Antonio Alzate, Mexico, 37: 71–86 (1919)

321
Ohmura, S. Nippon-jin shōka-sen no kaibōgaku-teki, soshikigaku-teki, narabi-ni byōrigaku-teki kenkyū (Anatomical, histological and pathological study on the pineal gland of the Japanese), Nippon ika daigaku zasshi 2: 30–68, 139–202 (1931)

322
Ohmura, S., and Anraku, E. Shōka-sen no lipoid ni tsuite (Studies on the lipoids of the pineal gland), Nippon byōrigakkai kaishi 25: 611–613 (1935)

323
Ohmura, S., and Anraku, T. Shōka-sen no lipoid ni tsuite (Lipids of the pineal gland), Nippon ika daigaku zasshi 6: 1264 (1935)

324
Ohmura, S., and Ubukata, M. Hito shōka-sen narabi-ni nō-myakurakusō ni okeru Kon gin-karyū (Kon's argentaffin granules in the human pineal gland and the choroid plexuses), Nippon ika daigaku zasshi 8: 1587–1592 (1937). Abstracted in: Nippon byōrigakkai kaishi 28: 42–43 (1938)

325
Ohnisi, K. Hōsan senjo (Bufo formosus) ni okeru shōka-sen no hassei ni kan-suru ichi kōsatsu (Development of the pineal gland of Bufo formosus), Kaibōgaku zasshi 5: 818–835 (1932)

326
Ohnisi, K. Senjo shōka-sen no hatsuiku ni tsuite (Development of the pineal gland of the toad, Bufo formosus), Kaibōgaku zasshi 5: 873–892 (1932)

327
Ohnisi, K. Chōsen-san Hynobius ni okeru shōka-sen no hassei ni tsuite (Development of the pineal gland in Hynobius native to Korea), Kaibōgaku zasshi 5: 898–907 (1932)

328
Ohnisi, K. Hōsan sake ni okeru shōka-sen no hassei ni kan-suru ichi kosatsu (One observation of the development of the pineal gland of the salmon native to Japan), Kaibōgaku zasshi 5: 1257–1268 (1933)

329
Orlandi, N. Sulla struttura della pineale nella prima infanzia, Rev. sudamer. endocr. 11: 363–387 (1928)

330
Orlandi, N., and Guardini, B. Sulla struttura della pineale umana, Rev. sudamer. endocr. 12: 465–495 (1929)

331
Ostroumoff, A. K voprosu o tret'em glaze pozvonochnykh (On the question of the third eye of vertebrates), Obshchestvo estestvoispytatelei; Protokoly zasyedani, Kazan, no. 96 (1887–1888)

332
Ovsiannikov, F. Ueber das dritte Auge bei Petromyzon fluviatilis, nebst einigen Bemerkungen über dasselbe Organ bei anderen Tieren, Mém. Acad. Imper. des Sciences, St. Petersbourg, vol. 36 (series 7), no. 9 (1888)

333
Ovsiannikov, F. Obzor izsledovanii o temiannom glazie u zemnorodnykh presmykaiushchikh i ryb (Research on the medial eye of terrestrial reptiles and of fish), Viestnik estestvoznaniia; Izdanie S. Peterburgskago obshchestva estestvoizpytatelei, 2 (no. 3): 100–111 (1891)

334
Owen, C. B. On the homology of the conario-hypophysial tract or the so-called pineal and pituitary glands, J. Linnean Soc., Zool., 16: 131–149 (1881–1883)

335
Owen, R. Structure du cerveau des marsupiaux, Ann. sc. nat., Zoöl., 8 (series 2): 175–185 (1837)

336
Papouschek, K. Untersuchung am Ependym von Amphibien; zur Frage der Kernsekretion, Zschr. mikr. anat. Forsch. 42: 148–164 (1937)

337
Pastori, G. Sull'anatomia macro-microscopica della "Epiphysis cerebri" nei mammiferi e nell'uomo, Pubbl. Univ. Cattol. Sacro Cuore (Milano): Serie prima—Sci. filos. 1 (fasc. 4): 19–65 (1924)

338
Pastori, J.   Contribution à l'étude de l'épiphysis cerebri (corps pinéale),
Arch. ital. biol. 78: 1–17 (1927)

339
Pastori, G.   Pineali accessorie e relazioni tra gli organi pineale e subcommessurale, Cervello 6: 1–16 (1927)

340
Pastori, G.   Pineali accessorie e relazioni tra gli organi pineali e sub-
commessurale, Pubbl. Univ. Cattol. Sacro Cuore (Milano); Serie sesta–
Sci. biol. 4 (fasc. 2): 97–115 (1928)

341
Pastori, G.   Qualche osservazione sulla patogenesi delle calcificazioni
pineali, Pubbl. Univ. Cattol. Sacro Cuore (Milano); Serie sesta–Sci. biol.
4 (fasc. 3): 117–129 (1928)

342
Pastori, G.   Ueber Nervenfasern und Nervenzellen in der Epiphysis
cerebri, Zschr. ges. Neur. Psychiat. 117: 202–211 (1928)

343
Pastori, G.   Alcuni reperti recenti riguardanti l'innervazione della epiphysis cerebri, Monit. zool. ital. 40: 518–521 (1929)

344
Pastori, G.   Ein bis jetzt noch nicht beschriebenes sympathisches Gang-
lion und dessen Beziehungen zum Nervus conari sowie zur Vena magna
Galeni, Zschr. ges. Neur. Psychiat. 123: 81–90 (1930)

345
Patten, W.   On the morphology and physiology of the brain and sense
organs of Limulus, Q. J. Micr. Sc. 35: 1–96 (1893–1894)

346
Pawlas, T.   W sprawie czarnego pigmentu w organizmach (Black pigment in animals), Kosmos, Lwow, 51: 262–310 (1926)

347
Pawlowsky, A.   Ueber den Fasernverlauf in der hinteren Gehirnkommis-
sur, Zschr. wiss. Zool. 24: 284–290 (1874)

348
Pesonen, N.   Ueber das subkommissuralorgan beim Meerschweinchen,
Acta Soc. med. Duodecim. 22 (series A): 53–78 (1940; published, 1947)

349
Pesonen, N.   Ueber das subkommissuralorgan beim Menschen, Acta Soc.
med. Duodecim. 22 (series A): 79–114 (1940; published, 1947)

350
Pesonen, N., and Setälä, K. Ueber die mit dem Subkommissuralorgan zusammenhängende Zellanhäufung, Acta Soc. med. Duodecim. 23 (series A): 46–58 (1940; published, 1947)

351
Pettit, A., and Girard, J. Sur la function secrétoire et la morphologie des plexus choroïdes des ventricules latéraux du système nerveux central, Arch. anat. micr. 5: 213–264 (1902–1903)

352
Peytoureau, S. La glande pinéale et le troisième œil des vertèbres. Thesis, no. 95, Bordeaux, 1887

353
Piccioli Marino, M. T. Contributo alla miglior conoscenza della regione parafisale degli Anfibi, Arch. ital. anat. 53: 160–174 (1948)

354
Pines, L. Ueber ein bisher unbeachtetes Gebilde im Gehirn einiger Säugetiere; das subfornikale Organ des dritten Ventrikels, J. Psychol. Neur., Leipzig, 34: 186–193 (1926–1927)

355
Pines, L. Ueber die Innervation der Epiphyse, Zschr. ges. Neur. Psychiat. 111: 356–369 (1927)

356
Pines, L. Allgemeine Ergebnisse unserer Untersuchungen über die Innervation der innersekretorischen Organe, Arch. ges. Physiol. 228: 373–390 (1931)

357
Pines, L., and Maimon, R. Weitere Beobachtungen über das subfornikale Organ des dritten Ventrikels der Säugetiere, Anat. Anz. 64: 424–437 (1928)

358
Polezhaev, N. O temiannom organie zrieniia pozvonochnych v ego otnoshenii k bokovym glazam (The relationship of the medial eye to the lateral eyes in vertebrates), Viestnik estestvoznaniia; Izdanie S. Peterburgskago obshchestva estestvoizpytatelei, 2 (no. 5): 178–187 (1891)

359
Polvani, F. Studio anatomico della glandola pineale umana, Fol. neurobiol., Leipzig, 7: 655–695 (1913)

360
Polvani, F. Studio anatomico della glandola pineale umana, Rass. stud. psichiat., Siena, 3: 3–5 (1913)

361
Preisler, O.   Zur Kenntnis der Entwicklung des Parietalauges und des Feinbaues der Epiphyse der Reptilien, Zschr. Zellforsch. 32: 209–216 (1942–1943)

362
Prenant, A.   Sur l'œil pariétal accessoire, Anat. Anz. 9: 103–112 (1893–1894)

363
Prenant, A.   Les yeux pariétaux accessoires d'Anguis fragilis sous le rapport de leur situation, de leur nombre et de leur fréquence, Bibl. anat. 2: 223–229 (1894)

364
Presse, E. A.   Findet eine Involution der Zirbeldrüse (Epiphysis cerebri) beim Haushund (Canis familiaris) statt? (Erster Beitrag zur Alters-anatomie des Haushundes). Inaug. Diss., Vet. Med., Hannover, 1939

365
Purvis, G. C.   On the pineal eye of Lamna cornubica or Porbeagle shark, Proc. R. Phys. Soc. 11: 62–67 (1890–1892)

366
Pussep, L., and Voss, H. E. V.   Studien über das Subcommissuralorgan; i—das Subcommissuralorgan beim Menschen, Fol. neuropath. eston. 2: 13–21 (1924)

367
Quast, P.   Zur Histologie der Zirbeldrüse des Menschen, Verh. anat. Ges. 37: 65–70, 1928

368
Quast, P.   Beiträge zur Histologie und Cytologie der normalen Zirbel-drüse des Menschen; i—das Parenchympigment der Zirbeldrüse, Zschr. mikr. anat. Forsch. 23: 335–434 (1931)

369
Quast, P.   Beiträge zur Histologie und Cytologie der normalen Zirbel-drüse des Menschen; ii—Zellen und Pigment des interstitiellen Gewebes der Zirbeldrüse, Zschr. mikr. anat. Forsch. 24: 38–100 (1931)

370
Quercy, P., Gay, R., et al.   Essai d'analyse des calculs de la pinéale par les rayons X, J. méd. Bordeaux 124: 570–571 (1947)

371
Quercy, P., de Lachaud, R., and Durand, R.   Sur l'épiphyse et des formations paraépiphysaires chez l'homme adulte, Rev. neur. 69: 483–490 (1938)

372
Quercy, P., and de Lachaud, R.   Sur les terminaisons annulaires libres des fibres névrologiques; iv–a, L'écorce cérébrale; b, Le bulbe olfactif; c, L'épiphyse, Rev. neur. 68: 733–739 (1937)

373
Quercy, P., de Lachaud, R., and Sittler, G.   Un organe de la fente de Bichat; le sac dorsal; son anatomie chez l'homme adulte, J. méd. Bordeaux 119: 144–146 (1942)

374
Quercy, P., de Lachaud, R., and Sittler, G.   Sur la région épiphysaire; i–Le sac dorsal; ii–Le canal de Bichat, Rev. neur. 76: 11–19 (1944)

375
Quercy, P., and Rigaldies, R.   Sur la région épiphysaire; le sac dorsal; sa calcification, J. méd. Bordeaux 124: 378–381 (1947)

376
Quercy, P., Rigaldies, R., Carles, J., and Quercy, D.   Sur la région épiphysaire; i–Le sac dorsal; ii–Les calculs de l'épiphyse et du sac dorsal, Rev. neur. 79: 401–412 (1947)

377
Rass, T.   Zur Morphologie des Gehirns der Knochenfische, Anat. Anz. 68: 70–80 (1929)

378
Reich, H.   Ueber die anatomische Lage der Zirbeldrüse nebst einer Bemerkung zu ihrer Funktion, Zschr. ges. Neur. Psychiat. 104: 818–820 (1926)

379
Reich, H. W.   Studie über die Lage von Epiphyse und Hypophyse, Zschr. ges. Neur. Psychiat. 109: 1–14 (1927)

380
Reichold, S.   Untersuchungen über die Morphologie des subfornikalen und des subkommissuralen Organs bei Säugetieren und Sauropsiden, Zschr. mikr. anat. Forsch. 52: 455–479 (1942)

381
Retzius, G.   Ueber den Bau des sog. Parietalauges von Ammocoetes, Biologische Untersuchungen 7 (new series): 22–25 (1895)

382
Riech, F.   Epiphyse und Paraphyse im Lebenscyclus der Anuren, Zschr. vergl. Physiol. 2: 524–570 (1924–1925)

383
del Rio-Hortega, P.   Sobre la naturaleza de las celulas epifisarias, Bol. Soc. espan. biol. 5: 22–26 (1916)

384

del Rio-Hortega, P.   Constitución histologica de la glandula pineal, Arch. neurob., Madrid, 3: 359–389 (1922). Also published in: Libro en honor de Ramon y Cajal, Madrid, 1: 315–359 (1922)

385

del Rio-Hortega, P.   Anatomia microscopica del cuerpo pineale, Conferencias y reseñas cientificas de la Soc. esp. de hist. nat. 1: 113–134 (1926)

386

del Rio-Hortega, P.   Constitución histologica de la glandula pineal; ii—Substratum neurologico, Arch. neurob., Madrid, 9: 26–68 (1929). Also published in: Progr. clin., Madrid, 36: 178–197 (1928)

387

del Rio-Hortega, P.   Constitución histologica de la glandula pineal; iii—Actividad secretora de las celulas parenquimatosas y neurologicas, Arch. neurob., Madrid, 9: 139–167 (1929)

388

Ritter, W. E.   The parietal eye in some lizards from the western United States, Bull. Mus. Comp. Zool., Harvard, 20: 209–228 (1891)

389

Ritter, W. E.   On the presence of a parapineal organ in Phrynosoma coronata, Anat. Anz. 9: 766–772 (1893–1894)

390

Rohon, J. V.   Ueber Parietalorgane und Paraphysen, Ceské spolecnosti nauk; Sitzungber. der Kgl. Böhmischen Gesellschaft der Wissenschaften —Mathematisch-naturwissenschaftliche Klasse, no. 33, pp. 1–15 (1899)

391

Romieu, M., and Jullien, G.   Sur l'existence d'une formation lymphoïde dans l'épiphyse des gallinaces, C. rend. Soc. biol. 136: 626–628 (1942)

392

Romieu, M., and Jullien, G.   Caractères histologiques et histophysiologiques des vésicules épiphysaires des gallinaces, C. rend. Soc. biol. 136: 628–630 (1942)

393

Romieu, M., and Jullien, G.   Évolution et valeur morphologique des vésicules closes de la glande pinéale des oiseaux, C. rend. Soc. biol. 136: 630–632 (1942)

394

Romieu, M., and Jullien, G.   Observations sur l'anatomie microscopique de la glande pinéale du nouveau-né humain, C. rend. Soc. biol. 136: 691–692 (1942)

395
Romieu, M., and Jullien, G.   Structure histologique et cytologie de l'épiphyse du nouveau-né, C. rend. Soc. biol. 136: 692–693 (1942)

396
Romieu, M., and Jullien, G.   Sur l'existence d'hemorragies capillaires et de phénomènes d'hémocrinie dans la glande pinéale du nouveau-né, C. rend. Soc. biol. 137: 249–250 (1943)

397
Romieu, M., and Jullien, G.   Cul-de-sac terminal du recessus et hydrencephalocrinie épiphysaire, C. rend. Soc. biol. 137: 456–457 (1943)

398
Roofe, P. G.   The endocranial blood vessels of Amblystoma tigrinum, J. Comp. Neur. 61: 257–293 (1935)

399
Roofe, P. G.   The histology of the paraphysis of Amblystoma, J. Morph. 59: 1–10 (1936)

400
Roussy, G., and Mosinger, M.   Les corrélations épiphyso-hypophysaires, Ann. anat. path. 15: 847–858 (1938)

401
Roussy, G., and Mosinger, M.   La neurocrinie épiphysaire et le complexe neuro-endocrinien épithalamo-épiphysaire, C. rend. Soc. biol. 127: 655–657 (1938)

402
Roux, P.   La glande pinéale ou épiphyse. Rennes: Oberthur, 1937

403
Ruiz Santolaya, P.   Histología del organo pineal, Siglo med. 77: 470–471 (1926)

404
Runnström, J.   Ueber die Anlage des Parapinealorgans bei Petromyzon, Zschr. mikr. anat. Forsch. 3: 283–294 (1925)

405
Sacristan, J. D.   Alteraciones especiales del conectivo en la glandula pineal humana, Bol. Soc. espan. biol. 3: 98–99 (1914)

406
Sacristan, J. M.   Einige Bemerkungen zu H. Josephy's Artikel: "Die feinere Histologie der Epiphyse," Zschr. ges. Neur. Psychiat. 69: 142–157 (1921)

407
Saint-Remy, G.   Notes tératologiques; 1–Ébauches épiphysaires et para-

[243]

physaires paires chez un embryon de poulet monstrueux, Bibl. anat. 5: 156–158 (1897)

408

Saitta, S.   Osservazioni sull'organo subcommessurale in alcuni mammiferi, Scritti biologici, Siena, 5: 419–428 (1930)

409

Salensky, W.   Recherches sur le développement du sterlet (Acipenser ruthenus), Arch. de biol. 2: 233–341 (1881)

410

Sanders, A.   Contributions to the anatomy of the central nervous system in Ceratodus forsteri, Ann. Mag. Nat. Hist., London, 3 (series 6): 157–188 (1889)

411

Sargent, P. E.   Reissner's fibre in the canalis centralis of vertebrates, Anat. Anz. 17: 33–44 (1900)

412

Sarteschi, U.   Ricerche istologiche sulla glandula pineale, Fol. neurobiol., Leipzig, 4: 675–685 (1910)

413

Scatizzi, I.   Ricerche sulla fine costituzione dell'epifisi dei Cheloni, Arch. zool. ital. 18: 407–420 (1933)

414

Scevola, D.   Ricerche istologiche sull'organo sottofornicale del terzo ventricolo, Monit. zool. ital. 49 (suppl.): 146–150 (1939)

415

Scevola, D.   Ulteriori indagini sulla struttura e morfogenesi dell'organo sotto-fornicale, Arch. ital. anat. 45: 195–205 (1941)

416

Scharrer, E.   Ueber die Zwischenhirndrüse der Säugetiere, Sitzber. Ges. Morph., München, 42: 36–41 (1933)

417

Scharrer, E.   Die Bildung von Meningocyten und der Abbau von Erythrocyten in der Paraphyse der Amphibien, Zschr. Zellforsch. 23: 244–252 (1935–1936)

418

Schewiakoff, W.   Beiträge zur Kenntnis des Acalephenauges, Morph. Jahrb. 15: 21–60 (1889)

419

Schlesinger, H.   Ueber die Zirbeldrüse im Alter, Arb. neur. Inst. Wien. 22: 18–40 (1917–1919)

[244]

420
Schmidt, W. J. Ueber ein Nebenparietalauge bei Lacerta agilis, Anat. Anz. 32: 137–140 (1908)

421
Schmidt, W. J. Beiträge zur Kenntnis der Parietalorgane der Saurier, Zschr. wiss. Zool. 92: 359–426 (1909)

422
Selenka, E. Das Stirnorgan der Wirbeltiere, Biol. Zbl. 10: 323–326 (1890–1891)

423
Shellabarger, C. J. Studies on the pineal body in the white Leghorn cockerel; Part IV—Observations on the pineal in the white Leghorn capon and cockerel. Ph.D. Thesis, Department of Zoology, Indiana University, 1952

424
Shirai, M. Hikaku-kaibōgaku-teki narabi-ni hasseigaku-teki kenchi yori mitaru shōka-sen to zugai to no kankei (The relation of the pineal gland to the cranium from the standpoint of comparative anatomy and of genetics), Kanazawa ika daigaku kaibōgaku kyōshitsu gyōseki 34: 85–92 (1940)

425
Sittler, G. A. R. Sur la région épiphysaire; le sac dorsal; le canal de Bichat. Thesis, Bordeaux, 1944

426
Slonimski, P. L'épiphyse pendant le développement postembryonnaire de l'Axolotl, C. rend. Soc. biol. 141: 1107–1108 (1947)

427
Sorenson, A. D. The pineal and parietal organ in Phrynosoma coronata, J. Comp. Neur. 3: 48–50 (1893)

428
Sorenson, A. D. Comparative study of the epiphysis and roof of the diencephalon, J. Comp. Neur. 4: 12–72, 153–170 (1894)

429
Spencer, W. B. The parietal eye of Hatteria, Nature 34: 33–35 (1886)

430
Spencer, W. B. Preliminary communication on the structure and presence in Sphenodon and other lizards of the median eye described by Von Graaf in Anguis fragilis (communicated by Prof. H. N. Moseley), Proc. R. Soc., London, 40: 559–565 (1886)

[245]

431
Spencer, W. B. On the presence and structure of the pineal eye in Lacertilia, Q. J. Micr. Sc. 27: 165–238 (1887)

432
Spencer, W. B. The pineal eye of Mordacia mordax, Proc. R. Soc. Victoria, Melbourne, 2: 102–105 (1890)

433
Spronck, C. H. H. De epiphysis cerebri als rudiment van een derde of parietaaloog, Ned. tschr. geneesk. 23: 174–179 (1887)

434
Ssobolew, L. W. Zur Lehre über die Entwicklung von Paraphysis und Epiphysis bei den Schlangen, Arch. mikr. Anat. 70: 318–329 (1907)

435
Staderini, R. Intorno alla ghiandola pineale dei mammiferi, Monit. zool. ital. 8: 241–254 (1897)

436
Staderini, R. L'occhio parietale di alcuni rettili e la sua funzionalità, Monit. zool. ital. 15: 341–343 (1904)

437
Staderini, R. I Saurii e il loro occhio parietale, Monit. zool. ital. 16: 61–64 (1905)

438
Stefko, W. Die vergleichende mikroskopische Anatomie der endokrinen Drüsen einiger Affengattungen und die Bedeutung des inkretorischen Systems in der Evolution der Primaten, Zschr. mikr. anat. Forsch. 16: 295–330 (1929)

439
Stemmler, J. Die Entwicklung der Anhänge am Zwischenhirndach beim Gecko (Gehyra oceanica und Hemidactylus mabouia); ein Beitrag zur Kenntnis der Epiphyse, des Parietalorgans und der Paraphyse. Inaug. Diss., Leipzig, 1900

440
Strahl, H. Das Leydigsche Organ bei Eidechsen, Sitzungsber. Ges. Beförd. ges. Naturwiss., Marburg, pp. 81–83 (1884)

441
Strahl, H., and Martin, E. Die Entwickelung des Parietalauges bei Anguis fragilis und Lacerta vivipara, Arch. Anat. Entw., pp. 146–161 (1888)

442
Studnicka, F. K. Sur les organes pariétaux de Petromyzon planeri,

Ceské spolecnosti nauk; Sitzungsberichte der Kgl. Böhmischen Gesellschaft der Wissenschaften—Mathematisch-naturwissenschaftliche Klasse, no. 1, pp. 1–50 (1893)

443
Studnicka, F. K.   Zur Anatomie der sogenannten Paraphyse des Wirbeltiergehirns, Ceské spolecnosti nauk; Sitzungsberichte der Kgl. Böhmischen Gesellschaft der Wissenschaften—Mathematisch-naturwissenschaftliche Klasse, no. 5, pp. 1–13 (1895)

444
Studnicka, F. K.   Beiträge zur Anatomie und Entwicklungsgeschichte des Vorderhirns der Kranioten, Ceské spolecnosti nauk; Sitzungsberichte der Kgl. Böhmischen Gesellschaft der Wissenschaften—Mathematisch-naturwissenschaftliche Klasse, section 1, no. 33, pp. 1–42 (1895), and section 2, no. 15, pp. 1–32 (1896)

445
Studnicka, F. K.   Zur Kritik einer Angaben über die Existenz eines Parietalauges bei Myxine glutinosa, Ceské spolecnosti nauk; Sitzungsberichte der Kgl. Böhmischen Gesellschaft der Wissenschaften—Mathematisch-naturwissenschaftliche Klasse, no. 21, pp. 1–4 (1898)

446
Studnicka, F. K.   Ueber den feineren Bau der Parietalorgane von Petromyzon marinus L., Ceské spolecnosti nauk; Sitzungsberichte der Kgl. Böhmischen Gesellschaft der Wissenschaften—Mathematisch-naturwissenschaftliche Klasse, no. 37, pp. 1–17 (1899)

447
Studnicka, F. K.   Untersuchungen über den Bau des Ependyms der Nervösen Centralorgane, Anat. Hefte; Abt. I—Arbeiten 15: 301–432 (1900)

448
Studnicka, F. K.   Zur Kenntnis der Parietalorgane under der sog. Paraphyse der niederen Wirbeltiere, Verh. anat. Ges., Jena, 14: 101–110 (1900)

449
Studnicka, F. K.   Die Parietalorgane, in: Oppel, A., Lehrbuch der vergleichenden mikroskopischen Anatomie der Wirbeltiere, vol. 5, Jena: Fischer, 1905

450
Sugimoto, H.   Shōka-sen bunpi kiten no saihōgaku-teki kenkyū; shōka-sen jisshitsu-saihō no kaku ni tsuite (Cytological studies on the mechanism of secretion in the pineal gland; the nuclei of the cells of the parenchyma of the pineal gland), Kaibōgaku zasshi 9: 1153–1164 (1937)

451
Sugiura, R.   Shiro-nezumi shōka-sen no keitaigaku-teki hassei narabi-ni soshiki-hasseigaku-teki kenkyū (Morphogenetic and histogenetic studies on the pineal gland of the white rat), Aichi igakkai zasshi 42: 2049 (1935)

452
Sugiura, R.   Shiro-nezumi shōka-sen no soshikigaku-teki kenkyū (Histological studies on the pineal gland of the white rat), Kaibōgaku zasshi 8: 20–21 (1935)

453
Sugiura, R.   Shōka-sen no hanashi (A talk on the pineal gland), Nagoya seibutsugakkai kiroku 3: 27–34 (1935)

454
Sugiura, R.   Ratte shōka-sen no keitai-hassei narabi-ni soshiki-hasseigaku-teki kenkyū (Morphogenetic and histogenetic studies on the pineal gland of the rat), Kaibōgaku zasshi 9: 409–448 (1936)

455
Suzuki, N., Eguchi, T., and Satō, M.   Shōka-sen no nenrei-teki henka ni tsuite (Changes in the pineal gland with age), Shinkeigaku zasshi 28: 617–618 (1928)

456
Suzuki, Y.   Beiträge zur Anatomie des Epithalamus, besonders der Epiphyse, bei den Primaten, Arb. anat. Inst. Univ. Sendai 21: 45–141 (1938)

457
Takemura, H.   Ryōseirui ni okeru shōka-sen no hassei ni tsuite (The development of the pineal gland in the amphibians), Kaibōgaku zasshi 20: 225–226 (1942)

458
Takemura, H.   Hōsan ryōseirui ni okeru shōka-sen no hassei ni tsuite; Megalobatrachus japonicus (Development of the pineal gland in amphibians native to Japan; Megalobatrachus japonicus), Hokuetsu igakkai zasshi 58: 331–347 (1943)

459
Takemura, H.   Hōsan ryōseirui ni okeru shōka-sen no hassei ni tsuite; Hynobius lichenatus (Boulenger) (Development of the pineal gland in amphibians native to Japan; Hynobius lichenatus, Boulenger), Hokuetsu igakkai zasshi 59: 93–100 (1944)

460
Takemura, H.   Hōsan ryōseirui ni okeru shōka-sen no hassei ni tsuite;

Polypedates buergeri, Schlegel (Development of the pineal gland in amphibians native to Japan; Polypedates buergeri, Schlegel), Hokuetsu igakkai zasshi 59: 103–113 (1944)

461
Takeyama, K. Morphologische Studien über die Nervendigungen in der Zirbeldrüse, Mitt. med. Akad., Kioto, 18: 83–93 (abstr. 325–326) (1936)

462
Terry, R. J. The morphology of the pineal region in teleosts, J. Morph. 21: 321–358 (1910)

463
Teruyama, N. Hito no shōka-sen no kaibō oyobi byōri (Anatomy and pathology of the human pineal gland), Naibunpitsugakkai zasshi 1: 593–623 (1925)

464
Tilney, F. The morphology of the diencephalic floor; a contribution to the study of craniate homology, J. Comp. Neur. 25: 213–282 (1915)

465
Tilney, F. Further evidence in support of the glandular nature of the pineal body, J. Nerv. Ment. Dis. 46: 442 (1917)

466
Tilney, F., and Warren, L. F. The morphology and evolutionary significance of the pineal body; being part 1 of a contribution to the study of the epiphysis cerebri with an interpretation of the morphological, physiological and clinical evidence. Amer. Anat. Mem., no. 9, Wistar Institute of Anatomy, Philadelphia, 1919

467
Togari, C., Sugiura, R., Fujita, D., and Itō, M. Kesshirui shōka-sen saihō ni tsuite (The pineal gland cells of the Rodentia), Kaibōgaku zasshi 23: 7 (1947)

468
Trautmann, A. Zur Frage der physiologischen Involution der Epiphysis cerebri, Deut. tieraerztl. Wschr. 42: 599–602 (1934)

469
Tretjakoff, D. Die Parietalorgane von Petromyzon fluviatilis, Zschr. wiss. Zool. 113: 1–112 (1915)

470
Turkewitsch, N. Zur Entwicklung des Zwischenhirndaches beim Menschen; Organon praecommissurale, Anat. Anz. 75: 463–468 (1932–1933)

471
Turkewitsch, N.   Die Entwicklung der Zirbeldrüse des Menschen, Morph. Jahrb. 72: 379–445 (1933)

472
Turkewitsch, N.   Die Entwicklung der Zirbeldrüse beim Rind (Bos taurus L.), Morph. Jahrb. 77: 326–356 (1936)

473
Turkewitsch, N.   Die Entwicklung des subkommissuralen Organs beim Rind (Bos taurus L.), Morph. Jahrb. 77: 573–586 (1936)

474
Turkewitsch, N.   Eigentümlichkeiten der embryologischen Entwicklung des Epiphysengebiets des Schafes (Ovis aries L.), Morph. Jahrb. 79: 305–330 (1937)

475
Turkewitsch, N.   Eigentümlichkeiten in der Entwicklung des Epiphysengebiets des Kaninchens (Lepus cuniculus L.), Morph. Jahrb. 79: 634–649 (1937)

476
Turner, W.   The pineal body (Epiphysis cerebri) in the brains of the walrus and seals, J. Anat. Physiol., London, 22: 300–303 (1888)

477
Ubukata, M., and Omura, S.   Demonstration der Kon's Silberpräparat der Gl. pinealis und des Plexus chorioideus des Menschen, Tr. Soc. path. jap. 28: 42–43 (1938)

478
Uemura, S.   Zur normalen und pathologischen Anatomie der Glandula pinealis des Menschen und einiger Haustiere, Frankf. Zschr. Path. 20: 381–488 (1917)

479
Ussow, M.   De la structure des lobes accessoires de la moelle épinière de quelques poissons osseux, Arch. de biol. 3: 605–658 (1882)

480
Utsu, N.   Senjo shōka-sen no hassei-hatuiku ni kan-suru saihōgaku-teki kenkyū (Cytological studies on the origin and development of the pineal gland of the toad), Kaibōgaku zasshi 6: 719–743 (1933)

481
de Varigni, H.   Le troisième œil des reptiles, Revue scientifique, 12 (series 3): 806–809 (1886)

482
del Vecchio, G.   Sul reperto di fibre muscolari striate nell'epiphysis cerebri umana, Osp. psichiat., Napoli, 2: 371–379 (1934)

483
del Vecchio, G.   Sui reperti di fibre muscolari striate nell'epifisi cerebrale; qualche osservazione in rapporto alla nota del Dr. Godina, Monit. zool. ital. 50: 182–184 (1939)

484
Vialli, M.   L'apparato epifisario degli Anfibi, Arch. zool. ital. 13: 423–451 (1929)

485
Voeltzkow, A.   Epiphyse und Paraphyse bei Krokodilen und Schildkroten, Abh. Senckenb. Naturf. Ges., Frankfurt, 27: 163–178 (1903)

486
von Volkmann, R.   Histologische Untersuchungen zur Frage der Sekretionsfunktion der Zirbeldrüse, Zschr. ges. Neur. Psychiat. 84: 593–616 (1923)

487
Waldschmidt, J.   Zur Anatomie des Nervensystems der Gymnophionen, Jena. Zschr. Naturwiss. 20: 461–476 (1887)

488
Walter, F. K.   Ueber den histologischen Bau der Zirbeldrüse; Vorläufige Mitteilung, Sitzungsber. Abh. naturf. Ges. Rostock 5: 3–6 (1913)

489
Walter, F. K.   Beiträge zur Histologie der menschlichen Zirbeldrüse, Zschr. ges. Neur. Psychiat. 17: 65–79 (1913)

490
Walter, F. K.   Ueber die normale und pathologische Histologie der Zirbeldrüse, Vortrag, gehalten auf d. 14. Jahresvers. d. nordd. Psych. Neur. zu. Lubeck (1914). Abstracted in: Zschr. ges. Neur. Psychiat. (Referate) 10: 269 (1914)

491
Walter, F. K.   Zur Histologie und Physiologie der menschlichen Zirbeldrüse, Zschr. ges. Neur. Psychiat. 74: 314–330 (1922)

492
Walter, F. K.   Weitere Untersuchungen zur Pathologie und Physiologie der Zirbeldrüse, Zschr. ges. Neur. Psychiat. 83: 411–463 (1923)

493
Warren, J.   The development of the paraphysis and the pineal region in Necturus maculatus, Am. J. Anat. 5: 1–27 (1906)

494
Warren, J.   The development of the paraphysis and pineal region in Reptilia, Am. J. Anat. 11: 313–377 (1910–1911)

495
Warren, J.   On the pineal region in human embryos, Proc. Amer. Assoc. Anat., 33. Sess., Anat. Rec. 11: 428–429 (1916–1917)

496
Warren, J.   The development of the paraphysis and pineal region in mammalia, J. Comp. Neur. 28: 75–104 (1917)

497
Watt, J. C.   Deposition of calcium salts in areas of calcification, Arch. Surg. 15: 89–101 (1927)

498
Weigert, C.   Beiträge zur Kenntnis der normalen menschlichen Neuroglia, Abh. Senckenb. naturf. Ges., Frankfurt, 19: 65–213 (1895)

499
Westhoff, F.   Neues über das sogenannte dritte Auge der Wirbeltiere, Jahrb. Naturwiss., Freiburg im Breisgau, 5: 317–319 (1889–1890)

500
Whitwell, J. R.   The epiphysis cerebri in Petromyzon fluviatilis, J. Anat. Physiol., London, 22: 502–504 (1888)

501
Wiedersheim, R.   Das Gehirn von Ammocoetes und Petromyzon planeri mit besonderer Berücksichtigung der spinalartigen Hirnnerven, Jena. Zschr. Naturwiss. 14: 1–23 (1880)

502
Wiedersheim, R.   Skelet und Nervensystem von Lepidosiren annectens, Jena. Zschr. Naturwiss. 14: 155–192 (1880)

503
Wiedersheim, R.   Ueber das Parietalauge der Saurier, Anat. Anz. 1: 148–149 (1886)

504
Winterhalter, W. P.   Untersuchungen über das Stirnorgan der Anuren, Acta Zool. 12: 1–68 (1931)

505
Wislocki, G. B.   Peculiarities of the cerebral blood vessels of the opossum; diencephalon, area postrema and retina, Anat. Rec. 78: 119–131 (1940)

506
Wislocki, G. B., and Dempsey, E. W.   The chemical histology and cytology of the pineal body and neurohypophysis, Endocrinology 42: 56–72 (1948)

507
Wislocki, G. B., and Leduc, E. H. Vital staining of the hematoencephalic barrier by silver nitrate and trypan blue, and cytological comparisons of the neurohypophysis, pineal body, area postrema, intercolumnar tubercle and supraoptic crest, J. Comp. Neur. 96: 371–413 (1952)

508
Wright, R. On the nervous system and sense organs of Amiurus, Proc. R. Canad. Inst., Toronto, 2: 352–386 (1884)

509
Yamada, H. Hari-mogura no shikyū-jōbu koto-ni shōka-tai no kaibōgaku-teki chiken (Anatomical information on the upper part of the thalamus, especially the pineal body, in the echidna), Arb. anat. Inst. Univ. Sendai 21: 149–171 (1938)

510
Yamada, H. Beiträge zur Anatomie der Epiphyse bei Beuteltieren, Arb. anat. Inst. Univ. Sendai 24: 169–231 (1941)

511
Yoshizumi, G. Kikutō-kōmori no shōka-sen no hassei (The development of the pineal gland of the chrysanthemum-headed bat), Kaibōgaku zasshi 24: 105 (1949)

512
Yoshizumi, G. Denshobato (Columba livia var. domestica, L.) shōka-sen no shoki hassei (First stages of the development of the pineal gland of the carrier pigeon), Niigata igakkai zasshi 63: 531 (1949)

513
Yoshizumi, G. Honyū-dōbutsu toku-ni kikutō-kōmori shōka-sen no shoki-hassei (Development in the initial stages of the pineal gland in mammals, especially in the chrysanthemum-headed bat), Igaku to seibutsugaku 17: 267–270 (1950)

514
Zancla, A. Sulla fine struttura del Conarium umano, Arch. anat. pat. 2: 161–169 (1906)

Reviews and Related Papers

1
A., J. L'étrange glande pinéale, Lyon méd. 132: 225–230 (1923)

2
Adriani, S. L'epifisi, Policlinico; Sezione medica 32: 105–116 (1925)

3
Andriani, S. La epifisis, Rev. sudamer. endocr. 8: 694–705 (1925)

4
Araki, C. Surgical removal of pineal tumors; a critical review of the literature, Arch. jap. chir. 14: 1193–1206 (1937)

5
Aschner, B. Die Erkrankungen der Zirbeldrüse, in: Hirsch, M., Handbuch der inneren Sekretion, 3^1: 247–273. Leipzig: Kabitzsch, 1928

6
Aschner, B. Physiologie der Zirbeldrüse, in: Hirsch, M., Handbuch der inneren Sekretion 2^1: 375–384. Leipzig: Kabitzsch, 1929

7
Aschner, B. Technik der experimentellen Untersuchungen an der Hypophyse und am Zwischenhirn, in: Abderhalden, E., Handb. biol. Arbeitsmeth., Abt. v, Teil 3B, Heft 2, ss. 125–148. Berlin: Urban & Schwarzenberg, 1938

8
Askanazy, M. De l'influence de certaines tumeurs sur le développement précoce des organes génitaux, Congrès français de médecine 10: 333–337 (1908)

9
Askanazy, M. Chemische Ursachen und morphologische Wirkungen bei Geschwülstkranken, insbesondere über sexuelle Frühreife, Zschr. Krebsforsch. 9: 393–421 (1910)

10
Askanazy, M. Die Zirbel und ihre Tumoren in ihrem funktionellen Einfluss, Frankf. Zschr. Path. 24: 58–77 (1921)

11
Atkinson, F. R. B. The hormones of the pineal gland, Bull. Soc. roumain. endocr. 5: 119–125 (1939)

12
Bailey, P. The pineal body, in: Cowdry, E. V., Special Cytology 2: 787–796. 2nd ed. New York: Hoeber, 1932

13
Bargmann, W. Die Epiphysis cerebri, in: Mollendorff, W. von, Handb. mikr. Anat. Menschen 6 (part 4): 309–502. Berlin: Springer, 1943

14
Belluzzi, I. Contributo allo studio della ghiandola pineale; sua patologia e fisiologia, Med. prat., Napoli, 13: 10–17 (1928)

15
Benda, C. Die Zirbeldrüse, in: Hirsch, M., Handbuch der inneren Sekretion 1: 1098–1159. Leipzig: Kabitzsch, 1932

16
Berblinger, W. Zur Frage der Zirbelfunktion, Virchows Arch. 237: 144–153 (1922)

17
Berblinger, W. Die Glandula pinealis (Corpus pineale), in: Henke, F., and Lubarsch, O., Handbuch der spez. path. Anat. und Histol. 8: 681–759. Berlin: Springer, 1926

18
Berblinger, W. Bemerkungen über die Zirbelgeschwülste, zur Arbeit von P. Kutscherenko "Tumor glandulae pinealis," Zbl. allg. Path. 38: 1–6 (1926)

19
Berblinger, W. Die Theorien über die Zirbelfunktion und ihre anatomischen Grundlagen, Arch. Psychiat. 85: 586–590 (1928)

20
Berblinger, W. Zur Frage der pinealen Frühreife und der pineal bedingten genitalen Hypertrophie beim Erwachsenen, Deut. med. Wschr. 55: 1956–1959 (1929)

21
Berblinger, W. Physiologie und Pathologie der Zirbel, Erg. ges. Med. 14: 245–312 (1930)

22
Berblinger, W. Zirbel (Epiphysis cerebri) und Frühreife, Neue deut. Klin. 10: 790–797 (1932)

23
Berkeley, W. N. Comments on the function and clinical uses of the pineal gland, Med. Rec. 97: 12–14 (1920)

24
Berkeley, W. N. Diseases of the pineal gland with incidental comment on its function, Am. Med. 30: 627–631 (1924)

25
Beutlerus, J. W. Disputatio medica de glandulae pinealis statu naturali et praeternaturali. Thesis, Marpurgi Cattorum (Marburg), 1680

26
Biach, P., and Hulles, E. Ueber die Beziehungen der Zirbeldrüse (Glandula pinealis) zum Genitale, Wien. klin. Wschr. 25: 373–375 (1912)

27
Bing, J. F., Globus, J. H., and Simon, H. Pubertas praecox: a survey of the reported cases and verified anatomical findings; with particular reference to the pineal body, J. Mount Sinai Hosp. 4: 935–965 (1937–1938)

28
Bliss, A. R. The endocrine compounds—the pineal gland, Drug and Cosmet. Indust. 44: 38–39 (1939)

29
Borell, U., and Örström, A. On the function of the epiphysis, Acta psychiat. neur., København, 47 (supplement): 144 (1947)

30
Born, A. Die Geschwülste der Zirbeldrüse. Inaug. Diss., Heidelberg, 1934

31
Buonomo la Rossa, B. Pinealomi e tumori della regione pineale, Rass. internaz. clin. ter. 29: 395–397 (1949)

32
Businco, A. Trattato italiano de anatomia patologia, part VII, pp. 360–363. 2nd ed. Torino: U. T. E. T., 1949

33
Calvet, J. L'épiphyse (glande pinéale). Paris: Baillière, 1934

34
van Caneghem, D. Over de physiologische en physio-pathologische beteekenis van de Hypophysis en van het Corpus pineale, Vlaamsch geneesk. tschr. 2: 345–364 (1921)

35
Cannavo, L. Azione opposta di estratti epifisari sulla chetonemia, Boll. Soc. ital. biol. sper. 11: 273–274 (1936)

36
Catalán, E. Las ideas de Descartes sobra la glandula pineal y la fisio-patologia moderna, Rev. crim., B. Aires, 12: 406–425 (1925)

37
Cattaneo, C. Ghiandola pineale, Atti dell'vIII Congresso pediatrico italiano (1913), pp. 444–448. Bologna, 1914

38
Charles, J. A. M. The pineal body; its function and disorders, Univ. Durham Coll. M. Gaz. 15: 102–107 (1914–1915)

39
Comby, J. Syndromes hypophysaires et épiphysaires, Arch. med. enf. 37: 539–554 (1934)

40
von Cyon, E. Les fonctions de l'hypophyse et de la glande pinéale, C. rend. Acad. sc., Paris, 144: 868–869 (1907)

41
Dandy, W. E. An operation for the removal of pineal tumors, Surg. Gyn. Obst. 33: 113–119 (1921)

42
DeCourt, J. L'opothérapie épiphysaire est-elle justifiée? Progr. méd., Paris, 2: 2125–2134 (1932)

43
Dendy, A. The pineal gland, Science Prog., 20th Cent., London, 2: 284–306 (1907–1908)

44
Descartes, R. De homine; figuris et latinitate donatus a Florentio Schuyl. Leyden: P. Leffen & F. Moyardus, 1662

45
Descartes, R. Les passions de l'âme, articles xxxi–xxxii, pp. 66–68. Paris: Compagnie de libraires, 1726

46
Dewey, M. Review of the development of the pituitary and pineal organs, Internat. J. Orthodont. 9: 346–351 (1923)

47
Dohrn, M., and Hohlweg, W. Die Stellung der Zirbeldrüse im endo-krinen System, Naturwissenschaften 17: 920 (1929)

48
Editorial. Diseases of the pineal body, J. Am. M. Ass. 34: 941–942 (1900)

49
Editorial. The pineal body, Prescriber, Edinburgh, 17: 366–369 (1923)

50
Editorial. Pineal body as an endocrine organ, Brit. M. J. 2: 544–545 (1936)

51
Editorial. Functions of the pineal, Lancet 1: 558 (1936)

52
Engel, P. Ueber die hormonalen Eigenschaften der Zirbeldrüse, Wien. klin. Wschr. 48: 481–486 (1935)

53
Engel, P. Die physiologische und pathologische Bedeutung der Zirbeldrüse, Erg. inn. Med. 50: 116–171 (1936)

54
Engel, P. Ueber den heutigen Stand unseres Wissens von der Zirbelfunktion, Wien. klin. Wschr. 50: 1219–1222 (1937)

55
Engel, P. Nuevos aspectos de la función de la glandula pineal, Rev. Acad. columb. cienc. 7: 233–235 (1946)

56
Engel, P., and Bergmann, W. Die physiologische Funktion der Zirbeldrüse und ihre therapeutische Anwendung, Zschr. Vitamin-, Hormon- und Fermentforschung 4: 564–594 (1952)

57
Farrant, R. The causation and cure of certain forms of insanity, Brit. M. J. 1: 882–883 (1916)

58
Fay, H. M. L'épiphyse: glande de l'intelligence, Méd. scol., Paris, 22: 176–183 (1933)

59
Fiandaca, S. La fisiopatologia dell'epifisi, Riformia med. 50: 1015–1017 (1934)

60
Fiessinger, N. Physiopathologie de la glande pinéale, Rev. gén. clin. thér. 50: 657–662 (1936)

61
Foa, C. Le mie ricerche sulla ghiandola pineale, Fiziol. zhur. (Sechenov Journal of Physiology of the U.S.S.R.) 19: 103–111 (1935)

62
Foerster, O. Die Hirntumoren und ihre moderne Diagnostik und Therapie, Neue deut. Klin. 16: 449–468 (1939)

63
Ford, F. R. Diseases of the Nervous System in Infancy, Childhood and Adolescence. 3rd ed. Springfield, Illinois: Thomas, 1952

64
von Frankl-Hochwart, L. The relations of internal secretion to mental conditions, Am. J. M. Sc. 146: 186–195 (1913)

65
Frankl-Hochwart, L. Ueber die Einwirkung der Zirbeldrüsenstörung auf die Psyche, Med. Klin. 10: 1460 (1914)

66
von Frankl-Hochwart, L. Ueber die Einwirkung der Zirbeldrüsenzerstörung auf die Psyche, Jahrb. Psychiat. Neur. 35: 159–163 (1915)

67
Frenzel, W. Wozu Zirbeldrüse, Umschau, 38: 969–972 (1934)

68
Friedreich, J. B. Versüch einer Literärgeschichte der Pathologie und Therapie der psychischen Krankheiten. Würzburg: Strecker, 1830

69
Fujikawa, Y. Zōki ryōhō; rinshō-jō no kansatsu (Organotherapy; clinical observations), Chiryō shinpō, no. 11: 114 (1903)

70
Fujikawa, Y. Zōki seizai oyobi sono shuchi; iii–Shōka-sen seizai (Organ extracts and their principal therapeutic uses; iii–Pineal gland extract), Chiryō shinpō, no. 11: 123 (1903)

71
Funk, E. H. The pineal body, Progr. Med., Philadelphia, 2: 325–329 (1921)

72
Galen, C. De anatomicis administrationibus, book ix, pp. 127–128. Paris: Simon de Colines, 1531

73
Galen, C. De usu partium corporis humani, book viii, chap. xiii, pp. 488–489. Lyons: Rouillius, 1550

74
Gastaldi, L. L'accrescimento somatico dell'uomo e le glandole endocrine con particolare riguardo all'ipofisi ed epifisi, Pathologica 17: 299–302 (1925)

75
Gentili, A. Malattie del sistema endocrino e gravidanza, Atti Soc. ital. ostet. 24: 114–330 (1925)

76
Gierke, E. Hypophysis und Epiphysis bei Diabetes insipidus, Verh. deut. path. Ges. 17: 200–208 (1921)

77
Globus, J. H. Pinealoma, in: Third International Congress of Scientific and Social Campaign against Cancer, p. 96. Atlantic City, 1939

78
Goldzieher, M. A. Diseases of the pineal gland, in: Litchfield, H. R., and Dembo, L. H., Therapeutics of Infancy and Childhood 3: 2739–2742. Philadelphia: Davis, 1942

79
Gordon, M. B. The role of the pineal in pediatrics; a review of the literature, Endocrinology 3: 437–453 (1919)

80
Gordon, M. B. Disorders of the internal secretions in children; thyroid, thymus and pineal glands, New York M. J. 113: 239–243 (1921)

81
Gouget, —. Les fonctions de la glande pinéale, Presse méd. 21: 769–770 (1913)

82
Granel, M. La glande pinéale; anatomie comparée et fonctions, Gaz. hebd. sc. méd. Montpel. 9: 361–365 (1887)

83
Griesinger, W. Mental Pathology and Therapeutics, p. 429. London: New Sydenham Society, 1867

84
Halban, J. Tumoren und Geschlechtscharaktere, Zschr. ges. Anat.; Abt. ii–Zschr. Konstit.-lehre 11: 294–326, 1925

85
Halliburton, W. D. The appendages of the brain, Ned. tschr. geneesk. 66: 1134–1146 (1922)

86
Hanson, A. M. Histology of the pineal gland and its probable physiologic function, Minnesota M. 20: 78–81 (1937)

87
Herdman, W. A. Recent discoveries in connection with the pineal and pituitary bodies of the brain, Proc. Liverpool Biol. Soc. 1: 18–25 (1886)

88
Herold, L. Zusammenfassende Aufsätze über den heutigen Stand der Medizin; I–Die physiologische und pathologische Bedeutung der Zirbeldrüse, Zschr. ärtzl. Fortbild. 38: 8–11 (1940)

89
Hofling, C. K. The pineal body, Cincinnati J. M. 29: 210–218 (1948)

90
Hofstätter, R. Ergebnisse und Aussichten der experimentellen Zirbelforschung, Jahrb. Psychiat. Neur. 37: 179–236 (1917)

91
Hofstätter, R. Beitrag zur therapeutischen Verwendung von Zirbelextrakten, Wien. klin. Wschr. 62: 338–339 (1950)

92
Hofstätter, R. Die therapeutische Verwendung von Zirbelextrakten ist kein Versüch mehr, Wien. med. Wschr. 10: 89–92 (1951)

93
Horrax, G. The pineal body, in: Metropolitan State Hospital (Waltham, Mass.), Collected Lectures of the 6th Postgraduate Seminar in Neurology and Psychiatry (1940–1941), pp. 69–71. Waltham, 1941

94
Horrax, G. Pineal body, in: Metropolitan State Hospital (Waltham, Mass.), Collected Lectures of the 7th Postgraduate Seminar in Neurology and Psychiatry (1941–1942), pp. 515–524. Waltham, 1942

95
Horrax, G. Pineal tumors of childhood, J. Pediat. 20: 397–400 (1942)

96
Horrax, G. The role of pinealomas in the causation of diabetes insipidus, Ann. Surg. 126: 725–739 (1947)

97
Horrax, G. The diagnosis and treatment of pineal tumors, Radiology 52: 186–192 (1949)

98
Hutton, J. H. Pineal gland and its function, Med. J. and Rec. 120: 476–477 (1924)

99
Iriarte Peixoto, R. Terapeûtica das afecoes da epifise, in: Terapeûtica das doenças endócrinas, chap. III, pp. 95–101. Lisboa: Livraria Luso-Espanhola, 1946

[261]

100
Itō, K. Nōkasuitai to shōka-sen (Hypophysis cerebri and pineal gland), Rinshō bunka 8: 4–5 (1941)

101
Itō, K. Seishin-bunretsu-byō no gen-in ni kan-suru shōka-sen no igi (The significance of the pineal gland in the causes of schizophrenia), Kurume igakkai zasshi 11: 103–106 (1948)

102
Itō, K. Kasuitai-kei to shōka-tai-kei (Pituitary type and pineal type; part 1), Seishin-shinkeigaku zasshi 50: 2–3 (1948)

103
Itō, K. Descartes to shōka-sen (Descartes and the pineal gland), Sōgō igaku 5: 413, 462–463 (1948)

104
Itō, K. Naibunpigaku-teki seikakugaku ni tsuite (The science of personality from the standpoint of endocrinology), Seishin-shinkeigaku zasshi 50 (no. 1): 5–8 (1948) and 50 (no. 5): 7–10 (1949)

105
Itō, K. Kasuitai-kei to shōka-tai-kei (Pituitary type and pineal type; part 2), Seishin-shinkeigaku zasshi 51: 2–3 (1950)

106
Itō, K. Kasui-tai-kei to shōka-tai-kei (Hypophysis type and pineal type), Sōgō igaku 9: 47–49 (1952)

107
Jelliffe, D. The pineal body; its structure, function and diseases, New York M. J. 111: 235–240, 269–275 (1920)

108
Jordan, H. E. Results of recent studies on the mammalian epiphysis cerebri, Tr. Am. Micr. Soc., Decatur, Ill., 31: 231–242 (1912)

109
Jores, A. Fortschritte der Hormontherapie; v–Therapie mit Parathormon, Thymus- und Epiphysenextrakt, Fortsch. Ther. 13: 503–509 (1937)

110
Jores, A. Die Krankheiten der Zirbeldrüse, in: Bumke, O., and Foerster, O., Handbuch der Neurologie 15: 389–393. Berlin: Springer, 1937

111
Jumon, H. Introduction à l'étude de l'endocrinologie; viii–L'épiphyse ou glande pinéale, Bull. méd., Paris, 53: 789–791 (1939)

112
Kidd, L. H. Pineal experimentations, Brit. M. J. 2: 2002–2003 (1910)

113
Kidd, L. J. The pineal body; a review, Med. Chron., Manchester, 24 (series 4): 154–184 (1912–1913)

114
Kidd, L. J. The pineal body; a review, Rev. Neur. Psychiat., Edinburgh, 11: 1–21, 55–75 (1913)

115
Kitay, J. I. Pineal lesions and precocious puberty: a review, J. Clin. Endocrinol. Metab. 14: 622–625 (1954)

116
Köbcke, H. Ueber den heutigen Stand der Epiphysenforschung, Deut. med. Wschr. 62: 1134–1137 (1936)

117
Koopman, J. Bijdragen tot de geschiedenis der ontwikkelung van de endocrinologie; II–De pijnappelklier, Bijdr. gesch. geneesk. 8: 96–100 (1928)

118
Krabbe, K. H. Corpus pineale, Ugeskr. Laeger 73: 1617–1625 (1911)

119
Krabbe, K. H. Valeur réciproque des syndromes hypophysaires et épiphysaires, Rev. neur. 38: 698–702 (1922)

120
Krabbe, K. H. The pineal gland, especially in relation to the problem of its supposed significance in sexual development, Endocrinology 7: 379–414 (1923)

121
Krabbe, K. H. Experimentelle undersogelser over corpus pineales funktion (exstirpationsforsag), Nord. med. tidskr. 5: 362–371 (1933)

122
von Kup, J. Die Wirkung psychischer Reize auf das Zirbel-Hypophysen Gleichgewicht, Frankf. Zschr. Path. 53: 101–104 (1939)

123
Laignel-Lavastine, M. Glande pinéale, Traité de physiologie normale et pathologique 4: 357–402 (1928)

124
Laire, G. Sur le système épithalamo-épiphysaire; ses connexions avec le complexe hypothalamo-hypophysaire. Thesis, Marseille, 1939

[263]

125
Lawson, H. The present status of the thymus and the pineal as endocrine organs, Kentucky M. J. 38: 345–348 (1940)

126
Legros, J. Étude sur la glande pinéale et ses divers états pathologiques. Thesis, Paris, 1873

127
Leiner, J. H. Pubertas praecox with especial attention to mentality, Endocrinology 4: 369–380 (1920)

128
Lepore, M. Le funzioni della glandula tiroide, dell'ipofisi e della glandula pineale, Gazz. osp. 49: 1603–1608 (1928)

129
Lereboullet, P. Rôle de l'hypophyse et de l'épiphyse dans les dystrophies infantiles, Gaz. Hôp. 95: 951–952 (1922)

130
Leschke, E. Beiträge zur klinischen Pathologie des Zwischenhirns; ɪ—Mitt., Klinische und experimentelle Untersuchungen über Diabetes insipidus, seine Beziehungen zur Hypophyse und zum Zwischenhirn, Zschr. klin. med. 87: 201–279 (1919)

131
Majima, T. Shōka-sen shuyō no shōkō oyobi shindan (Symptoms and diagnosis of tumors of the pineal gland), Naikagaku zasshi 6: 187–194 (1914)

132
Marburg, O. Die Adipositas cerebralis; ein Beitrag zur Pathologie der Zirbeldrüse, Wien. med. Wschr. 58: 2618–2622 (1908)

133
Marburg, O. Die Klinik der Zirbeldrüsenerkrankungen, Erg. inn. Med. 10: 146–166 (1913)

134
Marburg, O. Neue Studien über die Zirbeldrüse, Arb. neur. Inst. Wien. 23: 1–35 (1920–1922)

135
Marburg, O. Die Physiologie der Zirbeldrüse, in: Bethe, A., and Bergmann, G. von, Handbuch der normalen und pathologischen Physiologie, 16¹: 493–509. Berlin: Springer, 1930

136
Martino, G. Breves noticias physiologicas de endocrinología e opoterapia; vɪ—Epiphise, Arq. biol., Sao Paulo, 16: 143–144 (1933–1934)

137
McCord, C. P. The pineal gland, Interstate M. J., St. Louis, 22: 354–370 (1915)

138
McCord, C. P. The pineal gland's influence upon growth and differentiation, with particular reference to its influence upon prenatal developments, Am. J. Obst. 76: 678 (1917)

139
Migliucci, C. Il significato morfologico e funzionale dell'epiphisis cerebri; il dispinealismo in contrapposto al dispituitarismo, Gior. internaz. sc. med., Napoli, 34 (new series): 269–273 (1912)

140
Miura, K. Naibunpi-sen to shinkei-keitō koto-ni kōkan-sinkei to no kankei ni tsuite (The relation of the endocrine glands to the nervous system, especially to the sympathetic nerves), Shinkeigaku zasshi, 25: 189–196 (1925)

141
Molfino, F. Fisiopatologia della ghiandola pineale. Roma: Pozzi edit., 1935

142
Molfino, F. Physio-pathologie de la glande pinéale, Gaz. hôp. 109: 1274–1275 (1936)

143
de Monchy, S. J. R. De Ziekten der Glandula pinealis, Ned. tschr. geneesk. 67: 1419–1425 (1923)

144
Mori, S. Shōka-sen naibunpi (Internal secretion of the pineal gland), Naibunpi oyobi jikken chiryō 7: 615–624 (1939)

145
Mori, S. Naibunpigaku (Endocrinology), pp. 268–277. 2nd ed. Tokyo: Nanzandō, 1941

146
Mori, S., Hayashi, T., Ojima, A., Nonouchi, Y., and Sakatoku, J. Naibunpi-zōki shuyō no tōkei-teki kansatsu (Statistical observation of the neoplastic diseases in the endocrine organs), Gann 41: 152–154 (1950)

147
Mori, S., and Nakayama, K. Naibunpi-sen no sōgō-kankei; shōka-sen to ji-ta naibunpi-sen to no sōgō-kankei (Interrelations of the endocrine glands; interrelations of the pineal gland and other endocrine organs), Naibunpi oyobi jikken chiryō 5: 876–878 (1937)

148
Münzer, A. Die Zirbeldrüse, Berl. klin. Wschr. 48: 1669–1676 (1911)

149
Mygind, S. H. The function of the parietal eye, Acta psychiat. neur.,
København, 24: 607–627 (1949)

150
Nahmmacher, E. Organtherapie, Scientia Pharmaceutica 11: 43–44
(1940)

151
Nakata, M., Sakai, T., and Sōma, Y. Kōjō-bu dai-san nōshitsu-zōrō jutsu
(Posterior-superior third ventriculostomy), Nō to shinkei 2: 241–243
(1950)

152
Nassetti, F. Contributo alla conoscenza dei tumori della ghiandola pineali; considerazioni ed esperienze intorno alla possibilità di un intervento
chirurgico, Atti Accad. fisiocr., Siena, 4 (series 5): 19–21 (1912)

153
Nassetti, F. Dell'operabilità e delle vie di accesso ai tumori della ghiandola pineale, Policlinico; Sezione chirurgica 20: 497–501 (1913)

154
Niehans, P. Die endokrinen Drüsen des Gehirns; Epiphyse und Hypophyse. Bern: Hüber, 1938

155
Nishio, N. Nōkasuitai no jikken-teki kenkyū; nōkasuitai no kannō ni
tai-suru igi (Experimental studies on the hypophysis cerebri; the role
of the hypophysis on the interbrain—thalamencephalon), Nippon byōrigakkai kaishi 27: 505–506 (1937)

156
Ochi, S. Hormon ni tsuite; shōka-sen no Hormon (Hormones; the hormone of the pineal gland), Tōzai igaku taikan, 10 (Seirigaku; Hormon):
29–31 (1929)

157
Ogata, T. Naibunpi-sen no kinō-teki bunrui ni tsuite no shiken e no
tsuika (A supplement to the author's opinion of the functional classification of the endocrine glands), Byōrigaku zasshi 1: 544–545 (1942)

158
Olivetti, R. Recenti acquisizioni a proposito della funzione ormonica
epifisaria, Arch. ital. med. sper. 2: 349–359 (1938)

159
Orlandi, N. Lo stato attuale delle nostre conoscenze sulla glandola
pineale, Osp. maggiore, Milano, 10 (series 3): 223–233 (1922)

160
Parhon, C. I. L'épiphyse au point de vue endocrinologique, Bull. et mém. de la Sect. d'endocr. 4: 349–404 (1938)

161
Parhon, C. I. Aperçu général sur la pathologie et la physiologie de l'épiphyse; corrélations de cet organe; opothérapie épiphysaire; problèmes nouveaux en rapport avec cet organe, Bull. Acad. méd. roumaine 14: 783–810 (1943)

162
Parhon, C. I. Les travaux récents des endocrinologistes roumains concernant l'épiphyse, Biol. et méd., Marseille, 59–66 (1947)

163
Parhon, C. I. Le rôle de l'épiphyse dans les phénomènes métaboliques; revue générale, Medicina romana, Bucarest, 3: 3–4 (1948)

164
Pende, N. Recenti acquisizioni sulla fisiopatologia e sulla clinica della ghiandola pineale, Acta medica latina 4: 193–197 (1931). Also published in: Rinnovamento medico 9 (no. 1): 3–4 (1932)

165
Pende, N. Recenti acquisizioni sulla fisiopatologia e sulla clinica della ghiandola pineale, Med. argent. 11: 1478–1480 (1932)

166
Pennybacker, J. Pituitary, pineal and third ventricle tumors, Postgrad. M. J., London, 26: 141–154 (1950)

167
Polya, E. Hirnhäute, Gehirn, Zirbeldrüse; Uebersichtsreferat, Jahrber. ges. Chir. 26: 309–338 (1920)

168
Poppi, A. L'ipofisi cerebrale, faringea e la glandola pineale in patologia, Bologna, 1911

169
Rabl-Rückhard, H. Zur Deutung der Zirbeldrüse (Epiphyse), Zool. Anz. 9: 405–407 (1886)

170
Raybaud, A. État actuel de nos connaissances sur l'épiphyse, Marseille méd. 64: 775–785 (1927)

171
van Rijnberk, G. Organes sans appareils nerveux locaux, Arch. neerl. physiol. 8: 394–413 (1923)

172
Robbins, F. The pineal gland, Med. Rev. of Rev. 26: 237–243 (1920)

173
Robert, J. Epiphyse, Bull. méd., Paris, 53: 721–726 (1939)

174
Robert, J. La glande pinéale, Progr. méd., Paris, 79: 612–621 (1951)

175
Rolleston, H. D. The Endocrine Organs in Health and Disease, with an Historical Review, pp. 451–470. London: Oxford Univ. Press, 1936

176
Roussy, G., and Mosinger, M. Le complexe épithalamo-épiphysaire; ses corrélations avec le complexe hypothalamo-hypophysaire; le système neuroendocrinien du diencéphale, Rev. neur. 69: 459–470 (1938)

177
Roussy, G., and Mosinger, M. Les glandes à fonction neuricrine de cerveau, Schweiz. med. Wschr. 21: 581–583 (1940)

178
Roussy, G., and Mosinger, M. Les glandes neuricrines de l'encéphale (Formations épendymaires, hypendymocytaires et physocytaires), Rev. neur. 73: 521–546 (1941)

179
Roux, P. Contribution à l'étude historique de la glande pinéale, Hippocrate, Paris, 4: 527–551 (1936)

180
Saar, H. Pubertas praecox bei Gliom des Zwischenhirnes; ein Beitrag zur Frage der innersekretorischen Funktion der Zirbeldrüse, Frankf. Zschr. Path. 50: 451–461 (1937)

181
Sachs, E. Diagnosis and Treatment of Brain Tumors and Care of the Neurosurgical Patient. 3rd ed. St. Louis: Mosby, 1949

182
Sainton, P., and Dagnan-Bouveret, J. Descartes et la psychophysiologie de la glande pinéale, N. iconog. Salpêtrière, Paris, 25: 171–192 (1912)

183
Schächter, M. Nos connaissances actuelles concernant l'épiphyse, Bull. et mém. de la Sect. d'endocr. 1: 227–235 (1935)

184
Schächter, M. Nos connaissances actuelles concernant l'épiphyse, J. méd. Paris 56: 343–345 (1936)

185
Schächter, M. La macrogénitosomie précoce, syndrome de Pellizzi, n'est pas d'origine pinéale, Paris méd. 113: 244–247 (1939)

186
Seguy, J., and Jamain, B. Quelques données expérimentales récentes sur l'épiphyse, Médecine 19: 309–314 (1938)

187
Seigneur, P. Étude critique sur la glande pinéale normale et pathologique. Thesis, Paris, 1912

188
Selye, H. Textbook of Endocrinology. 2nd ed. Montreal: Acta Endocrinologica, 1949

189
Sezary, A. Les tumeurs de la glande pinéale, Gaz. hôp. 87: 1141–1147, 1205–1209 (1914)

190
Souques, A. Descartes et le siège de l'âme dans la glande pinéale, Bull. Soc. fr. hist. méd. 32: 14 (1938)

191
Souques, A. Glande pinéale et esprits animaux, d'après Descartes, Rev. neur. 77: 7–30 (1945)

192
Sternberg, J. L'épiphyse, glande endocrine, Rev. méd. Univ. de Montréal 3: 49–61 (1951)

193
Stevenin, H., and Deparis, M. Données récentes sur l'épiphyse, Le Phare médical de Paris, pp. 355–358, Oct., 1937

194
Takase, K. Sinkei-byō to naibunpi; shōka-sen no shitsubyō (Nervous diseases and internal secretion; diseases of the pineal gland), Nagasaki igakkai zasshi 7: 564–565 (1929)

195
Takeya, H. Shōka-sen no shuyō ni tsuite (Tumors of the pineal gland), Ōsaka iji shinshi 6: 82–93 (1935)

196
Takeya, H. Shōka-sen no naibunpigaku-teki chiken ni kan-suru rekishi-teki kaiko (Historical review of endocrinological information on the pineal gland), Nippon naibunpigakkai zasshi 12: 1–11 (1936)

197
Talbot, N. B., Sobel, E. H., McArthur, J. W., and Crawford, J. D. Functional Endocrinology from Birth through Adolescence. Cambridge, Mass.: Harvard Univ. Press, 1952

198
Termeer, G. Ovarialgeschwülste im Kindesalter und Pubertas praecox, Arch. Gyn. 127: 431–462 (1926)

199
de los Terreros, C. S. Glandula pineal y patología infantil, Rev. iber. amer. cienc. med. 36: 105–112 (1916)

200
Tilney, F. Is the pineal body a gland or a vestige? J. Nerv. Ment. Dis. 48: 154–156 (1918)

201
Tilney, F. Is the pineal body a gland or a vestige? New York M. J. 107: 887–888 (1918)

202
Tilney, F. The pineal gland, in: Cowdry, E. V., Special Cytology 1: 501–548. New York: Hoeber, 1928

203
Tokumitsu, Y. Naibunpi ni tsuite (Internal secretion), Tōhoku igaku zasshi 1: 66–104 (1916)

204
Tokumitsu, Y. Naibunpi-ki ketsuraku shōkō no byōri hassei ni tsuite (The pathological development of symptoms following the loss or failure in function of endocrine organs), Nippon naibunpigakkai zasshi 26: 5 (1950)

205
Trautmann, A. Die Zirbel, Corpus pineale, in: Ellenberger, W., Handbuch der vergleichenden mikroskopischen Anatomie der Haustiere 2: 169–176. Berlin: Parey, 1911

206
Trivus-Katz, F. A. Smena zubov v svjazi s funksijej endokrinnykh zhelez (The change from temporary to permanent teeth in relation to the functions of the endocrine glands), Voprosy izucheniia i vospitaniia lichnosti, Leningrad, no. 3/4, pp. 35–53 (1927)

207
de Velasco y Castellanos, R., and Rodriguez-Sarabia, L. Estudio fisiologico del timo y de la epifisis, Cron. med. quir. Habana 61: 179–182 (1935)

208
Vermeulen, H. A. Epiphyse gezwellen, Ned. tschr. geneesk. 68: 2951–2952 (1924)

209
Vincent, S.   Internal Secretions and the Ductless Glands, pp. 405–411. London: Arnold, 1912

210
Vogel, K.   Von der Bedeutung der Hirnanhänge. Inaug. Diss., Würzburg, 1828

211
Wakeley, C. P. G.   Hunterian lecture on the surgery of the pineal gland, Med. Press and Circ., London, 188: 145–149, 189–196 (1934)

212
Wakida, K.   Shōwa 13-nendo ni okeru honpō shōka-sen kenkyū no gaikan (A survey of research in Japan on the pineal gland in 1938), Tōkyō iji shinshi, no. 3135, pp. 1389–1391 (1939)

213
Wakida, K.   Shōwa 14-nendo ni okeru honpō shōka-sen kenkyū wo kaerimite (A review of research in Japan on the pineal gland in 1939), Ikai tenbō, no. 275: 9 (1940)

214
Wakida, K.   Shōka-sen ni kan-suru jikken-teki narabi-ni rinsyō-teki kenkyū; sōsetsu (Experimental and clinical studies on the pineal gland; general discussion), Nippon Fujinkagakkai zasshi 37: 549–561 (1942)

215
Wolff, G. J.   Diss. inaug. quaestiones medicas varii argumenti (De conario et acervulo cerebri). Thesis, Harderwyck, 1791

216
Wright, S.   Thymus and pineal glands, Brit. M. J. 1: 874–875 (1937)

217
Yamao, K.   Shōka-sen ni tsuite (The pineal gland), Igaku oyobi igaku-jin 4: 18–19 (1921)

218
Yokomori, K.   Shōka-sen no shikkan (Diseases of the pineal gland), Igaku shūran, chap. 4: 1–16, 1930

219
Zimmerman, A.   Az anatomia köreböl (Concerning anatomy), Terme-szettudomanyi mozgalmak 49: 170–171, 1917; and 57: 57–59, 1925

220
Zimmerman, L.   Az epiphysisrol, Allatorv. lap. 59: 389–390 (1936)

INDEX

[276]